Life's too short
for ordinary.
That's why we've
spent 25 years
finding, visiting and
choosing brilliant
places to stay.

For people who
love special.

First edition
Copyright © 2019
Alastair Sawday Publishing Co. Ltd
Published in 2019
ISBN-13: 978-1-906136-94-9

Sawday's,
Merchants House, Wapping Road,
Bristol BS1 4RW, UK
Tel: +44 (0)117 204 7810
Email: info@sawdays.co.uk
Web: www.sawdays.co.uk

Series Editor Alastair Sawday
Content Manager Wendy Ogden
Editors Nicola Crosse, Chris Elmes, Wendy Ogden
Production coordinators Sarah Cottam, Antonica Eikli
Writing Claire Baranowski, Becca Bill, Jo Boissevain, Nicola Crosse, Antonica Eikli, Zoe Grafton, Carmen McCormack, Sue Nottingham, Wendy Ogden, Annie Shillito
Inspections Jan Adam, Edna Allbrooke, David Ashby, Mandy Barnes, Charlotte Barr, Sarah Barratt, Jennie Biggs, Becky Brunning, Angie Collings, Rachel Conway, Sarah Cottam, Anne Cousin, Nicola Crosse, Mary Dixon, Fiona Duby, Peter Evans, Julie Franklin, Catherine Gledhill, Pamela-Ann Godwin, Naomi Gorvin, Zoe Grafton, Becca Harris, Carmen McCormack, Claire Morgan, Véronique Nelson, Wendy Ogden, Valerie Penny, Aideen Reed, Scott Reeve, Karen Roden, Sally Shervington, Annie Shillito, Alison Skinner, Diana Tamlyn, Nicky Tennent, Peter Thurlow, Rebecca Whewell, Jane Wilson, Mandy Wragg
Designer Megan Silcocks
Marketing & PR Emily Enright, Ella Perryman
+44 (0)117 204 7801
marketing@sawdays.co.uk

We have made every effort to ensure the accuracy of the information in this book at the time of going to press. However, we cannot accept any responsibility for any loss, injury or inconvenience resulting from the use of information contained therein.

Production Pagebypage Co. Ltd
Maps Maidenhead Cartographic Services
Printing Pureprint, Uckfield
Distribution Travel Alliance, Bath
info@pelotongrey.com

LIST OF SYMBOLS

  ♿   At least one bedroom and bathroom accessible for wheelchair users. Phone for details.

 Children of all ages are welcome. Cots, highchairs etc are not necessarily available.

 Pets welcome; please let the owner know if you want to bring pets.

Cover front photo: Dunhill Barn, page 183
Cover back photo: Hoopells Torr, page 58

Photo opposite: Trevigue, page 47

Sawday's

Great British
Bed & Breakfast
Guide

Contents

SCOTLAND
p412–443

NORTH
EAST
p382–388

NORTH
WEST
p338–354

YORKSHIRE
AND
HUMBER
p358–379

EAST
MIDLANDS
p284–304

WEST
MIDLANDS
p308–335

WALES
p392–408

EAST
OF
ENGLAND
p246–281

LONDON
p228–243

SOUTH EAST
p162–224

SOUTH WEST
p28–156

For the love of B&Bs

B&Bs are a great British institution. Places where you'll be treated like a valued friend and where you get the chance to engage with the owners and sometimes other guests. Places where there may be an unexpected glass of wine on a sunny evening in the garden, breakfast that goes on and on because the conversation is so good, tips about where to go and what to do, the offer of some goose eggs/home-grown spinach/jar of marmalade to take home with you and that warm feeling you get when you truly connect with other people. These are what make staying in a B&B special.

A very funny article called '10 reasons why I hate B&Bs' recently appeared online. It was peppered with advice on how to dodge chit-chat with well-meaning but irritating owners, tips on engineering a solitary breakfast for those who can't speak before coffee and suggestions for overcoming the embarrassment of making eye contact with the occupants of the room next door, whose every sigh and shuffle you've been listening to all night.

A good lampooning is fun and sometimes necessary, but we are changing the hearts and minds of people who would rather starve, or camp in a bus shelter, than stay in a B&B. They're non-conformists, free thinkers who enjoy experiencing something new, something never imagined, something special and never realise that they can find all those things in a good old British B&B.

This battalion of B&Bs is unique – the experience of staying in them cannot be replicated anywhere else. Vineyards where you can taste the wine and join in with the harvest, independent spaces with a bistro with rooms above and a bakery where you wake to the smell of your croissant gently rising. They're all breaking the mould of the traditional B&B.

You'll find diverse architecture: a 12th-century priory, ancient castles chock-full of history, elegant Georgian townhouses, thatched cottages in villages straight from *Midsomer Murders*, Victorian potteries and mills, a growing band of very modern architect-designed eco houses and a beautiful London houseboat to name just some.

You can learn something too. Take an old piece of furniture and give it a facelift, bake bread, start yoga, paint pictures or learn to screenprint, fly fish and throw pots, or finish your novel at a library of 150,000 books.

From these places you can immerse yourself in little patches of Britain intimately known by their owners, who can help you unearth their charms. You can wander forgotten bridleways, scramble to private beaches, join coast paths from gardens, swim in lakes and rivers, climb behind waterfalls, row to a picnic spot, shop for vintage finds in little markets, watch the judging at an agricultural show, borrow bikes for miles of quiet pedalling and search for Nessie on the shores of the loch.

And most importantly (it's true, B&B non-believers) the people you meet will enrich all those experiences. Our B&B owners are as distinct as their places – that's why we've chosen them. Farmers, artists, business coaches, writers, landscape gardeners, explorers, film-makers, foodies and an expert on the endangered wild Bactrian camel. Yes, you might talk over breakfast, but it'll be fascinating.

So whether you've experienced horrors in the past, or always been a fan, take a deep breath and plunge into the warm waters of a Sawday's B&B. You may be taken you somewhere you weren't expecting, but that's part of the adventure and one of thousands of reasons to love B&Bs.

The Malabar, page 344

The Malabar, page 344

What we look for

We look for special.
We've visited every one of them.
We've written about them honestly.

Our B&Bs are not uniform. We look for differences not similarities,
so you'll find ancient stately homes surrounded by acres of parkland,
modern cabins in town gardens and lots of interesting places in between
that defy a label. What binds them is not their outward appearance but
what it feels like to be there as a guest. We look for:

Warm, engaging owners

There are some people in this world born to be
hosts and we seek them out. True people-lovers
look forward to meeting strangers and turning
them into friends as much as children look
forward to Christmas. They relish making their
guests feel relaxed, comfortable and happy.

Character

We like our B&Bs to be as idiosyncratic and lively
as they please. Travelling is dull if you stay in
places reflecting nothing more interesting than
somebody else's take on boutique bling. The
B&Bs we choose have the character of their
owners stamped right through them – however
that manifests itself. We love surprises!

Lack of rules

We like fuss-free B&Bs with a wide-open door
policy, not places where you are restricted by
notices and signs. We prefer bedrooms without
locks, long chatty breakfasts and suppers at one
affable table, kitchens one can wander into for a
chat and gardens you are free to roam. We
particularly applaud owners who encourage their
guests to do a lot of joining in.

Good food

It's quite likely you'll eat as well, or even better, in
one of our B&Bs than in a swanky hotel with a
chef. This is partly about catering for fewer
people but also about how the food is sourced.

Eggs are often from owners' hens, sometimes
bacon and sausages from their own pigs, beef or
lamb from the fields around you. Many of our
owners bake their own bread, make their own
marmalade and bottle fruit from their gardens.
At most places you'll be offered homemade cake
or scones when you arrive and if the owners do
supper it'll be worth staying in for good British
cooking with plenty of home-grown vegetables.

Generosity of spirit

Our B&B owners are dab hands at offering you a
lift from the nearest station, finding you the best
spot in the garden to have your sundowner,
popping a hot water bottle in your bed when it's
chilly, lending maps – and sometimes dogs – for
a special walk, drying your wet kit, letting you put
your wine in their fridge, heating up baby food
and any number of random acts of kindness.

A sense of place

Our guests like digging a bit deeper into the
places they stay, so we choose owners who love
to celebrate where they live – whether it's by
offering local soaps and lotions, cheese from the
artisan producer down the road, beer from a
nearby micro-brewery or meat and vegetables
from their own farms and gardens. Staying at
these places will teach you much about Great
Britain – county by county.

Upper Red House, page 395

Dunhill Barn, page 183

The Slate Shed at Graig Wen, page 403

Sawday's top 6

These categories represent just some of the things we love about our B&Bs: beautiful gardens for morning coffee, story-filled historic buildings, one-of-a-kind spaces and inspirational modern design. We've also picked out places where you can get active or try something new, from canoeing and canyoning to photography and floristry, as well as choosing our favourites for the sociable atmosphere so unique to B&Bs.

Whittling down a host of great contenders to just six for each category was extremely difficult. The ones we've picked stand out for their creativity and their approach in one particular regard, but we're confident that all the places in this book offer the warmth and character that we've always looked for.

Gardens

A little stroll in the garden after breakfast is always a pleasure. These places, bursting with colour and calm, sculpture and topiary, are our favourite for finding a quiet bench and listening to the birds.

I. HEREFORD OAST, KENT

This charming, friendly oast house B&B is set back from a country road and gazes over fields. Its rural Kent location also means it has a large, open garden full of birds and superb views over the fields. Owner Suzy loves bringing guests tea and cake in the garden and on sunny summer days you'll be in sheer heaven.

PAGE 215

2. ALLT-Y-BELA, MONMOUTHSHIRE

A beautiful renaissance farmhouse that sits in its own secret valley reached down a quiet country lane. You'll find a magical garden created by one of the owners, Chelsea Gold Medal winner Arne Maynard, with formal topiary, dramatic earth sculptures and gentle native planting. In the spring there are massed snowdrops and wild narcissus which give way to carpets of primroses and bluebells.

PAGE 393

Great Chalfield Manor, page 135

3. GREAT CHALFIELD MANOR, WILTSHIRE

A National Trust house and a rare example of the English medieval manor complete with 14th-century church and great hall. The gardens are exquisite and filled with clipped yew houses, upper and lower moats, herbaceous borders, a woodland and huge lawns. You can also walk around the orchard, which is immaculately tended and enhanced by the owner's love of roses.

PAGE 135

4. KING JOHN'S LODGE, SUSSEX

Deep in the High Weald and down a maze of country lanes is this enchanting 1650s house in eight acres of heaven. The garden is owner Jill's pride and joy, and she does a brilliant job of keeping it blooming. Enjoy sweeping lawns, wild gardens, ancient apple trees and heading out on long woodland walks.

PAGE 207

Allt-y-bela, page 393

5. BROADGATE, CUMBRIA

A lovely Georgian country house with stunning views to the sea and a beautiful walled garden, which fades into its woodland setting. High stone walls, covered with climbers and old roses, enclose wide herbaceous beds and an old glasshouse. This is a garden in the most wonderful setting and which Diana constantly adds to for year-round interest.

PAGE 343

6. CREED HOUSE, CORNWALL

At Jonathon and Annabel's there's a comforting sense of all being well. Discover a sunken cobbled yard thought to have been a carriage wash, snowdrops and daffodils in their thousands and an outstanding tree and shrub collection. A maze of secret paths covered in rhododendrons, camellias, azaleas and magnolias leads from gently sloping lawns deep into woodland.

PAGE 39

Creed House, page 39

OUR TOP 6 FOR
Activities

Learning or experiencing something new is the best kind of souvenir. Take guided hikes and wine tasting tours, master the potter's wheel or weave your own willow basket at our favourite places for activities.

I. WOOD HOUSE, CUMBRIA

A 1600s farmhouse set in the glorious Buttermere valley with private access to Crummock Water. Your host Tony will help to make your stay as adventure-fuelled as you like; there's canoeing and canyoning, guided walks, world-class mountain biking, rock climbing and wild swimming all on offer. The Via Ferrata, a thrilling cable walk takes you across the top of a mountain, is also close by for any adrenaline junkies.

PAGE 349

2. SWALLOW BARN, SOMERSET

Views sweep over the hills from this eco-friendly barn conversion and you can join the Macmillan Way walking trail from your doorstep. Penny provides you with maps and binoculars, as well as all her recommended coffee stops en route. Quirky green heritage bikes are on offer too, so spend the day riding the Sustrans Route24 cycle path and exploring all the nearby villages.

PAGE 115

Swallow Barn, page 115

3. THE BEECHES, SUSSEX

Creative guests will love their stay at this beautiful Grade II listed country house in the heart of the Sussex countryside. Within the grounds sits an 18th-century oak framed barn which has been converted into a hub of creative activity. Sandy offers courses in pruning, propagation and planting schemes, as well as creative willow work, knitting, crochet, floristry and photography.

PAGE 200

Vinegar Hill Pottery, page 179

4. VINEGAR HILL POTTERY, HAMPSHIRE

Talented hosts introduce you to their sylvan setting and stylish ceramics workshop at this lovely coastal B&B in Milford on Sea. Learn a new skill or take pottery courses, choosing from a one-day class to a whole weekend. Your host Dave, an experienced potter, will teach you to use the wheel and create ceramics that have a rich glaze and beautiful contemporary finish.

PAGE 179

The Flint Barns, page 204

5. THE FLINT BARNS, SUSSEX

Unwind in the stunning South Downs at this lovely B&B on a pioneering English vineyard. Arrive to a glass or wine or pot of tea; there are regular wine nights with talks and you can book a tour of the vineyard with a tasting and lunch. There are also ample walks from your door - join the South Downs Way or the footpath that leads all the way to the sea.

PAGE 204

6. ASHLEY COURT, DEVON

This country house is full of delightful surprises, with much unchanged since the early 1930s. Settle in the morning room with its interesting library or join in with a yoga class. There's a full retreat on offer too, if you'd like to come and restore your soul. In between classes, wander through the mature woodlands or sit among the rhododendrons and get lost in a book.

PAGE 72

Wood House, page 349

History

It's incredible to stay somewhere that makes you feel like you're living in another time. These are favourites for getting a taste of Georgian manor houses, Tudor hunting lodges and ancient monastic life.

I. HARLINGTON MANOR, BEDFORDSHIRE

An ancient dream of a manor house that dates back to the 14th century, set in a village just north of London. Listen out for old tales of John Bunyan, who was said to have been imprisoned here, and Charles II who came to stay. Today, the manor is full of David's impressive antiques and eclectic art. There's a grand piano to play if you wish and rich carvings to admire in the magnificent Tudor dining room.

PAGE 247

2. THE OLD PRIORY, SOMERSET

A relaxed and artistic home where books and antiques abound. Jane's 12th-century home is as much a haven for reflection today as it was to the monastic community who lived here centuries ago. Find Venetian red walls in low ceilinged living rooms, a 14th-century fireplace and a deeply traditional four-poster bedroom that will transport you back in time.

PAGE 106

Harlington Manor, page 247

3. MANOR HOUSE FARM, STAFFORDSHIRE

A Jacobean farmhouse layered with history on a working rare-breed farm set in the Churnet Valley. Chris inherited the house and has worked tirelessly to expand and improve the grounds. An extensive perennial border sports a huge stone table, which was once part of Lancaster's municipal baths, a railway carriage is now a garden summerhouse and sculptures peek out from the greenery.

PAGE 335

4. PENTILLIE CASTLE, CORNWALL

The approach up to Pentillie is gorgeous, with Dartmoor National Park in the distance and the river Tamar in view. The romantic castle dates back to 1698 and you'll find it has kept many of its original features. During your stay, enjoy ladies' lunches with speakers, outdoor theatre, wine tastings and special seasonal dinners that run throughout the year.

PAGE 44

Pentillie, page 44

5. HAFOD Y GARREG, POWYS

A unique opportunity to stay in the oldest house in Wales, which dates all the way back to 1402 and was built for Henry IV as a hunting lodge. Owners Annie and John have filled it with a charming mix of Venetian mirrors, Indian rugs, pewter plates, rich fabrics and impressive oak pieces. Enjoy a candlelit dinner in the romantic dining room before retreating with a nightcap by the fire.

PAGE 400

6. YARLINGTON HOUSE, SOMERSET

There's something to astound at every turn of this impressive Georgian manor, from the traditional to the downright quirky. There are fine copies of 18th-century wallpapers, elegant antiques and tremendous art, as well as traditional bedrooms with glorious views of the parkland. Beyond is a short woodland walk with shrubs and an impressive 200-year-old Cedar of Lebanon.

PAGE 109

Yarlington House, page 109

The Malabar, page 344

Contemporary

These are the places we feel are bringing a real contemporary edge to the B&B, turning the traditional cottage image completely on its head. There are Indian influences, incredible artworks and inspiring designs.

I. MOUNT PLEASANT FARM, SOMERSET

A boutique B&B full of surprises, with market-find furniture and fun, arty decor. Daisy has restored the cottage using reclaimed everything: painted or gold-leafed pieces, polished boards, beautiful bedheads and Indian banisters. Each of the bedrooms is individually styled and all to the highest spec; enjoy a soak in the copper bath tub or head out for a dip in the pool.

PAGE 120

2. HIR KEMMYNS, CORNWALL

From the moment you drive through the gates you get a sense of crisp modernity combined with the most inspiring sea views. The two B&B rooms have their own entrances from the back garden and are decorated in cool, calming colours. Each morning you'll wake to the light on the waves as you look out across to St Mawes and beyond.

PAGE 37

3. THE MILL, SUFFOLK

Paul and Claire have done a brilliant job of turning their Grade II listed mill into a contemporary boutique B&B. Each beautifully furnished room is separate from the main house, with private parking and an individual entrance. One room boasts the original Tudor turrets of Melford Hall and a great brass bath, while the other has its own log-burner and a private walled garden.

PAGE 260

4. LULWORTH HOUSE, DORSET

Breathtaking views, coastal walks, wildflowers and pretty beaches all lie on the doorstep of this remote B&B on a peaceful lane. Each bedroom comes with its own terrace, perfect for an evening drink on sunny days, as well as crisp white sheets and colourful furnishings. Enjoy delicious breakfasts out on your terrace or all together around the large dining table.

Mount Pleasant Farm, page 120

PAGE 88

5. THE MALABAR, CUMBRIA

Fiona and Graham have turned the barn next to their farmhouse into deeply comfortable, smart spaces influenced by Graham's time spent in India. You'll spot elephant-shaped coffee tables dotted around and tapestry-inspired bedspreads up in the bedrooms. The real star of the show however are the yellow and purple roll top baths, which are extremely inviting after a long walk along the Howgill Fells.

PAGE 344

6. HOOPPELLS TORR, DEVON

Jeeva and Simon have created the ultimate place to relax in their rambling farmhouse. In the bedrooms, old features like original wood floors and beams are mixed with bold contemporary colours, linen furnishings and fabulous roll top baths. There are six acres of grounds for you to explore as well as a secret beach, but sometimes a swim in the saltwater pool is all you need.

The Mill, page 260

PAGE 58

One of a kind

We love a place that simply defies categorisation, whether it's a renovated barge, an aircraft control tower or just an inspiring interior hiding behind a familiar facade. These are top picks for individuality.

I. ARA, LONDON

This is a truly fascinating B&B on a barge in Battersea, originally used for shipping grain and now transformed into a unique home. You'll love having a taste of river living in such a luxurious space. Settle into the guest room by the wood-burner, hop up a ladder into a little wheelhouse library and look out onto the water from your chaise longue.

PAGE 237

2. PONDEN HALL, YORKSHIRE

A special house brimming with atmosphere and said to be the inspiration for Wuthering Heights. Julie's knowledge of the history is impressive and she offers tours of her fascinating home. Bedrooms have just the right balance of luxury and individuality: an amazing box bed, rocking horse, raftered ceilings and log stoves in two.

PAGE 359

Coes Faen Lodge, page 404

3. THE CONTROL TOWER, NORFOLK

The Control Tower was originally an iconic landmark on the former RAF North Creake airfield, which dates back to the 1940s. Today, it is a unique slice of history. The restoration has been a labour of love and Ni and Claire's attention to detail is remarkable; expect a mix of modernism and art deco design in full flow, gleaming bathrooms, cocktail cabinets and WWII books.

PAGE 280

4. GLADSTONE'S LIBRARY, FLINTSHIRE

Lose yourself happily in this stunning historic building with fabulous books and peaceful rooms. You have 150,000 books, silence, space and convivial company if you need it as well as the Eucharist, which is held every weekday. Delicious local food is served in the bistro and you'll find an open fire and sofas in the Gladstone room.

PAGE 408

Ponden Hall, page 359

5. WOODCHESTER VALLEY VINEYARD BARNS, GLOUCESTERSHIRE

How often do you get to stay over at one of the UK's leading vineyards. These B&B suites are in a creatively restored barn, overlooking fields of vines on one side and stunning Cotswolds views on the other. Taster days and evenings are on offer during your stay: visit the winery, learn about the grapes and the process before tasting the estate's outstanding wines.

PAGE 141

6. COES FAEN LODGE, GWYNEDD

This historic but brightly renovated country estate in dense, ancient woodland is a wonderful outdoorsy retreat. Go fishing on the Tay, pick vegetables from the garden and walk through the forest. With very few rules, your four-legged friend can accompany you throughout the day. Head to the restaurant and try scallops hand-dived on the west coast and venison from the Meikleour Forest.

PAGE 404

Woodchester Valley Vineyard Barns, page 141

Sociable atmosphere

One of the best things about B&Bs is gathering round a big table, swapping stories and plans with fellow travellers. These are our favourite places for a good chat with welcoming owners and like-minded guests.

I. DUNHILL BARN, HAMPSHIRE

This gloriously rustic B&B has a friendly and relaxed vibe so you'll feel right at home from the minute you walk through the door. Breakfasts are in the living area, where light streams in through big windows as you tuck into homemade banana muffins, granola, berries or a full breakfast. You'll meet lots of interesting folk on your stay, who you can chat to over coffee or down at the local pub.

PAGE 46

2. TY'R CHANTER, POWYS

Your host Tiggy loves to welcome and entertain, so you'll be guaranteed the finest hospitality during your stay. You can help to collect eggs and feed the lambs, there are heaps of books to get stuck into and a long convivial table for sociable meals. Tiggy is a qualified fishing instructor and loves taking her guests down to Usk to catch a trout. After a busy day, there's always homemade cake and whisky to help yourself to.

PAGE 398

Bistro Lotte, page 112

3. STOKENHAM HOUSE, DEVON

This lovely B&B gazes at the sea and the bird-rich Slapton Ley. Iona and Paul are energetic and thoughtful hosts who have created a fabulous South Hams base. Chill out on the cushions on the lawn or in the summerhouse - or have a BBQ by the pool. You can also learn to cook or grow vegetables; courses are a great chance to meet other guests.

PAGE 273

4. OLD HARBOUR VIEW, DORSET

There's lots to enjoy at this friendly Georgian harbourside house. You're in the heart of Old Weymouth's hustle and bustle, with its colourful boats and fishermen coming in with their catch. Peter and Anna are brilliant hosts and are on hand to help with anything you need. Breakfasts are served around the large table and there are ample opportunities to chat with other guests.

PAGE 86

Old Harbour View, page 86

5. BISTRO LOTTE, SOMERSET

Lotte and her team are always on hand to make you feel relaxed and comfortable. The bistro downstairs hums with happy people, windows are flung open in the summer and comfortable bedrooms above have their own entrance so you can come and go as you please. Enjoy French platter breakfasts, late lunches and convivial dinners on candlelit tables.

PAGE 112

6. WINTERTON, ARGYLL & BUTE

With only two rooms and creative, well-travelled hosts, being at Winterton is like staying with old friends. The house has stunning mountain views from a sun lounge dotted with sofas and cosy chairs. Sleep soundly in luxurious, quiet bedrooms and enjoy laid-back breakfasts with a delicious twist that set you up for a wonderful day exploring the peninsula and islands.

PAGE 432

Winterton, page 432

South West

Trevigue, page 47

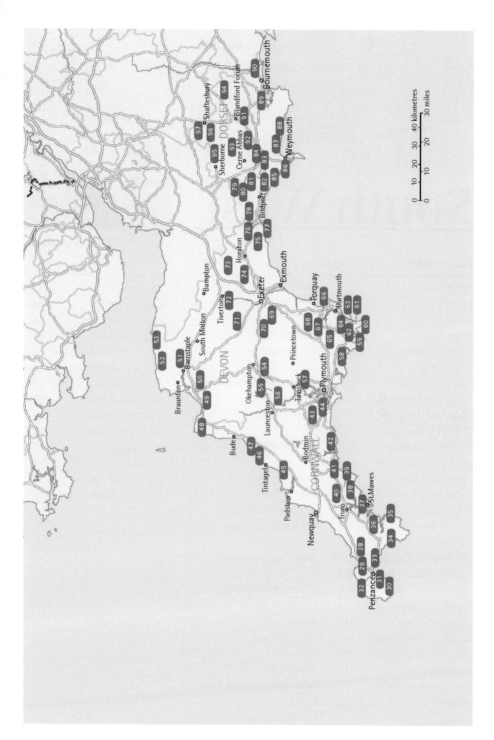

25

South West

The Curious Cabinet, page 126

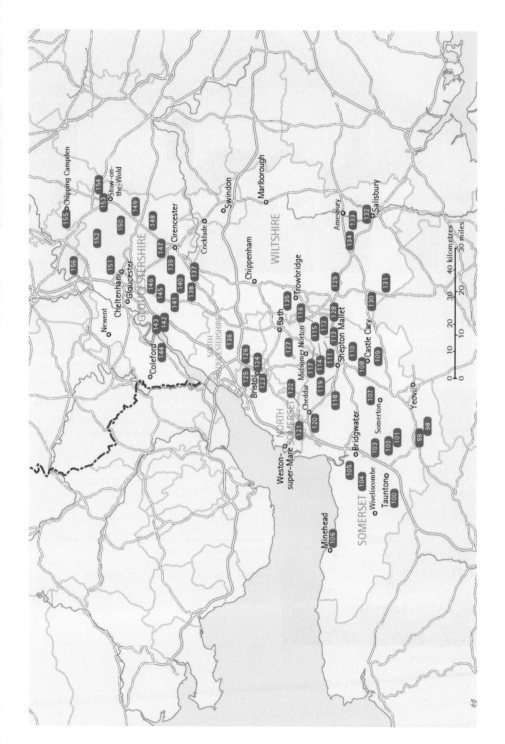

House at Gwinear

An island of calm, this grand old rambling vicarage sits in rare bird-filled acres, just a short drive from St Ives. Come for peace and quiet and a classic Cornish welcome from owners Charles and Diana who are devoted to encouraging the arts and crafts. Find English shabby chic with loads of character and no stuffiness – fresh flowers on the breakfast table, a piano in the corner, rugs on polished floors, masses of books. Your bedroom is in a separate wing with its own sitting room and a fine view of the church from the bath. In summer you can eat breakfast in the Italianate courtyard, play a game of tennis on the ancient courts and wander the large, lawned gardens. Ask for supper or walk half an hour to the pub. *French & Italian spoken.*

Rooms	1 twin/double with separate bath & sitting room: £85-£95.
Meals	Supper, 2 courses with wine, £25. Pub 1.5 miles.
Closed	Rarely.

Charles & Diana Hall
House at Gwinear,
Gwinear, St Ives, TR27 5JZ

Tel   +44 (0)1736 850444
Email   charleshall@btinternet.com

The Firs

There's real warmth and a hint of romance in the air here. This attractive Edwardian villa was author Rosamunde Pilcher's childhood home, there are dreamy views of the garden from airy bedrooms, and Marie greets you with tea and cake. Breakfast is served at a shared table overlooking the garden – with the sun streaming in through the huge bay window. It's a generous continental spread including fruit, yogurt, cheese and meats – and you can order a daily cooked special too if you fancy more. Walk to the flawless sands of Porthkidney, spot the many birds on the estuary or play golf at the local course. Stroll down the terraced lawns and you'll reach a tiny station, hop on a clifftop train and enjoy one of the most scenic routes in the country. Eight minutes of spectacular coastal views later and you can be exploring the galleries and beaches of St Ives. Stay for dinner or head back to spend the evening in one of Lelant's cosy village pubs.

Rooms	2 doubles: £135.
Meals	Restaurants 5-minute walk.
Closed	Occasionally.

Tel	+44 (0)1736 757830
Email	stay@thefirslelant.com
Web	www.thefirslelant.com

Marie Britten
The Firs,
Riverside, Lelant, TR26 3DW

Cove Cottage

Down a long lane to a rose-clad cottage in the most balmy part of Cornwall... peace in a private cove. Your own door leads up steps to a gorgeous suite with luxurious linen on an antique four-poster, art, sofas... and a flowery balcony with spectacular views of the sea and subtropical gardens. Settle in happily to the sound of the waves. Sue is friendly and serves a great breakfast in the garden room: home-laid eggs, homemade jams and their own honey. The Penwith peninsula hums with gardens, galleries and stunning sandy beaches; Minack Theatre and Lamorna are close. Arrive to a salad supper chosen from a small but special menu. Paradise! *Minimum stay: 3 nights in high season.*

Rooms	1 suite for 2: £145.
Meals	Salad suppers from £12.50 available on the night of arrival. Pub/restaurant 3 miles.
Closed	November – February.

Sue White
Cove Cottage,
St Loy, St Buryan,
Penzance, TR19 6DH

Tel   +44 (0)1736 810010
Email   thewhites@covecottagestloy.co.uk
Web   www.covecottagestloy.co.uk

The Old Pilchard Works

Hidden down the side of Tracey's house are two little flats each with their own door. One has stairs to an airy bedroom and a glimpse of the sea. Find a calm, sleek feel with modern white furniture, cool linen, snug wool blankets; zinc coat hooks, bright cushions, clever lighting add interest. Tracey leaves you a niftily upcycled 7UP box stuffed with homemade granola, croissants, pain au chocolat, homemade compote and yogurt, fruit, organic oatmeal porridge, agave syrup... Eat outside on the shared suntrap terrace – or in bed if you fancy. Stroll along the harbour, book a boat trip; St Ives and atmospheric Minack Theatre are nearby. *Minimum stay: 2 nights. Nearby car park £3 for 24 hours.*

Rooms	1 twin/double; 1 double with separate shower room: £80-£105.
Meals	Pubs/restaurants 2-minute walk.
Closed	Rarely.

Tel	+44 (0)1736 732699
Email	tracey.wearnes@gmail.com

Tracey Wearne
The Old Pilchard Works,
6 Chapel Street, Mousehole,
Penzance, TR19 6SB

Venton Vean

Everything at Venton Vean is tip-top. Immensely helpful owners Philippa and David moved from London with their family and have transformed a dilapidated Victorian house into a supremely cool and elegant B&B. Moody colours, mid-century design classics and interesting reclamation finds make for a stunning and eclectic interior. Food is a passion – expect freshly ground coffee in your room and some of the most tantalising breakfasts around: Mexican, Spanish, even a good old full English will have you dashing down in the morning. Arty Penzance is a joy as is the craggy-coved beauty all around. *Minimum stay: 2 nights.*

Rooms	4 doubles: £72-£100. 1 family room for 4: £110-£140. Singles £71-£87.
Meals	Packed lunch from £5. Cream tea £4. Pubs/restaurants 8-minute walk.
Closed	Christmas.

Philippa McKnight
Venton Vean,
Trewithen Road,
Penzance, TR18 4LS

Tel	+44 (0)1736 351294
Email	info@ventonvean.co.uk
Web	www.ventonvean.co.uk

Ednovean Farm

There's a terrace for each fabulous bedroom (one truly private) with views to the wild blue yonder and St Michael's Mount Bay, an enchanting outlook that changes with the passage of the day. Come for peace, space and the best of eclectic fabrics and colours, pretty lamps, Christine's sculptures, fluffy bathrobes and handmade soaps. The beamed open-plan sitting/dining area is an absorbing mix of exotic, rustic and elegant; have full breakfast here (last orders nine o'clock) or continental in your room. A footpath through the field leads to the village; walk to glorious Prussia Cove and Cudden Point, or head west to Marazion.
Over 16s welcome.

Rooms	2 doubles, 1 four-poster: £100-£145.
Meals	Pub 5-minute walk.
Closed	Rarely.

Tel	+44 (0)1736 711883
Email	info@ednoveanfarm.co.uk
Web	www.ednoveanfarm.co.uk

Christine & Charles Taylor
Ednovean Farm,
Perranuthnoe,
Penzance, TR20 9LZ

Halzephron House

The coastal path runs through the grounds of this former smugglers' house and the view is to die for – you can see St Michael's Mount on a clear day. Be greeted by homemade treats and coffee: lovely Lucy and Roger are foodies as well as designers. A contemporary and quirky suite awaits you, throw open the drawing room door and there's a big private deck overlooking the garden where you can soak up the stunning sunsets. Then drift off in a big antique French bed to the sound of the waves. The handsome house sits in four acres of lawns and wildflower meadow and has a 'secret' cliff top garden and amphitheatre. You can walk to three amazing beaches, a 13th-century church, a golf course and a gastropub. This is a landscape for creatives, begging to be painted, sketched and described. You'll be in good company, the guest book flows with the words of actors, musicians and authors including AA Milne and Conan Doyle. Your hosts will happily tell you more house secrets over breakfast at the sunny communal table. *Minimum stay: 2 nights; 7 in high season.*

Rooms	1 suite for 2: £130-£150. Extra bed £30-£45. Self-catering cottage available & 2 cabins on Canopy & Stars.
Meals	Pub 0.25 miles. Continental/Cornish breakfast in the drawing room: enquire with owner.
Closed	Rarely.

Lucy Thorp
Halzephron House,
Gunwalloe,
Helston, TR12 7QD

Tel	+44 (0)1326 240517
Mobile	+44 (0)7899 925816
Email	info@halzephronhouse.co.uk
Web	www.halzephronhouse.co.uk

Glendurgan

In 1827 a thatched cottage stood where the light-filled family house now surveys the valley. Charles's paintings of plants and trees line the stairwell and there are family pieces, books and art galore. Caroline trained as a cook and her breakfasts are superb, with homemade marmalade and jams – some from garden fruit. Bedrooms have sensational views; Violet and Magenta are as an Edwardian aunt would have liked. No TV but a grand piano, harp, and the view to Helford river is stunning. Outside is magical, exotic and wooded, and there's a sense of discovery as you wend down steep paths to Durgan beach. Splendid in spring with magnolias, bluebells and primroses, and summer, to quote Charles's excellent book, "breaks in a wave of whiteness, with eucryphia, hoheria, myrtus and that 'bombe Alaska' of rhododendrons, 'Polar Bear', while autumn is awash with bulbs – amaryllis, colchicum, crinum and nerine". There's interest in winter too and, even in the wildest weather, it's a deeply romantic place to be. There's much to explore and Charles, garden designer and leader of tours, will advise.

Rooms	2 twins: £130. Singles £90.
Meals	Restaurant within walking distance.
Closed	Occasionally.

Tel	+44 (0)1326 250326
Email	fox@glendurgan.plus.com

Charles & Caroline Fox
Glendurgan,
Mawnan Smith,
Falmouth, TR11 5JZ

Bosvathick

A huge old Cornish house that's been in Kate's family since 1760 – along with Indian rugs, heavy furniture, ornate plasterwork, portraits and a piano... even a harp. Historians will be in their element: pass three Celtic crosses dating from the 8th century before the long drive finds the imposing house (all granite gate posts and lions) and a rambling garden with grotto, lake, pasture and woodland. Bedrooms are traditional, full of books, antiques and pots of flowers; bathrooms are spic and span, one small and functional, two large. Come to experience a 'time warp' and charming Kate's good breakfasts. Close to Falmouth University, too. *French spoken.*

Rooms	2 twin/doubles: £110-£120. 2 singles: £70. Extra bed/sofabed £25-£35 per person per night.
Meals	Supper from £25. Packed lunch £5-£10. Pubs 2 miles.
Closed	Rarely.

Kate & Stephen Tyrrell
Bosvathick,
Constantine,
Falmouth, TR11 5RZ

Tel	+44 (0)1326 340103
Email	kate@bosvathickhouse.co.uk
Web	www.bosvathickhouse.co.uk

Hir Kemmyns

The two B&B rooms have their own entrances from the back garden. There's a help-yourself drinks and biscuit station, and you wake to views over the sailing waters of St Mawes and the sea beyond. It's an upside-down house with bedrooms downstairs. Continental breakfast is laid out on a long table in the dining room, opening onto a balcony overlooking the sea. Lucy gives you freshly baked bread and croissants, homemade jams and compote, cereals and fruit salad, with special treats on Sundays. Children can come too – kit and toys can be provided as well as a cot and fold-out bed. Sit on your sunny patio, delve into books and magazines – and it's a stroll to the sea, Castle and Lamorran Gardens. *Minimum stay: 2 nights.*

Rooms	2 doubles: £90-£95. Extra bed available for children, £20 per night. Cot available, £10 per night.
Meals	Pubs/restaurants 10-minute walk.
Closed	Rarely.

Tel	+44 (0)1326 279103
Email	lucy@hir-kemmyns.com
Web	www.hir-kemmyns.com

Lucy Cullen
Hir Kemmyns,
Upper Castle Road,
St Mawes, TR2 5BZ

Hay Barton

Giant windows overlook many acres of farmland, and Jill and Blair look after you so well! Breakfasts are special with the best local produce, homemade granola, yogurt and more. Arrive for tea and lovely home-baked cake, laid out in a comfortable guest sitting room with a log fire and plenty of books and maps. Bedrooms are fresh and pretty with garden flowers, soft white linen on big beds and floral green walls. Gloriously large panelled bathrooms have long roll top baths and are painted in earthy colours. You can knock a few balls around the tennis court, and you're near to good gardens and heaps of places to eat. *Minimum stay: 2 nights in summer.*

Rooms	3 twin/doubles: £90-£100. Singles £70-£75.
Meals	Pubs 1-2 miles.
Closed	Rarely.

Jill & Blair Jobson
Hay Barton,
Tregony, Truro, TR2 5TF

Tel	+44 (0)1872 530288
Mobile	+44 (0)7813 643028
Email	jill.jobson@btinternet.com
Web	www.haybarton.com

Creed House

In Jonathon and Annabel's house and garden there's a comforting sense of all being well. Inside the 1730s house, wooden floors are covered with Persian rugs and light pours into every elegant corner; big guest rooms exude taste and simplicity and you breakfast well in the panelled dining room. This is one of Cornwall's loveliest private gardens, a tribute to the hard work and brilliant plantsmanship devoted to these seven acres. Jonathon's parents arrived in 1974 to find a Miss Havisham of a garden – today it is a fabulous rectory garden. Discoveries include a sunken cobbled yard thought to have been a carriage wash. Snowdrops and daffodils bloom in their thousands; the shrub collection is outstanding; rhododendrons, camellias, azaleas and magnolias (many 40 years old) and secret paths lead from gently sloping lawns deep into woodland. There's much to admire: four obelisks in the walled garden are adorned by 40 sweet-smelling Cornish roses, and there's a wonderful collection of trees, many chosen for autumn colour – of particular note is a magnificent Cornus Controversa Variegata on the front lawn. *Children over 8 welcome.*

Rooms	1 double, 1 twin/double: £110.
Meals	Pub/restaurant 1 mile.
Closed	Christmas & New Year.

Tel	+44 (0)1872 530372
Email	jrcroggon@btinternet.com
Web	www.creedhouse.co.uk

Jonathon & Annabel Croggon
Creed House,
Creed, Grampound,
Truro, TR2 4SL

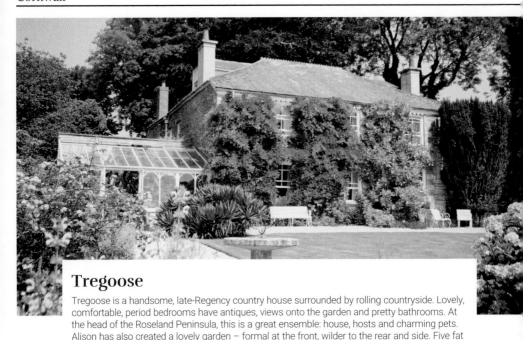

Tregoose

Tregoose is a handsome, late-Regency country house surrounded by rolling countryside. Lovely, comfortable, period bedrooms have antiques, views onto the garden and pretty bathrooms. At the head of the Roseland Peninsula, this is a great ensemble: house, hosts and charming pets. Alison has also created a lovely garden – formal at the front, wilder to the rear and side. Five fat Irish yews and a tumbledown wall were the starting point... but having reconstructed the walls to create a sunken garden, things started to look up. The L-shaped barn was a good backdrop for planting, so in went yellow privet, flame-coloured alstroemerias, show-stopping *Crocosmia solfaterre* and agapanthus for contrast. The sunken walled garden protects *Aloysia citrodora*, leptospermum, and *Acacia baileyana purpurea*. Palm-like dracaena, Monterey pines and cypresses and the Chusan palm do well, as does the spectacular *Rhododendron arboreum*. Snowdrops flower from November to March – spectacular. A potager supplies produce for dinners and flowers for the house, and Alison knows all about Cornish plants and gardens. *Children by arrangement.*

Rooms	1 four-poster, 1 twin; 1 double with separate bath: £98-£110.
Meals	Dinner from £28. BYO. Pub/restaurant 1 mile.
Closed	Christmas & Easter.

Alison O'Connor
Tregoose,
Grampound,
Truro, TR2 4DB

Tel	+44 (0)1726 882460
Email	tregoose@tregoose.co.uk
Web	www.tregoose.co.uk

Antonia's Pearls, The Studio

Tucked behind the oldest part of a handsome listed Georgian house is a small but exquisite bolthole for two with a private, sunny garden. Its style is contemporary, stylish and fun, thanks to its creative owners. Step in to find white walls and white rafters, painted floorboards, quirky touches (two little sconces sport sea urchin shades), a charcoal sofa in a corner and a big gorgeous bed; there's just room for a crib too. The compact living space is partitioned off from a white-and-slate galley kitchen where wine and seasonal treats await, along with a dishwasher, a butler's sink and gleaming pots and pans. If you want a night off, Antonia will cook for you, beautifully – enjoy local produce and lobster from the fisherman. Lined curtains are clasped with leather, Venetian blinds control the light, the shower will drench you and you can smell the salt on the air. Venture back down the path and you are on the edge of Charlestown's quay where the tall ships lie – Phoenix, Kaskelot and Earl of Pembroke. This World Heritage site is still a working harbour, ever the film director's backdrop of choice! It is a privilege to stay.

Rooms	1 studio for 2: £160-£220
Meals	Breakfast on request, £15.
	Dinner on request, 2 courses, £20.
	Pubs/restaurants 2-minute walk.
Closed	Never.

Tel	+44 (0)1726 68966
Email	antonia@antoniaspearls.co.uk
Web	www.antoniaspearls.co.uk

Antonia & David Shields
Antonia's Pearls, The Studio,
Charlestown Harbour,
Charlestown, PL25 3NX

Tredudwell Manor

Winding lanes lead to this handsomely refurbished Queen Anne style house. Surrounded by lawns and mature trees the views are south to the sea and the total peace is just the tonic. Inside is a marble bar for more reviving and the mix of sofas, mini-ottomans, parquet floors with Persian rugs and family portraits make for a genteel atmosphere. First floor bedrooms are large enough to waltz in with toile de Jouy wallpaper, antiques and views. In the roof space are more compact but delightful rooms – uncluttered and calm with low beams, shuttered windows and modern bathrooms. Breakfast is a treat with the best produce from nearby Fowey. *Pets by arrangement.*

Rooms	6 doubles: £70-£130.
	1 family room for 4: £125-£165.
	Singles £75-£100.
	Extra bed £10-£20 per person per night.
Meals	Pubs/restaurants 2 miles.
Closed	Rarely.

Justin & Valérie Shakerley
Tredudwell Manor,
Lanteglos, Fowey, PL23 1NJ

Tel	+44 (0)1726 870226
Email	info@tredudwell.co.uk
Web	www.tredudwell.co.uk

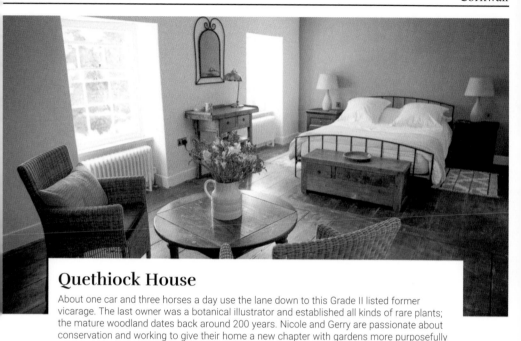

Quethiock House

About one car and three horses a day use the lane down to this Grade II listed former vicarage. The last owner was a botanical illustrator and established all kinds of rare plants; the mature woodland dates back around 200 years. Nicole and Gerry are passionate about conservation and working to give their home a new chapter with gardens more purposefully wild than manicured. Your own entrance leads upstairs to three rooms – two share a bathroom so are perfect for family or friends; fall asleep to the hooting of owls. Wake to breakfast in a basket delivered to your room: homemade bread and jams, local honey, yogurt, fruit salad, warm croissants and their own apple juice. Eat on the Victorian terrace on sunny mornings – and spot a kingfisher fishing in the spring-fed pond. Wander down mown paths and over bridges, spy flycatchers and tree creepers, marvel at the stars in the dark skies. *Minimum stay: 2 nights in high season. Babes in arms & children over 10 welcome.*

Rooms	1 double; 1 double, 1 twin sharing bathroom: £75-£100.
Meals	Pubs/restaurants 10-minute drive.
Closed	Rarely.

Tel	+44 (0)1579 388896
Mobile	+44 (0)7747 610359
Email	nicole.qh@zen.co.uk

Nicole Yde-Poulsen
Quethiock House,
Quethiock, PL14 3SL

Pentillie Castle

A gorgeous approach with Dartmoor National Park in the distance, a long flower-lined drive, then the river Tamar coming into view and lastly the romantic castle. It's as well run as any hotel (with chef, smiley staff and eclectic wine list) but it's got an informal family feel with 'help yourself' suppers by the Aga along with a note saying, 'don't wash up!'. Fill up on dry cured bacon and eggs before visiting 55 acres of Humphry Repton and Lewis Kennedy designed gardens with orchard, summer house and kitchen gardens linked by paths. You don't really have to leave once you get here as there are events aplenty: ladies' lunches with speakers, outdoor theatre, wine tastings and special seasonal dinners. Swim in the outdoor solar-heated pool, order a picnic the night before and find a shady spot on a sunny day; wild swimmers can hop straight into the river from its banks. You can walk to a pub in Halton Quay and Plymouth and Tavistock are a short drive. Return to much comfort, original artwork and nice things from St Kitts Herbery in the bathrooms. Choose from a menu of kitchen suppers or a three-course affair in the dining room with wine. You can even get married here.

Rooms	8 twin/doubles: £160-£225. 1 four-poster suite for 2: £220-£240. Singles £145-£225.
Meals	Dinner, 3 courses, £35. DIY supper, 2 courses, £18. Afternoon tea £22.50. Picnic hamper £30 for 2. Pub 3 miles.
Closed	Rarely.

Sammie Coryton
Pentillie Castle,
St Mellion,
Saltash, PL12 6QD

Tel	+44 (0)1579 350044
Email	contact@pentillie.co.uk
Web	www.pentillie.co.uk

The Corn Mill

This restored mill in a quiet Cornish valley is a relaxed and friendly home. You'll find tea and cake when you get there, perhaps a drink in the evening. Art and country lovers will fit right in – artist Suzy has her studio in a folly and fills her house with flowers. Suzy and Jem make their home yours. Sleep in pretty bedrooms, have a convivial breakfast at the long table in the farmhouse kitchen: a locally sourced spread with home-baked bread. Little ones will love exploring the large garden, home to a spreading chestnut tree planted as a sapling when the Bishops first moved in, while you sit and read in a sunny spot. Suzy's oil paintings are a reminder of North Cornwall's nearby stunning coastline.

Rooms	1 double: £100-£120.
	1 family room for 4: £100-£120.
Meals	Pub/restaurant 2 miles.
Closed	Christmas & New Year.

Tel	+44 (0)1208 851079
Email	jemandsuzie@icloud.com

Susan Bishop
The Corn Mill,
Port Isaac Road,
Trelill, Bodmin, PL30 3HZ

The Old Parsonage

On the southern fringe of Boscastle lies this handsome Georgian parsonage, a grand base for exploring the Cornish coast. Behind the picture-perfect exterior find elegant, light-filled spaces and four big, bright, modern bedrooms. After a restful sleep take a seat at the convivial table in the pine-floored dining room. This is a breakfast well worth waking up for. Jon and Delyth are big foodies and like to show off local produce, so along with their homemade bread it's the perfect fuel for your seaside adventures. Hikers can stride out onto a spectacular stretch of the South West Coast path, boat spotters can wander down to Boscastle harbour, and the more laid back may relax with an afternoon tea watching the Cornish world go by. *Over 12s welcome.*

Rooms	4 twin/doubles: £108-£138.
Meals	Packed lunch £6.95.
	Pub/restaurant 600yds.
Closed	November – January.

Jon & Delyth Ward
The Old Parsonage,
Forrabury,
Boscastle, PL35 0DJ

Tel	+44 (0)1840 250339
Mobile	+44 (0)7377 063722
Email	enquiries@old-parsonage.com
Web	www.old-parsonage.com

Trevigue

Not far up the single track road from Crackington Haven and close to wildly beautiful Strangles Bay you'll find Trevigue hunkering down, as it has for 700-ish years. There's history in the stone floors, oak beams and crackling open fires, but it's the Crockers' love for the place that shines most brightly. Their passion for sustainable living is infectious. All furnishings are locally sourced and some of the cushion covers are made from recycled water bottles. Breakfasts include home-laid eggs, local free-range sausages and bacon and slow-cooked Aga porridge with a topping of fruit, agave syrup and seeds. Pack up your swimmers and take the donkey path that snakes down the cliff to a very nearly private beach for swimming or sunbathing. Say hello to the farm animals on your way back. *Children over 7 welcome.*

Rooms	1 double, 3 twin/doubles: £80-£120. Singles £70-£110.
Meals	Pubs/restaurants 1.5 miles.
Closed	Christmas.

Tel	+44 (0)1840 230492
Mobile	+44 (0)7903 110037
Email	trevigue@talk21.com
Web	www.trevigue.com

Gayle Crocker
Trevigue,
Crackington Haven,
Bude, EX23 0LQ

Hartland Mill

Cathy and James live with Ruby the labrador, in a storybook house on the edge of the world. The welcome couldn't be warmer, your hosts want to make your stay the very best. From the big airy guest sitting room to the candlelit dining room, all is as neat as a new pin. Breakfast has an outstanding menu that changes daily – overnight oats, full English with Cathy's slow roasted herby tomatoes, potato rösti, freshly baked muffins, pancakes, avocado on toast...

No wonder guests don't leave the convivial table for hours. The seclusion is blissful – all you hear is the stream. From the garden you can take a walk to the coastal path. Hartland Abbey with its bluebell woods and garden is close by too. Cathy will prepare a home-cooked dinner for your return or you can try The Farmers Arms, a new favourite in nearby Woolsery; your generous hosts will drop you off. *Minimum stay: 2 nights in high season. Over 12s welcome.*

Rooms	2 doubles, 1 twin/double: £95-£115.
Meals	Dinner, 2 courses, £17.50. BYO wine. Pubs/restaurants 10 minutes.
Closed	Rarely.

Cathy Walker
Hartland Mill,
Hartland, Bideford, EX39 6DS

Tel	+44 (0)1237 440181
Email	hello@hartlandmill.co.uk
Web	www.hartlandmill.co.uk

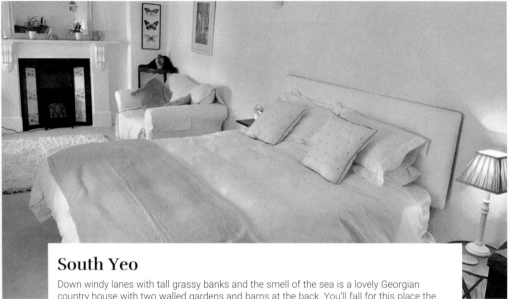

South Yeo

Down windy lanes with tall grassy banks and the smell of the sea is a lovely Georgian country house with two walled gardens and barns at the back. You'll fall for this place the moment you arrive, and its owners: Jo used to run an interiors business; Mike keeps the cattle and sheep that graze all around. Bedrooms are inviting; the double, overlooking the valley, has a cream French bed, a pretty quilted cover, a claw-foot bath and a little sitting room (adjoining) with TV. There's an elegant drawing room with a fire too. Delicious breakfasts with home-laid eggs and homemade jams are brought to a snug room that catches the morning sun.

Rooms	1 double: £90-£100. 1 twin/double with sitting room: £95-£105. Singles £75.
Meals	Pub 1.5 miles.
Closed	Rarely.

Tel	+44 (0)1237 451218
Email	stay@southyeo.co.uk
Web	www.southyeo.co.uk

Joanne Wade
South Yeo,
Yeo Vale, Bideford, EX39 5ES

Old Keepers Cottage

A traditional family home just north of Bideford – with the South West Coast Path a 10-minute drive away. Lucy welcomes you with a cream tea – or drinks if you arrive after teatime – and there's plenty of space to spread out, including a sitting room made cosy with wood-burner and comfy armchairs, and a music room with a piano. Fabulous river Torridge views accompany your breakfast, a generous table of cereals, yogurts, local bacon, kedgeree and eggy bread or eggs done any which way. Plan your day – perhaps catch a ferry to Lundy Island from Bideford Quay to see puffins, wild goats and the Lundy ponies. Head to Westwood Ho! for seaside fun, and to Bideford for dinner – there's lots of choice. Return to pat Archie the Shetland pony and wander down to the river through the woods – a haven for tawny and barn owls, peregrine falcon, squirrels, badgers and deer.

Rooms	1 double, 1 twin/double; 1 double, 1 twin both with separate bathrooms downstairs: £60-£120. Singles from £45. Two doubles available as a suite, £120-£150. Extra bed/sofabed £20 p.p.p.n.
Meals	Restaurants 10-minute drive.
Closed	Christmas & New Year.

Lucy Giddy
Old Keepers Cottage,
Tennacott Lane, Bideford, EX39 4QD

Tel	+44 (0)1237 479113
Email	lucygiddy@btinternet.com
Web	www.oldkeeperscottage.net

Coombe Farm

Easy-going, foodie, country-lovers will fit right in here. Lisa and Matt, passionate about real food, cook home-grown dinners; charcuterie a speciality. Their fine old Devon long house sits in a green fold of farmland and you're free to wander the garden, chat to the pigs, plunge in the invigorating pool. Inside find a quirky mix of family and brocante finds, a snug sitting room full of art, colourful comfortable rooms and fab bathrooms. Breakfast is a delicious spread of homemade everything: granola, jams, sourdough bread, sausages and bacon from the rare breed pigs. No 3 cycle route is close by; Exmoor walks and coast are 20 minutes. *Minimum stay: 2 nights at weekends & in high season.*

Rooms	1 double, 2 twin/doubles: £75-£90.
Meals	Dinner from £25.
	Restaurants 15 minutes walk.
Closed	Rarely.

Tel	+44 (0)1271 324919	
Mobile	+44 (0)7775 941031	
Email	info@coombefarmgoodleigh.co.uk	
Web	www.coombefarmgoodleigh.co.uk	

Matthew Eckford
Coombe Farm,
Goodleigh, Barnstaple, EX32 7NB

Beachborough Country House

Welcome to this gracious 18th-century rectory with stone-flagged floors, lofty windows, wooden shutters and glorious rugs. Viviane is vivacious and spoils you with dinners and breakfasts from the Aga; dine in the elegant dining room before a twinkling fire. Hens cluck, horses whinny but otherwise the peace is deep. Ease any walker's pains away in a steaming roll top tub; lap up country views from big airy bedrooms. There's a games room for kids in the outbuildings and a stream winds through the garden – a delicious three acres of vegetables and roses. Huge fun.

Rooms	2 doubles, 1 twin/double: £95. Singles £70. Extra bed/sofabed £10-£30 per person per night. Extra single available.
Meals	Occasional dinner, 2-3 courses, £22.50-£27.50. Catering for house parties. Pub 3 miles.
Closed	Rarely.

Viviane Clout
Beachborough Country House,
Kentisbury, Barnstaple, EX31 4NH

Tel	+44 (0)1271 882487
Mobile	+44 (0)7732 947755
Email	viviane@beachboroughcountryhouse.co.uk
Web	www.beachboroughcountryhouse.co.uk

North Walk House

North Walk is one of a collection of guest houses on the promenade above Lynmouth Bay's dramatic seascape. Ian and Sarah are engaging hosts, happy to share their enthusiasm for this patch of Devon – stay a few days and unwind. They love to cook, so your stay starts with homemade cake or flapjack – along with those wonderful bay and sunset views, Aga-cooked meals are convivial with just-met guests often chatting round the table long afterwards. Breakfasts include local kippers or organic bacon and sausages, fruit, muesli, homemade bread – Ian's porridge always gets a thumbs up; dinners might be Ilfracombe fish or Devon beef, lamb or venison – seasonal and mostly organic. Discover Exmoor's coastal and moor walks, genteel Lynton and Lynmouth; return to armchairs by the log fire and drinks before dinner. *Dogs welcome in ground floor room.*

Rooms	2 doubles, 1 twin/double: £112-£175. Singles £70-£109.
Meals	Dinner, 4 courses, from £27. Pub/restaurant 0.25 miles.
Closed	1 November to 31 March.

Tel	+44 (0)1598 753372
Email	northwalkhousebb@gmail.com
Web	www.northwalkhouse.co.uk

Ian & Sarah Downing
North Walk House,
North Walk, Lynton, EX35 6HJ

Burnville House

Granite gateposts, Georgian house, rhododendrons, beech woods and rolling fields of sheep: that's the setting. But there's more. Beautifully proportioned rooms reveal subtle colours, elegant antiques, squishy sofas and bucolic views, stylish bathrooms are sprinkled with candles, there are sumptuous dinners and pancakes at breakfast. Your hosts left busy jobs in London to settle here, and their place breathes life – space, smiles, energy. Swim, play tennis, walk to Dartmoor from the door, take a trip to Eden or the sea. Or... just gaze at the moors and the church on the Tor and listen to the silence, and the sheep.

Rooms	3 doubles: £95-£105. Singles £65.
Meals	Dinner from £23. Pub 2 miles.
Closed	Rarely.

Victoria Cunningham
Burnville House,
Brentor, Tavistock, PL19 0NE

Tel	+44 (0)1822 820443
Mobile	+44 (0)7881 583471
Email	burnvillef@aol.com
Web	www.burnville.co.uk

Lee Byre

Food is important here – the kitchen garden is abundant with veggies and soft fruits; there are chickens and beehives, and spring water from the well in your bedroom. Anything that can't be grown, foraged or made is bought as locally as possible. Delicious meals are a relaxed affair around the big table; breakfast can be granola, bread, muffins, banana and cinnamon porridge or a full English. Book in for a two-course dinner paired with local wine. You're on the fringes of Dartmoor, footpaths shoot off from the door and you can take a packed lunch and follow the meandering river Lew. The family have tons of local knowledge and Guy can take you on guided walks through the National Park, or even out for a night-time stargaze. The bedrooms, two large and one huge, are part of the old milking parlour: comfortable, airy spaces to read or watch TV if it rains, with Judy's artwork brightening the walls. Sit in the garden watching birds dart around, gather round the fire pit in the evenings. *Minimum stay: 2 nights. Children over 10 welcome.*

Rooms	1 double, 1 twin/double: £90-£120. 1 suite for 2: £110-£140. Singles from £75. Extra bed in suite, £30 per night.
Meals	Packed lunch, £7.50. Dinner, 2 courses, £20. Pub 15-minute drive.
Closed	November – March.

Mobile	+44 (0)7969 994060
Email	info@leebyre.com
Web	www.leebyre.com/houserooms

Guy Barnes
Lee Byre,
Coryton, EX20 4PE

The Granary – Borough Farm

Follow the winding road, past Connemara ponies and rare-breed sheep, to a farm that's been here for centuries. Julia's natural warmth, and the Dartmoor views, will soothe ruffled souls. Hop up the granary's exterior steps to your room: white walls and wood floor, curvaceous French bed, sky windows for gazing at glittering stars, and a delicious French antique double-ended bath, basin and loo behind a screen. There's another beautiful bath in a tent (shared with two yurts), and your own garden with a firepit. The communal Loft has a fridge, kettle and toaster, comfy armchairs, church pews and trestle tables for wholesome breakfasts and suppers.

Rooms	1 double: £85-£125.
Meals	Continental breakfast included.
	Cooked breakfast £8.
	Dinner, 2 courses, from £12.
	Pubs/restaurants 4 miles.
Closed	November – February.

Julia Martin
The Granary – Borough Farm,
Kelly, Lifton, PL16 0HJ

Tel	+44 (0)1822 870366
Email	contactus@devonyurt.co.uk
Web	www.devonyurt.co.uk

The Cider House

Big mullion windows and contemporary classic interiors at this enchanting former refectory of a medieval abbey. Bryony and Bertie, an endearing young couple, give you stylish bedrooms with roll top tubs and views of garden or valley. Breakfasts are feasts of estate produce – apple juice, honey, rhubarb compote, eggs, bacon, sausages, just-baked bread – served on white china in the drawing room with stunning views of the gardens. There are 700 acres of woodland to explore and the ruined abbey as well as a kitchen garden heaving with soft fruit and vegetables; the framework of old buildings and stone walls are a magical setting. *Minimum stay: 2 nights at weekends. Over 16s welcome.*

Rooms	2 doubles, 1 twin/double, 1 four-poster: £135-£185. Singles £125-£170.
Meals	Pub within walking distance.
Closed	Rarely.

Tel	+44 (0)1822 259062
Email	indulge@cider-house.co.uk
Web	www.cider-house.co.uk

Bryony & Bertie Hancock
The Cider House,
Buckland Abbey, Yelverton, PL20 6EZ

Hooppells Torr

Time to unwind – from the tea and cake on arrival, to the reassuring comfort and luxury of the bedrooms, this is the place to exhale and simply relax. The rambling farmhouse, beautifully updated by Jeeva and Simon, has six acres of spectacular grounds for you to explore and even picnic in. From the conservatory you look out over a glorious English country garden straight out of a Merchant Ivory film, while Simon plies you with his Aga-cooked breakfast, featuring the best of what's local and seasonal. Sheltered, sandy Wonwell beach is just a 20-minute meander away, and the cheery local pub is closer still. Your thoughtful hosts have made sure their guest rooms have a private entrance so you can come and go as you please. Pleasingly understated, but not to be underestimated. *Minimum stay: 2 nights at weekends.*

Rooms	2 doubles: £145-£155.
Meals	Pubs 10-minute walk.
Closed	Rarely.

Jeeva & Simon Beckett
Hooppells Torr,
Kingston, Kingsbridge, TQ7 4HA

Mobile	+44 (0)7772 053919
Email	info@hooppellstorr.com
Web	www.hooppellstorr.com

Beadon Farmhouse

You're near to pretty Salcombe but it's deeply peaceful here and Caroline is brimming with ideas (especially food-related) to help you unwind. Over two acres of garden are yours to wander and there are plenty of spots to sit with a book or practice yoga. You'll also find a gate to a footpath which takes you to North Sands beach, the South West Coast path and the Winking Prawn restaurant. Breakfast is a real treat, taken in the dining room or out on the view-filled terrace and much is from the garden in season. Choose from oats soaked in almond milk with chia seeds, yogurt, fruit and honey; homemade granola; seasonal greens with hummus, quinoa and sunflower seeds, or a big Beadon breakfast with eggs however you like them. It's a 15-minute walk into the centre of Salcombe for shops, art galleries and good places to eat; it's great fun to sit by the harbour with an ice cream watching the boats, and people, come and go. Return to much comfort in your room or to the orchard for a nap in the hammock. *Minimum stay: 2 nights at weekends. Children over 10 welcome.*

Rooms	3 doubles: £115-£160.
Meals	Restaurants and pubs 15-minute walk.
Closed	Rarely.

Mobile	+44 (0)7837 879706
Email	enquiries@beadonfarmhouse.co.uk
Web	www.beadonfarmhouse.co.uk

Caroline Morris
Beadon Farmhouse,
Beadon Road, Salcombe, TQ8 8LX

Glebe House

Set on a hillside with fabulous views over the Coly valley, this late-Georgian vicarage is now a heart-warming B&B. The views will entice you, the hosts will delight you and the house is filled with interesting things. Chuck and Emma spent many years at sea – he a Master Mariner, she a chef – and have filled these big light rooms with cushions, kilims and treasured family pieces. There's a sitting room for guests, a lovely conservatory with vintage vine, peaceful bedrooms with blissful views and bathrooms that sparkle. All this, two sweet pygmy goats, wildlife beyond the ha-ha and the fabulous coast a hike away. *Minimum stay: 2 nights July & August weekends & bank holidays.*

Rooms	1 double, 1 twin/double: £90.
	1 family room for 4: £100-£130.
	Singles £60.
Meals	Dinner, 3 courses, £30.
	Pubs/restaurants 2.5 miles.
Closed	Christmas & New Year.

Emma & Chuck Guest
Glebe House,
Southleigh, Colyton, EX24 6SD

Tel	+44 (0)1404 871276
Mobile	+44 (0)7867 568569
Email	guestsatglebe@gmail.com
Web	www.guestsatglebe.com

Higher Beeson House

The 16th-century farmhouse and stables, arranged around a neat yard, have been kitted out with ground-source underfloor heating and natural slate floors. Bedrooms are in the stables: all are a good size, newly carpeted, spotless with good lighting. Find the chic summerhouse by the lake, replete with wood-burning stove and comfy chairs. Lynda and Charles give you a great local breakfast in the beamed dining room with views through the kitchen to their much loved garden. Originally four acres of boggy wilderness it now thrives. There's a pond stocked with rudd, visited by mallards and moorhens, and packed with flag irises and lilies. Then a series of steps and terraces (all built by clever Charles), bubbling fountains, timber decks, a waterfall, and a greenhouse. Lynda is the plantswoman and she goes for big plants! Gunnera, bamboo, echiums and a banana plant all zoom heavenward while yuccas, phormiums and agapanthus add to the exotic feel. In a perennial bed there are more traditional plants like roses and stocks. So peaceful, so much wildlife; pick a bench and delight in it all. Sometimes you can hear the sea. *Minimum stay: 2 nights.*

Rooms	2 doubles, 1 twin, 1 four-poster: £95-£115. Singles £80-£85.
Meals	Pub/restaurant 0.75 miles.
Closed	Rarely.

Tel	+44 (0)1548 580623
Mobile	+44 (0)7977 905836
Email	enquiries@higherbeeson.co.uk
Web	www.higherbeeson.co.uk

Lynda & Charles Rogers
Higher Beeson House,
Beeson, Kingsbridge, TQ7 2HW

Keynedon Mill

Welcome to an ancient stone mill, and beautiful rooms in the old miller's house. There's a big friendly kitchen with stone floors and a cheerful red Aga, a beamed dining room with a long polished table, a guest sitting room with a wood-burner, and a pretty garden with a stream running through – picnic, read, enjoy a glass of wine in peaceful corners. Elegant bedrooms have superb beds, antique linen curtains, fresh flowers, morning tea trays and decanters of port. A delicious breakfast of home-baked bread and local produce will set you up for the day: walk the coastal path, discover secluded coves. *Over 12s welcome.*

Rooms	2 doubles; 1 double, 1 twin both with separate bath/shower: £95-£125. Singles £75-£95. Extra bed/sofabed £30 per person per night.
Meals	Pub 0.5 miles.
Closed	Rarely.

Stuart & Jennifer Jebb
Keynedon Mill,
Sherford, Kingsbridge, TQ7 2AS

Tel	+44 (0)1548 531485
Mobile	+44 (0)7775 501409
Email	bookings@keynedonmill.co.uk
Web	www.keynedonmill.co.uk

Stokenham House

Lovely Stokenham House gazes at the sea and the bird-rich Slapton Ley. Iona and Paul – an energetic and thoughtful, imaginative couple – have created a super South Hams base: huge chill-out cushions on the lawn, summerhouse in the pretty banked garden, BBQ by the pool. It's grand yet laid-back, with a fine drawing room, big conservatory and a family-friendly feel. Learn to cook or grow veg, invite friends for dinner, host your own party: Iona is a superb cook. The funky large annexe suite is very private; generous bedrooms in the house are decked in vintage fabrics and papers, and have single rooms off. *Pets by arrangement.*

Rooms	1 twin/double, sharing separate bath with single: £120-£145. 1 suite for 2: £140. 1 family room for 4: £140-£210. 1 single: £100. Extra bed no charge.
Meals	Dinner from £30. Pubs/restaurants 2-minute walk.
Closed	Rarely.

Tel	+44 (0)1548 581257
Mobile	+44 (0)7720 443132
Email	ionajepson@googlemail.com
Web	www.stokenhamhouse.co.uk

Iona & Paul Jepson
Stokenham House,
Stokenham, Kingsbridge, TQ7 2ST

Strete Barton House

Contemporary, friendly, exotic and exquisite: French sleigh beds and Asian art, white basins and black chandeliers, and a garden with sofas for the views. So much to love – and best of all, the coastal path outside the door. Your caring hosts live the dream, running immaculate B&B by the sea, in an old manor house at the top of the village. Breakfasts are exuberantly local (village eggs, sausages from Dartmouth, honey from the bay), there's a wood-burner in the sitting room, warm toasty floors and Kevin and Stuart know exactly which beach, walk or pub is the one for you. Heavenly. *Children over 8 welcome. Dogs welcome in cottage suite only.*

Rooms	3 doubles, 1 twin/double; 1 twin/double with separate shower: £105-£155. 1 suite for 2: £150-£165.
Meals	Pub/restaurant 50 yds.
Closed	Rarely.

Stuart Litster & Kevin Hooper
Strete Barton House,
Totnes Road, Strete, Dartmouth, TQ6 0RU

Tel	+44 (0)1803 770364
Email	info@stretebarton.co.uk
Web	www.stretebarton.co.uk

Brooking

A whitewashed, wisteria-clad house in a gorgeous village... tea and cake will be waiting. Alison's is a relaxed and friendly home. You will sleep well in a peaceful, charming bedroom: luxurious linen on a brass bed, floral cushions, a jug of wild flowers on an antique wooden chest. Alison's breakfasts change with the seasons: homemade granola, jams and bread, fruit compotes and tasty cooked choices. The garden is walled, rambling and pretty with a tangle of climbers, a bright wooden summerhouse and places to sit in the sun. Head out for nearby Totnes (bustling and arty), great wood or moorland walks and fun on the river Dart. *Babysitting happily available if needed.*

Rooms	1 double: £85-£95. Extra room available; let to same party only. Travel cot, high chair, toys and books in house!
Meals	Soup, bread & local cheeses available. Children's meals available by arrangement. Pubs 2-minute walk.
Closed	Rarely.

Tel	+44 (0)1803 731037
Email	w.carlyon@btinternet.com
Web	www.brooking-ashprington.co.uk

Alison Carlyon
Brooking,
Ashprington, Totnes, TQ9 7UL

Avenue Cottage

The tree-lined approach is steep and spectacular; the cottage sits in 11 wondrous acres which overlook the river Dart and Sharpham Estate (local vineyard.) Richard is a gifted gardener and happy to guide you round his fascinating garden with its magical woodland trail and enviable range of hydrangeas. Find a quiet spot to read or absorb the tranquility with tea on the terrace. The house itself is comfortable and calm – rooms look over the sweeping valley and garden. The old-fashioned twin room has a balcony and large, recently refurbished bathroom with a walk in shower. The pretty village, vineyard café and pub are a short walk away.

Rooms	1 twin/double; 1 double, sharing shower room with owner: £70-£90. Singles £55-£75.
Meals	Pub 0.25 miles.
Closed	Rarely.

Richard Pitts & David Sykes
Avenue Cottage,
Ashprington, Totnes, TQ9 7UT

Tel	+44 (0)1803 732769
Mobile	+44 (0)7719 147475
Email	richard.pitts@btinternet.com
Web	www.avenuecottage.com

7 The Grove

In the heart of higgledy-piggledy Totnes you'll be welcomed by Bethan and John with your own floor and the use of a sunny sitting room. Breakfast is served when you wake – home-baked bread, fresh juice and compotes using fruit from the garden, a full English if you want. The big garden has plenty of hidden corners you're encouraged to explore and includes three small ponds and flower beds where wildflowers are allowed to romp. Behind a stone wall is a vegetable and fruit garden where priority is given to produce that is good to pick at and eat raw. It's a short walk to Totnes' high street, weekend markets, independent shops and restaurants. A half hour drive south gets you to sandy beaches for walking, swimming and surfing; the same distance west and you're on Dartmoor.

Rooms	2 twin/doubles sharing bath, let to same party only: £90. Singles £55.
Meals	Pubs/restaurants 300 yds.
Closed	Christmas.

Tel	+44 (0)1803 862866
Email	totnesgrove@yahoo.com
Web	www.totnesgrove.com

Bethan Edwards & John Paige
7 The Grove,
Totnes, TQ9 5ED

Bulleigh Barton Manor

Tea and scones will be waiting. Find long, leafy views to wake up to, a pool for lazy summer days, ponds and a big colourful garden with a summerhouse. Liz and Mark have restored their house with care, uncovering beams and lovely bits of old wood and filling it with original art and books. Bedrooms are inviting: sink-into beds, china pieces on white window sills, a pot of garden flowers, local fudge and homemade cake. They are keen on sourcing the best local produce and their host of hens lay your breakfast eggs. Dartmoor and the south coast are at your feet; return to a friendly hello from Zennor the dog by the fire. *Over 16s welcome.*

Rooms	2 doubles: £86-£135.
	1 suite for 2 with kitchenette:
	£90-£130. Singles £77-£120.
Meals	Pubs/restaurants 0.5 miles.
Closed	Rarely.

Liz & Mark Lamport
Bulleigh Barton Manor,
Ipplepen, Newton Abbot, TQ12 5UA

Email	liz.lamport@btopenworld.com
Web	www.bulleighbartonmanor.co.uk

Hannaford House

An inviting place to stay, with fabulous views across the valley to Haldon Forest. Kay and Simon give you a cosy annexe for two with a wood-burner, well-dressed bed, books and flowers; you have your own sunny courtyard as well with table, chairs and loungers where you can sit with an evening glass of something or your morning coffee. Breakfast is brought over to you; home-produced and tasty, it includes sausage and bacon from the pigs, eggs from the hens, tomatoes in season, homemade bread and jams. Find hammocks in the colourful garden, woods to explore, Exmouth estuary for boating fun and Dartmoor for hearty walks.

Rooms	1 annexe for 2: £100. Singles £70-£80.
Meals	Pub 1.5 miles.
Closed	Rarely.

Mobile	+44 (0)7752 701182/
	+44 (0)7902 920207
Email	kay@hannafordhouse.co.uk
Web	www.hannafordhouse.co.uk

Kay & Simon Wisker
Hannaford House,
Kennford, Exeter, EX6 7XZ

Brook Farmhouse

Tuck yourself up in the peace and quiet of Paul and Penny's whitewashed, thatched cottage, surrounded by glorious countryside. Inside find your own charming sitting room with a huge inglenook, good antiques, fresh flowers, and comfy sofa and chairs; breakfast here on homemade apple juice, eggs from the owners' hens and delicious local bacon and sausages. Up the ancient spiral stone stairs is your warm, beamed bedroom with smooth linen, chintzy curtains, lots of cushions. You are near Dartmoor and can reach Devon beaches and the north Cornish coast; perfect for hearty walkers, birdwatchers, surfers and picnic-lovers.

Rooms	1 double with separate bathroom: £80-£90. Singles £55-£65. Extra rooms available.
Meals	Pub 2 miles.
Closed	Rarely.

Paul & Penny Steadman
Brook Farmhouse,
Tedburn St Mary, Exeter, EX6 6DS

Tel	+44 (0)1647 270042
Email	penny.steadman@btconnect.com
Web	www.brook-farmhouse.co.uk

The Linhay

A peaceful hideaway for couples looking to escape from the city, this 18th-century thatched cottage sits in its own valley in the serene Devon countryside. With a running stream nearby, a pretty orchard and friendly Balwen sheep, this is a place for nature lovers. Owners Andrei and Holly have cleverly converted this three-level open-plan bolthole. They live just metres away in the main house. Expect a cosy, natural feel with rocking chairs by a log burner and a balcony looking out over apple and plum trees.

Home-cooked breakfasts are brought over whenever you wish: freshly-laid eggs, sausages from the pigs and artisan bread. They'll give you supper too if you don't want to venture out. Wellies and maps are waiting for you so set off over glorious fields or venture further to village pubs for long, lazy lunches. Hole up by the fire with a good book, or wander the garden and sit under the weeping willow. In summer the swallows swoop. *Minimum stay: 2 nights.*

Rooms	1 suite for 2 with kitchenette: £95.
Meals	Homecooked supper £30 for 2.
	Pubs/restaurants 3 miles.
Closed	Rarely.

Tel	+44 (0)1363 84386
Email	enquiries@smilingsheep.co.uk
Web	www.smilingsheep.co.uk

Holly Carter & Andrei Szerard
The Linhay,
Brendon Cottage, Copplestone,
Crediton, EX17 5NZ

Ashley Court

This Regency country house is full of delightful surprises with much unchanged since the early 1930s. Nigel and Tara have rewired and replumbed and left the good bits carefully alone. Settle in the morning room with its interesting library, join in with a yoga class, or ask for a guided tour of the house and garden – the restoration of both is purposely gentle and the history fascinating. Architectural historians will want to visit the intact stables – still with horses and still with the ladder up to the stable boy's quarters; cobbled paths through the mature woodlands and rhododendrons slowly being revealed; the bones of an ancient walled garden and greenhouses painstakingly being brought to life with advice from the Devon Gardens Trust. You're just a 15-minute walk from Tiverton and there are walks along the river or canal; you'll find good pubs in Cadeleigh and Bickleigh.

Rooms	3 doubles, 1 twin: £10-£120.
	2 singles: £45.
Meals	Pubs 10-minute drive.
Closed	Christmas, New Year & occasional weekends.

Nigel Jones
Ashley Court,
Ashley, Tiverton, EX16 5PD

| Mobile | +44 (0)7725 950683 |
| Email | nigel@yogajunction.co.uk |

Pounds Farm

A flock of white geese trot across the field, the cottage gardens are a summer-blooming feast of colour and the Blackdown Hills are the green backdrop. Inside is just as good: polished wood, original lithographs, oil paintings, comfy seats by the fire, airy bedrooms in apple-pie order and freshly picked flowers in every room. Enjoy the pool, wander the gorgeous gardens, have breakfast (free-range and delicious) outside in the sun – Diana wants you to feel at home. You're equidistant from Exmoor and the south coast, and you can wander down the hill for supper and a pint in the local. A friendly house with a timeless charm.

Rooms	1 double; 1 double with separate bathroom; 1 twin/double sharing bathroom with double, let to same party only: £80-£95.
Meals	Pubs/restaurants 10-minute walk.
Closed	Rarely.

Email	shillingscottage@yahoo.co.uk
Web	www.poundsfarm.co.uk

Diana Elliott
Pounds Farm,
Hemyock, Cullompton, EX15 3QS

Larkbeare Grange

Follow the tree-lined drive to this smart Georgian house and be warmly greeted by Charlie and Julia, homemade cake and tea at the ready. There's a peaceful air with the grandfather clock ticking away the hours. You'll sleep like a bear under goose down duvets; there's a suite for a small family and rooms to bring friends or grandparents along. Charlie, Savoy-trained, and Julia are fun and give you Aga breakfasts with heaps of choice: organic porridge, fresh and poached fruit (lots from the orchards), homemade bread, jams and yogurt, local bacon, slow-roasted sausages, smoked salmon and scrambled eggs, veggie options too. There's a holiday barn (self-cater if you have a dog in tow), acres to explore, dark skies and Exeter a short drive. Walk to The Thirsty Farmer to work up an appetite for supper. *Minimum stay: 2 nights some weekends.*

Rooms	2 doubles, 1 twin/double: £120–£150.
	1 suite for 4: £180–£200.
	Singles £95–£120.
Meals	Pub 1.5 miles.
Closed	Rarely.

Charlie & Julia Hutchings
Larkbeare Grange,
Larkbeare, Talaton, Exeter, EX5 2RY

Tel	+44 (0)1404 822069
Mobile	+44 (0)7762 574915
Email	stay@larkbeare.net
Web	www.larkbeare.net

Glebe Farm

Sheila and Tim make sure you're well fed. Start each morning at a big table in the kitchen with French windows flung open to the courtyard. Tim cooks sourdough in the Aga and smokes salmon, Sheila makes jam and compote, their chickens provide the eggs. You'll be welcomed with tea (or an aperitif) plus homemade shortbread, and you can ask about picnics. Three charming bedrooms look out over wildflowers, and there's a garden for pottering. You can feed the chickens, fire up the pizza oven or just relax – Tim will share his telescope, or you can borrow the Canadian canoe for lazy river paddling. South Pool is a sleepy village – it's where Salcombe regulars come for quiet – but you're close to Devon's best beaches. Nip over to Mill Bay on the foot ferry for cocktails and spa luxuries, and feast on fresh seafood at The Beach House in South Milton. *Minimum stay: 2 nights in high season.*

Rooms	2 doubles, 1 twin: £105-£120. Extra child's bed £20.
Meals	Pub 5-minute walk.
Closed	Christmas & occasionally.

Tel	+44 (0)1548 532850
Mobile	+44 (0)7802 808624
Email	hirsttim@gmail.com
Web	www.glebefarmsouthpool.co.uk

Timothy Hirst
Glebe Farm,
Kingsbridge, TQ7 2RP

Greenhill House

There's something timeless about Lyme and the views from the south-facing windows here are spectacular: rolling hills, the town and the bay lie before you. Sara and Ed live on the third floor with the rest of the house given over to their guests to come and go as they please. You'll feel very well looked after, from afternoon tea served next to the open fire in the drawing room or in the garden on arrival, to gourmet breakfasts served at an antique table in the formal cream-and-blue dining room. You can wander into town in 15 minutes – explore the many art galleries, look for fossils on the beach or wander along to the historic harbour. There are superb restaurants here too; HIX Oyster & Fish House is a 20-minute walk – you can easily get a taxi back.

Rooms	3 doubles: £150-£175. Singles £130-£155.
Meals	Pubs/restaurants 1 mile.
Closed	Christmas.

Sara & Ed Hollway
Greenhill House,
Somers Road,
Lyme Regis, DT7 3EX

Tel	+44 (0)1297 445497
Email	greenhillhousebandb@gmail.com
Web	www.greenhillhousebandb.co.uk

Old Monmouth

Tudor townhouse with a colourful past – the Duke of Monmouth, Oscar Wilde, a box of love letters found after WWII American soldiers stayed... Tony and Alex have loved discovering the history and bringing this old house back to life. They're a creative, immensely likeable pair and their vintage finds from French trips abound. Bedrooms are romantic with lavender-scented drawers, tea trays, perhaps an antique gilt mirror, Liberty wallpaper or flame-pink cushion. There's a summery breakfast room, wood fires burning bright all winter and orchids in every corner. Walk along The Cobb, explore the coast path; sailing, great restaurants, famous gardens too. *Pass to nearest car park provided.*

Rooms	4 doubles: £95-£140. Cot available.
Meals	Pubs/restaurants 2-minute walk.
Closed	Christmas, Easter and summer holidays.

Tel	+44 (0)1297 444124
Mobile	+44 (0)7919 858693
Email	oldmonmouth@gmail.com
Web	www.oldmonmouth.com

Tony & Alex Kossykh-Bearman
Old Monmouth,
12 Church Street,
Lyme Regis, DT7 3BS

Wodetone Vineyard

Deep Dorset with patchwork fields, miles of hedgerows, ancient oaks. Arrive at this farmstead with its old barns and rows of vines, and breathe in the peace. Mary and Nigel are relaxed hosts; find a happy mix of antique and retro, splashes of gingham, artworks, family photos, flowers. Solar heats the water; wood fires keep it all toasty. The elegant sitting room has two tables in the window for sunny breakfasts: seasonal fruit, homemade granola and jams, local bacon, good bread. Explore bluebell woods and footpaths, walk the coastal path. Mary has created a wonderful place to stay, and you can book vineyard tours and tastings too.
Minimum stay: 2 nights in high season.

Rooms	2 doubles: £90-£105. Singles £80-£95.
Meals	Pubs/restaurants 2.5 miles.
Closed	10 October to 12 February.

Mary Riddle
Wodetone Vineyard,
Spence Farm, Wootton Fitzpaine,
Bridport, DT6 6DF

Mobile	+44 (0)7966 751467
Email	info@vineyardbandb.co.uk
Web	www.vineyardbandb.co.uk

Wooden Cabbage House

Leafy lanes and a private drive lead you to Martyn and Susie's beautifully restored hamstone house, hidden in rolling West Dorset. Savour the total peace and stunning valley views in a home full of flowers, fine antiques and paintings. Cosy bedrooms have country-house charm; the suite is dog-friendly. Delicious breakfasts are served in the garden room: homemade granola and jams, garden fruit compote, local eggs, bacon, sausages, smoked trout; French windows open to a productive potager and terraced gardens. Good walks, and the Jurassic coast is 30 minutes; return to sofas by the log fire. Fabulous hosts – nothing is too much trouble. *Children over 6 welcome.*

Rooms	2 doubles, 1 twin/double: £120-£130.
	1 suite for 4: £145-£150. Singles £110.
Meals	Pubs/restaurants 3 miles.
Closed	1 November to 12 March.

Tel	+44 (0)1935 83362
Email	relax@woodencabbage.co.uk
Web	www.woodencabbage.co.uk

Martyn & Susie Lee
Wooden Cabbage House,
East Chelborough,
Dorchester, DT2 0QA

Old Forge

Snug in a stream-tickled hamlet, deep in Hardy country, this B&B is as pretty as a painting and wonderfully peaceful. Judy is charming and friendly – this is a happy place, a real country home, a no-rules B&B. The 17th-century farmhouse opposite is where you breakfast: Judy, ex Prue Leith, serves a neighbour's eggs, a friend's sausages and good coffee in an eclectically furnished room with bucolic views to garden, meadows and hills. Walk from the door or head to the Jurassic Coast for more demanding hikes, explore Bridport's vibrant Saturday market or beautiful Sherborne Abbey, discover Bronze Age forts. Judy is happy to give you a lift to and from the nearby pub.

Rooms	1 double: £100. Singles £60-£70. Stays of 2+nights: £80-£90.
Meals	Pub 1.5 miles.
Closed	Rarely.

Judy Thompson
Old Forge,
Lower Wraxall Farmhouse,
Lower Wraxall, Dorchester, DT2 0HL

Tel	+44 (0)1935 83218
Email	judyjthompson@hotmail.co.uk
Web	www.lowerwraxall.co.uk

Fullers Earth

Ian and Wendy greet you warmly with tea and homemade cake by the fire in their listed Georgian home – you'll feel relaxed in no time with such easy hosts. Upstairs you'll find roomy bedrooms with pretty village views, fresh flowers and interesting books to dip into. You breakfast well on sausages and bacon from the local farm, tomatoes from the greenhouse in season, rhubarb and gooseberry compotes from the garden and homemade jams. Plan your walks through this AONB or join the Macmillan Way (half a mile). Bring bikes and cycle the National routes which criss-cross the area, have a day of fossil hunting at the coast, climb Eggardon Hill or Golden Cap for far-reaching views – you're in the heart of Hardy country. Return to look around the village, visit 'the best village stores in Dorset', explore the church with the highest tower in Dorset, an Art Deco baptistry and a splendid William Morris window. It's well worth taking a turn in the beautifully-kept garden too. The local pub, the Fox and Hounds, is a short stumble from here. *Minimum stay: 2 nights at weekends & in high season.*

Rooms	1 double; 1 double, sharing bath/shower room with single, let to same party only: £115. Singles £75.
Meals	Pub 5-minute walk.
Closed	Christmas.

Tel	+44 (0)1300 320190
Mobile	+44 (0)7792 654543
Email	stay@fullersearth.co.uk
Web	www.fullersearth.co.uk

Wendy & Ian Gregory
Fullers Earth,
Cattistock, Dorchester, DT2 0JL

West Compton Manor

Drive down narrow lanes with tall hedges to this little hamlet and an old stone family house filled with photos, pictures, loads of books, a couple of friendly dogs and memorabilia. And a Tesla charger, although check the details before you stay. Bedrooms feel very private – you pretty much have your own wing of the house and you can come and go as you please. Breakfast will include home-laid eggs, bacon and sausages from a local farm, maybe some mushrooms foraged by Ashley. He loves cooking and will give you supper too if he has enough notice, so do ask. Walk along footpaths across Eggardon Hill into Askerswell and the Spyway Inn for good pub grub in about 40 minutes, or just over an hour to Three Horseshoes Inn at Powerstock. Beachcombers and fossil hunters can drive to Lyme in 30 minutes.
Minimum stay: 2 nights.

Rooms	1 double, 1 twin, both with separate bath/shower: £100-£140. 1 suite for 2: £120-£150. Singles £80-£100. Extra bed/sofabed £50 per person per night.
Meals	Pubs within 3 miles.
Closed	Rarely.

Ashley Stewart
West Compton Manor,
West Compton, Dorchester, DT2 0EY

Tel	+44 (0)1300 320400
Email	ashley@manorfarmwestcompton.com
Web	www.westcomptonmanor.co.uk

Manor Farm

Tessa's family have lived in the flint and stone house since 1860 so it's crammed with history but not in the least daunting. It's a real family home with books galore, pictures, maps and photographs and from all the windows views soar to the chalk hills. You breakfast by the wood-burner in the dining room: sometimes homemade granola, always homemade jams and marmalade, fruit from the garden in season and good bacon and sausages sizzled in the Aga. Supper can be two or three courses and sometimes simple, sometimes smart but always with garden vegetables and a pudding and eaten outdoors in summer. The Macmillan Way passes through the hamlet so join it in either direction for short or long walks. A two to three hour hike will take you to Abbotsbury – a unique coastal village with a swannery – you can always get a taxi back. The nearest decent pub is a 10-15 minute drive – The Spyway at Askerswell. Return to very private bedrooms up your own staircase.

Rooms	1 double, 1 twin sharing bath, let to same party only: £80-£95.
Meals	Dinner, 2-3 courses, from £15. Pub/restaurant 4 miles.
Closed	Rarely.

Tel	+44 (0)1308 482227
Mobile	+44 (0)7818 037184 (signal unreliable)
Email	tessa@cvfarms.co.uk
Web	www.manor-farm.uk.com

Tessa Russell
Manor Farm,
Compton Valence, Dorchester, DT2 9ES

Tudor Cottage

Come to feel very special and for truly exquisite breakfasts at the cosy table in the sitting room. Homemade muesli and granola, homemade jams, artful fruit salads, mushroom omelette, home-baked bread and more are served on pretty china with proper linen napkins. Cross the bridge over the river Frome from the village and enter a vast parkland criss-crossed with paths, ancient trees and bridle ways, take a packed lunch and head to pebble or sand beaches in under half an hour, eat well at the Royal Oak in Cerne Abbas or The Ollerod in Beaminster. Bridport is worth delving into for its quirky independent shops and arts centre, thriving markets and artisan food outlets. Return to the comforting sitting room – in winter the fire roars up the chimney behind the medieval overmantle – and sit back with tea and cake. *Over 16s welcome.*

Rooms	1 double, 1 twin: £90–£105.
Meals	Pubs/restaurants 2 miles.
Closed	Rarely.

Louise Clarke
Tudor Cottage,
9 Dorchester Road, Frampton,
Dorchester, DT2 9NB

Tel	+44 (0)1300 320382
Mobile	+44 (0)7970 282151
Email	stay@tudorcottagedorset.co.uk
Web	www.tudorcottagedorset.co.uk

Quintessential B&B

Treasures spill over from Bob's antique shop opposite and fill every space in his little cottage. Known locally as 'Bonkers Bob', he says he's put his heart and soul into creating a B&B like no other... Step into an eccentric home of quirky corners, art, fine linens, French finds and tropical and theatrical surprises. He used to live in Bordeaux and is a laid-back host who loves to chat and cook – tea and cakes when you get there, and Aga-cooked breakfasts (on big plates) that set you up for anything. Pretty Abbotsbury is well worth exploring, there's a good pub you can walk to for dinner (or book one of Bob's simple suppers) and you can blow your cobwebs away walking along nearby Chesil Beach. Return to very comfy rooms: guests always comment on their good night's sleep. *Minimum stay: 2 nights in high season.*

Rooms	2 doubles: £85-£120.
Meals	Dinner, 3 courses, £22.50.
	Pub 5-minute walk.
Closed	Rarely.

Mobile	+44 (0)7775 681081
Email	bobhure@gmail.com

Robert Curtis
Quintessential B&B,
8 West Street,
Abbotsbury, DT3 4JT

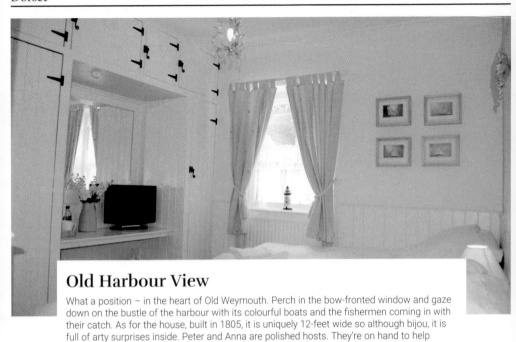

Old Harbour View

What a position – in the heart of Old Weymouth. Perch in the bow-fronted window and gaze down on the bustle of the harbour with its colourful boats and the fishermen coming in with their catch. As for the house, built in 1805, it is uniquely 12-feet wide so although bijou, it is full of arty surprises inside. Peter and Anna are polished hosts. They're on hand to help and give you homemade cake with a cuppa when you get there, and serve outstanding breakfasts on lovely china: homemade breads and jams, creamed mushrooms on puff pastry, smoked haddock and kippers from the Bridport Smokery. Wander along the medieval lanes, head for the sandy beach, book a boat trip, try one of the many seafood restaurants... Then it's back home to a very comfortable bed. *Ask about permits for parking, on booking. Minimum stay: 2 nights.*

Rooms	1 double, 1 twin/double: £98. Singles £80.
Meals	Pubs/restaurants within walking distance.
Closed	Christmas & New Year.

Peter Vincent
Old Harbour View,
12 Trinity Road, Weymouth, DT4 8TJ

Tel	+44 (0)1305 774633
Email	info@oldharbourview.co.uk
Web	www.oldharbourviewweymouth.co.uk

Marren

On the Dorset coastal path overlooking Weymouth Bay – a lovely spot for Jurassic Coast walking and crystal-clear swimming. Peter and Wendy have transformed this 1920s house and their style reflects their penchant for natural materials and country life. It's set in four acres of terraced gardens with Italianate overtones, that have been created by Wendy, a garden designer. Find strong structured evergreen 'cloud' pruned and clipped shrubs, exotic plants, swaying grasses, huge terracotta pots bursting with colour... a complete wildlife sanctuary. Bedrooms always have flowers too; one has a door onto the garden, while from the other you can watch the sun setting over the sea. Enjoy a breakfast of homemade bread, marmalade and jams, seasonal fruit salad and a full English, then wander down to the secluded beach below for a turquoise sea swim or a bracing picnic. *Minimum stay: 2 nights at weekends.*

Rooms	2 doubles: £100-£145.
Meals	Pub 1 mile.
Closed	Rarely.

Tel	+44 (0)1305 851503
Mobile	+44 (0)7957 886399
Email	peter@marren.info
Web	www.marren.info

Peter Cartwright
Marren,
Holworth, Ringstead, DT2 8NJ

Lulworth House

Down through hills, wild heaths and pine forests to Lulworth. Carole and John's home is set back from the cove in a peaceful lane; artist and garden designer, their 1980s house is a creative treasure, inside and out. Both the bedrooms are on the ground floor and one opens to its own terrace. Wake for a generous breakfast served upstairs in the open-plan living space – or outside on balmy days. It's worth a half hour drive to the Square and Compass pub in Worth Matravers for fossils, real ale and homemade pasties. Wander round a garden full of banana trees, ferns, deep borders and a pergola with scrambling abundant grapevines. Walk to the sea in 10 minutes or climb over the cliffs to secret Mupe Cove for an early morning swim. Lulworth Cove has various good places to eat out and you can walk there in a few minutes. *Over 12s welcome.*

Rooms	1 double; 1 double with separate shower room: £90-£125.
Meals	Pubs/restaurants within walking distance.
Closed	Occasionally.

John & Carole Bickerton
Lulworth House,
Bindon Road, West Lulworth,
Wareham, BH20 5RU

Tel	+44 (0)1929 406192
Email	lulworthhousebandb@gmail.com
Web	www.lulworthhousebandb.co.uk

Bering House

An immaculate harbourside retreat. Renate's attention to detail shows how much she loves running her B&B and welcoming guests. From fluffy dressing gowns and bathroom treats to biscuits and sherry – she and John look after you with heart-warming generosity. Bedrooms are really comfortable; the Harbour Suite is huge and has views across the sparkling harbour and over to the Purbeck Hills. The breakfast table gleams with Spode china and Renate offers a superb choice: exotic fruits with Parma ham, warm figs or Morello cherry compote with Greek yogurt and honey, 'posh porridge', smoked salmon, poached eggs, muffins, smoked haddock gratin... Sit out under the vine-covered arbour, walk through the park to the colourful huts by the sea, take a boat trip to Brownsea Island and spot red squirrels, Sika deer and masses of birds. *Minimum stay: 2 nights.*

Rooms	1 twin/double: £95.
	1 suite for 2 with kitchenette: £120.
	Singles £70-£110.
Meals	Pub 400 yds. Restaurant 500 yds.
Closed	Rarely.

Tel	+44 (0)1202 673419
Email	johnandrenate1@tiscali.co.uk
Web	www.beringhouse.co.uk

Renate & John Wadham
Bering House,
53 Branksea Avenue,
Hamworthy, Poole, BH15 4DP

Cedar House

It's a beautiful Georgian family home – grand, warm and welcoming, with four acres of garden next to a working farm. Owner Christopher can drive you (in a Bentley) from local airports and stations to the door, where you'll be greeted with fresh coffee and cake. Breakfast is eaten around a big table with other guests – separately if you prefer – or in the acre of private garden. Groups can have dinner at the house too, just ask. It's perfect for bigger groups as well as couples, with a conservatory ideal for a small convention. You're near the edge of the New Forest for walks and biking, Christchurch harbour is a 15-minute walk, beaches are close. Return to big stylish bedrooms with Bose speaker systems, Nespresso machines, fruit bowls and mini fridges. All have views over the gardens or fields, and some have balconies. *Minimum stay: 2 nights.*

Rooms	5 doubles, 1 twin: £120-£150. Extra bed available.
Meals	Pubs/restaurants 15-minute walk.
Closed	Christmas.

Christopher van Hagen
Cedar House,
29 Salisbury Road,
Christchurch, BH23 7JH

Mobile	+44 (0)7787 574939
Email	chrisvh29@gmail.com
Web	www.cedarhousebbnb.co.uk

Crawford House

Below, the river Stour winds through the valley and under the medieval, nine-arched bridge. Above, an Iron Age hill fort; between is Crawford House. The sun streams through the tall windows of the downstairs rooms and you feel very much at home. Andrea is fun and has lots of local knowledge. There are plenty of historic houses to visit, you can get to Poole with its stunning natural harbour in half an hour, and the gate from her garden leads on to the North Dorset Trailway – useful for dog walking. Sit out in walled gardens full of roses with lemon drizzle cake and tea, read by the open fire, sleep well in warm comfy bedrooms. Andrea's delicious breakfasts include homemade marmalade and seasonal berries.

Rooms	1 twin/double; 1 twin with separate bath, 1 twin with separate shower: £75-£80. Singles £40.
Meals	Pub 10-minute walk.
Closed	Rarely.

Tel	+44 (0)1258 857338
Email	andrea.lea888@gmail.com

Andrea Lea
Crawford House,
Spetisbury,
Blandford Forum, DT11 9DP

Abbots Court House

A refreshingly unfussy place, set in five acres with roaming chickens and pigs and a large kitchen garden. Jez and Niki are the most open and engaging couple and staying here will lift your spirits. Everything about Abbots Court feels warm and soulful. Dine by roaring fires on an outstanding menu (small, selective and only for guests) of home-grown, very local or freshly foraged ingredients. There's a snug for romantic pre-dinner drinks and little ones are well looked after too with early suppers, high chairs and a connecting family room. Cosy nights in big beds are followed by breakfasts of homemade breads, chef's porridge and a full Dorset cooked spread. Then if you've time to explore, get your wellies on and go den building in the copses or take a long, lazy walk through stunning countryside.

Rooms	5 doubles: £90-£180.
	1 family room for 4: £90-£180.
	Extra beds available.
Meals	Dinner approx. £28. 7-course tasting
	menu, £58. Pubs/restaurants 8 miles.
Closed	Occasionally.

Jez Barfoot
Abbots Court House,
East Street,
Winterborne Kingston, DT11 9BH

Email	info@abbots-court.co.uk
Web	www.abbots-court.co.uk

Lower Fifehead Farm

A passion for cooking here! The dramatic dining room has church pews at an oak refectory table; the log fire will be lit in winter, and you can eat on the terrace in summer. Hearty breakfasts include bacon and sausages from home-reared pigs, devilled mushrooms or eggs Benedict; Jessica makes the bread and preserves, and there's always freshly squeezed orange juice. It's a gorgeous house too – it's been in Jasper's family for many years and shines with pretty fabrics, antiques, hand-painted furniture, vintage pieces, rich colours, shelves of books – and seriously comfortable brass beds. Don't miss the candlelit dinners. *Minimum stay: 2 nights at weekends.*

Rooms	2 doubles, 1 twin/double: £75-£95. Singles from £55.
Meals	Dinner, 2-3 courses, £25-£30. Pubs/restaurants 2 miles.
Closed	Christmas & New Year.

Tel	+44 (0)1258 817335
Email	lowerfifeheadfm@gmail.com
Web	www.lowerfifeheadfm.co.uk

Jessica Miller
Lower Fifehead Farm,
Fifehead St Quinton,
Sturminster Newton, DT10 2AP

All Hallows Farmhouse

The farmhouse is on the edge of Wimborne St Giles, overlooking watercress beds. It's a relaxed family home combined with cookery school where Lisa enthusiastically shares her culinary knowledge with guests who come from all over the world. Sleep in bedrooms with garden views, rise for breakfast or brunch. Lisa bakes English muffins daily and changes the menu with the seasons – there's always fruit from the orchard and homemade Bircher muesli, then heaps of choice from pancakes and kedgeree to salmon fishcakes and slow-cooked gammon. In the evening, order a charcuterie platter or drive to The Drovers pub in the next village, Gussage All Saints (about three miles). Return to a generous sitting room just for guests where the fire burns in winter; settle in with a book or board game... replete and happy. *Minimum stay: 2 nights.*

Rooms	1 double; 1 double with separate bathroom: £80-£120.
Meals	Supper, sharing platters from £25.
Closed	Rarely.

Lisa Osman
All Hallows Farmhouse,
All Hallows,
Wimborne St Giles, BH21 5NJ

Tel	+44 (0)1725 551185
Email	lisa@allhallowsfarmhouse.co.uk
Web	www.allhallowsfarmhouse.co.uk

Caundle Barn

Take the pretty route... ramble through rich pasture, tiny hamlets and woodland to reach this attractive 17th-century stone barn. All is spotless, from the oak stairs and galleried landing to the antiques and exquisite curtains; Sarah has blended old and new beautifully. Your bedroom is sunny and sumptuous; the little shower room has scented oils and luxurious towels. Sarah cooks with the seasons and you'll enjoy homemade marmalade, fruits, local eggs, bacon and sausages. Views and walks are sublime, Sherborne is fun, there are gourmet pubs galore and Poppy the Jack Russell adds her charm to this friendly home.

Rooms	1 double: £80-£110. Singles £60.
Meals	Pubs/restaurants 4 miles.
Closed	Rarely.

Tel	+44 (0)1963 251264
Email	howes20@btinternet.com

Sarah Howes
Caundle Barn,
Purse Caundle, Sherborne, DT9 5DY

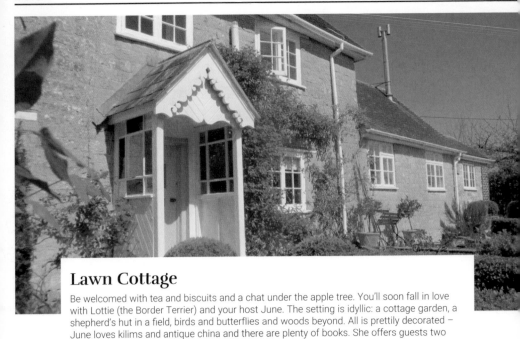

Lawn Cottage

Be welcomed with tea and biscuits and a chat under the apple tree. You'll soon fall in love with Lottie (the Border Terrier) and your host June. The setting is idyllic: a cottage garden, a shepherd's hut in a field, birds and butterflies and woods beyond. All is prettily decorated – June loves kilims and antique china and there are plenty of books. She offers guests two bedrooms on the ground floor (one with bunk beds) and a third upstairs; the shepherd's hut, surrounded by nature and with stunning views is the perfect hideaway for two and you can add extra beds or tents. Breakfasts of crispy bacon, locally baked bread and eggs from known hens can be taken in the dining room or on the terrace when fine. This is the Blackmore Vale – Thomas Hardy's 'Valley of the Dairies'. Many have gone, but you can still see cows dotted around the villages, including Stour Row. Stride across the fields to Duncliffe Wood; gaze on the views to Melbury Down; explore Shaftesbury Abbey museum and garden; have supper in the King's Arms in the village.

Rooms	1 twin/double; 1 double with separate bathroom: £80-£90. 1 single/bunk: £50. 1 shepherd's hut for 2 with separate bathroom in house: £90. Extra bed £20 per person per night.
Meals	Pub/restaurant 1 mile.
Closed	Rarely.

June Watkins
Lawn Cottage,
Stour Row, Shaftesbury, SP7 0QF

Tel	+44 (0)1747 838719
Mobile	+44 (0)7809 696218
Email	enquiries@lawncottagedorset.co.uk
Web	www.lawncottagedorset.co.uk

Gutchpool Farm

You stay in the private wing of the farmhouse with views over farmland, river or courtyard. There's a grass landing strip so it's possible to arrive by plane (by prior arrangement of course); horses can be stabled too. Breakfast choices change often – a convivial affair by the wood-burner in the big sitting room: eggs from the hens in the orchard, perhaps mushrooms on toast with chives, avocado on sourdough with chilli and lime or blueberry pancakes with maple syrup, homemade preserves and freshly-squeezed orange juice. Have supper at Rachel and Bill's favourite inn The Beckford Arms in Fonthill Gifford (a 20-minute drive); Rachel gives you a helpful list of other nearby eateries, interesting shops and places to visit too. *Minimum stay: 2 nights.*

Rooms	1 twin/double; 1 double, 1 twin both with separate bathroom: £100-£130.
Meals	Nearest recommended restaurant 10-minute drive. Packed lunch £10.
Closed	Christmas & occasionally.

Tel	+44 (0)1747 612345
Mobile	+44 (0)7836 763701
Email	beds@gutchpool.com
Web	www.gutchpool.com

Rachel Hall
Gutchpool Farm,
Gillingham, SP8 5QP

Fairways

The food, the views – amazing! Tim is a passionate cook, and he and Sarah want you to enjoy their friendly open house. Settle in with tea and Tim's high-rise scones and look out over Seaborough Hill. Their 1960s bungalow is immaculate: white walls, gleaming oak floors, toasty wood-burner and French windows onto the garden. Perfect bedrooms have inviting beds and pots of sweet peas; bathrooms sparkle. Pad through to breakfast in the airy sitting/dining room – or out on the sunny deck: eggs from across the valley, smoked salmon, Dorset bacon, organic tomatoes, homemade bread, granola and jams... It's a treat to stay here. *Minimum stay: 2 nights at weekends. Over 16s welcome.*

Rooms	2 doubles: £115. Singles £100.
Meals	Pub/restaurant 3 miles.
Closed	1 November to 28 February.

Sarah & Tim Dommett
Fairways,
Hewish Lane, Crewkerne, TA18 8RN

Tel	+44 (0)1460 271093
Mobile	+44 (0)7768 753045
Email	info@fairwaysbandb.co.uk
Web	www.fairwaysbandb.co.uk

Brook House

A relaxed home with no rules; arrive to tasty cake and tea or a tipple, settle in the sitting room by one of the wood-burners, chat in the kitchen, wander mown paths in the garden. The sunny open-plan kitchen/living room is the heart of the house; Becky is a keen cook so food is good, local, homemade; Crumpet, one of the terriers, snoozes by the Aga. Quiet, comfy bedrooms have tip-top linen, painted furniture, pots of flowers, garden views; the larger twin has a sofa by tall windows. Next door the Cider Mill has a farm shop, museum and tea rooms, the walks are great, the Jurassic coast is a short drive. A friendly place, a treat to stay. *Over 12s welcome.*

Rooms	1 double, 1 twin/double: £100-£110. Singles £75-£85.
Meals	Dinner, 3 courses, from £20. Pub 3 miles.
Closed	Occasionally.

Tel	+44 (0)1460 250860
Mobile	+44 (0)7841 594342
Email	becky@brookhousesomerset.com
Web	www.brookhousesomerset.com

Becky Jam
Brook House,
Dowlish Wake, Ilminster, TA19 0NY

Cider Barn

Arrive to a cheerful hello from Louise and head upstairs to the huge living space of her renovated old cider barn for tea and cake – or she'll bring you a tray outside. There's a sunny garden and the night skies are clear. Guest bedrooms lie privately on the ground floor. The West Apartment is self-contained with a kitchen and sitting room; this is usually let as self-catering but if you come as a group of six B&Bers you can all use its sunny sitting space

which opens onto the garden. Louise is a great cook and breakfast includes fruit salad, yogurts, croissants, bacon and tomatoes cooked in the oven and local, free-range eggs in different colours. Join footpaths to the river Tone, a café at Tonedale Mill, or to The Martlet Inn in Langford Budville for your dinner. You can catch a steam train from Bishops Lydeard to Williton and Watchet and be on the Quantock Hills in 25 minutes. *Pets by arrangement.*

Rooms	1 double, 1 twin/double: £90-£95.
	1 apartment for 2: £90-£95.
	Singles £70-£75.
Meals	Pub 1 mile.
Closed	Rarely.

Louise Bancroft
Cider Barn,
Runnington, Wellington, TA21 0QW

Tel	+44 (0)1823 665533
Email	louisegaddon@btinternet.com
Web	www.runningtonciderbarn.co.uk

Brewers Cottage

David and Rosie are relaxed hosts and everything slows down the moment you open the gate. If you enjoy your own space, spread out in the annexe with a wet room or find upstairs bedrooms white and fresh with lavender and Rosie's paintings. Breakfast in the neat cottage dining room or al fresco: honey from the bees plus anything you ask for; David might go foraging or catch a trout for supper; bring your own wine and wander the garden with a glass – masses of colour, rare trees, ample veg patch where five types of tomato grow! Cider tasting is just up the road, Barrington Court and market town Ilminster are close.

Rooms	1 double; 1 double with separate bathroom: £90-£100. 1 annexe for 2: £95-£105. Extra twin available sharing bathroom (let to same party only).
Meals	Dinner 3 courses with coffee, from £29.50. BYO. Pubs/restaurants 1 mile.
Closed	Occasionally.

Tel	+44 (0)1460 282900
Email	brewerscottagebandb@gmail.com
Web	www.bedandbreakfast atbrewerscottage.com

David & Rosie Darrah
Brewers Cottage,
Isle Brewers, Taunton, TA3 6QL

Brook Farm

The front door is open for your arrival... Step into the rich red hallway of this traditional Georgian-fronted farmhouse, and find cosy corners for reading, period prints, polished wood, and open fires in the winter. Maria gives you breakfast in a sunny dining/sitting room, where doors open out to the patio and garden beyond; the guest sitting room is snug with comfy sofas and plenty of books. Sink into luxurious beds in immaculate bedrooms; TVs are smart, WiFi is on tap, bathrooms gleam and views are green and peaceful. The Somerset Levels surround you, Glastonbury and Wells are close and there's a good pub in the village too. *Over 12s welcome.*

Rooms	1 double, 1 twin/double: £90-£105. Singles £75-£85.
Meals	Pubs/restaurants 1.2 miles.
Closed	Rarely.

Maria Laing
Brook Farm,
Newport Road, North Curry,
Taunton, TA3 6DJ

Tel	+44 (0)1823 491124
Email	maria.follett@hotmail.co.uk
Web	www.brookfarmbb.com

Maunsel House

There's so much to blurt out it's tricky to start. Let's begin with eccentric owner Ben, 7th Baronet, who has restored the family pile and is (incidentally) looking for the perfect provider of an heir. Beware, you must jump through hoops! The house is packed with history, furniture, guns, swords, stuffed animals, hats, surprises, nudes in the loos, books, board games and roaring fires. It's completely bonkers and huge fun and you must immediately get together a group and flock here for winter shenanigans. Couples alone will probably end up in one of the annexe rooms – perfectly comfortable, but not as mind-boggling.

Rooms	13 doubles , 4 twin/doubles, 2 twins: £80-£225.
Meals	Pubs/restaurants 5 miles. Dinners for groups available on request.
Closed	Open for B&B October to April. April to October – try your luck!

Tel	+44 (0)1278 661076
Email	stay@maunselhouse.co.uk
Web	www.maunselhouse.co.uk

Ben Slade
Maunsel House,
North Newton, Taunton, TA7 0BU

Bashfords Farmhouse

A feeling of warmth and happiness pervades this exquisite 17th-century farmhouse in the Quantock Hills. The Ritchies love doing B&B – even after over 20 years! – and interiors have a homely feel with well-framed prints, natural fabrics, comfortable sofas, and a sitting room with inglenook, sofas and books. Bedrooms are pretty, fresh and large and look over the cobbled courtyard or open fields. Charles and Jane couldn't be nicer, know about local walks (the Macmillan Way runs by) and love to cook: local meat and game, tarte tatin, homemade bread and jams. A delightful garden rambles up the hill; the pub is just a minute away.

Rooms	1 twin/double; 1 double with separate shower, 1 twin/double with separate bath: £90. Singles £55.
Meals	Dinner £27.50. Supper £22.50. Pub 75 yds.
Closed	Rarely.

Charles & Jane Ritchie
Bashfords Farmhouse,
West Bagborough, Taunton, TA4 3EF

Tel	+44 (0)1823 432015
Email	info@bashfordsfarmhouse.co.uk
Web	www.bashfordsfarmhouse.co.uk

Blackmore Farm

Come for atmosphere and architecture: the Grade I-listed manor-farmhouse is remarkable. Medieval stone, soaring beams, four-posters, ecclesiastical windows, giant logs blazing in the Great Hall. Ann and Ian look after guests and busy dairy farm with equal enthusiasm. Furnishings are rich, bedrooms are large and the oak-panelled suite (with secret stairway) takes up an entire floor. The stable rooms are simpler. Aga breakfasts with local sausages and jams are eaten at the long polished table in the Hall. Don't miss the excellent farm shop – there's a café too with cakes, drinks and produce from the area.

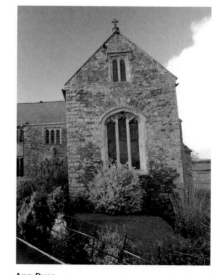

Rooms	1 double, 1 twin, 2 four-posters, 1 suite for 2: £120-£140. Singles £75-£85.
Meals	Occasional dinner from £27 for large parties only. Pubs/restaurants 5-minute walk.
Closed	Rarely.

Tel	+44 (0)1278 653442
Email	dyerfarm@aol.com
Web	www.blackmorefarm.co.uk

Ann Dyer
Blackmore Farm,
Cannington, Bridgwater, TA5 2NE

The Old Priory

Rambling, beamed and flagstoned, Jane's 12th-century home is as much a haven for reflection and good company today as it was to the monastic community who once lived here. Both house and hostess are unpretentious and friendly; Jane adds her own special artistic flair. Find Venetian-red walls in the low-ceilinged, time-worn living room with 14th-century fireplace, a deeply authentic four-poster bedroom with undulating oaken floor. Breakfasts are organic, local and very good: Alastair pronounced his, "one of the best breakfasts ever"! The bewitching walled garden perfectly complements Jane's ancient home... a place of peace and a wonderfully personal creation. A bounteous blend of formal touches with shrubs, small trees and climbers allowed to express themselves freely. A tall mimosa greets you at the little gate on a lane overlooked by the Castle, mature espaliered fruit trees line the path and then Jane's most formal touch, the square, knee-high hedged box garden. Informally planted herbaceous borders and a small lawn in front of the house complete the picture. You can wander into the church grounds next door through an archway.

Rooms	1 twin, 1 four-poster; 1 double with separate shower: £100. Singles by arrangement.
Meals	Pubs/restaurants 5-minute walk.
Closed	Christmas.

Jane Forshaw
The Old Priory,
Priory Green, Dunster, TA24 6RY

Tel	+44 (0)1643 821540
Email	oldprioridunster@gmail.com
Web	www.theoldpriory-dunster.co.uk

Keepers Cottage

Restored stable, hayloft and cottage... take your pick from imaginatively restored spaces. Oak-beamed bedrooms have well-dressed beds, sofas, reclamation finds, books and biscuits; "Hayloft" has a wood-burner; "Paddock" and "Orchard" can interconnect for a family. Amble over to the friendly kitchen in the main house for breakfast: homemade granola, organic porridge, all sorts of cooked choices – pop your menu-sheet in the 'bread bin' by the back door in the evening; Emma will bring over a continental breakfast to your room if preferred. Sunny sitting spots in the garden, a scramble up Glastonbury Tor, a stroll to a good supper at the pub... *Children over 10 welcome.*

Rooms	3 doubles: £105-£125. Singles £90-£100. Extra bed/sofabed £30 per person per night.
Meals	Pop-up restaurant, 5 courses, £37; usually 3rd Sat in month. Pubs/restaurants 10-minute walk.
Closed	Christmas.

Tel	+44 (0)1458 851103
Email	info@keeperssomerset.com
Web	www.keeperssomerset.com

Emma Taylor
Keepers Cottage,
Wood Lane, Butleigh, BA6 8TR

Ansford Park Cottage

An old farmworker's house, modernised and freshly spruced, stands proud in verdant countryside. Long views from the clipped garden drift into the distance; warm Sue (plus cute Jack Russells) greets you. You sleep in the extension to the front of the house; one bedroom has valley views, the other has views over the Mendips. Both have comfy beds, books, homely touches and peacefulness. Breakfast is a leisurely affair of local bacon and eggs. Tramp off on an inspiring walk – Leland trail, Macmillan Way – you're spoilt for choice. Escape London by train (95 minutes) – collection from the station can be arranged.

Rooms	1 twin/double; 1 twin/double with separate bath: £70-£85. Singles £70.
Meals	Dinner £25. Packed lunch £5. Pub/restaurant 1 mile.
Closed	Christmas & occasionally.

Susan Begg
Ansford Park Cottage,
Ansford Park, Maggs Lane,
Castle Cary, BA7 7JJ

Tel	+44 (0)1963 351066
Email	nigelbegg@lineone.net
Web	www.ansfordparkcottage.co.uk

Yarlington House

A mellow Georgian manor surrounded by impressive parkland, romantic rose gardens, apple tree pergola and laburnum walk. Your hosts are friendly and flexible artists with an eye for quirky detail; Carolyn's embroideries are everywhere, and there's something to astound at every turn: fine copies of 18th-century wallpapers, elegant antiques, statues with hats atop and tremendous art. Traditional bedrooms with glorious garden views and proper 50s bathrooms have a faded charm. Enjoy a full English breakfast, grape juice from the glasshouse vines, log fires and lovely local walks. Surprising and unique. *Heated pool in the summer.*

Rooms	2 doubles, 1 twin; 1 double with shared bathroom: £160. 1 bunk room for 4 with shared bathroom: £160. 1 family room for 4 with separate bath: £160-£210. Singles £80. Extra rooms available.
Meals	Pubs/restaurants within 0.5 miles.
Closed	Three weeks in August.

Tel	+44 (0)1963 440344
Email	carolyn.desalis@yarlingtonhouse.com
Web	www.yarlingtonhouse.com

Carolyn & Charles de Salis
Yarlington House,
Yarlington, Wincanton, BA9 8DY

Valley View Farm

It's very pleasant here in an isolated part of Somerset with ancient houses dotted about. This very ordinary 70s house is out of kilter with the architecture but great fun to stay here and your dog is welcome. Martin (and when she's back from the US, his lovely wife Bean) look after you with aplomb and a great deal of humour. Breakfast is a laidback affair at the big wooden table in the kitchen: home-baked bread (toast it how you want it), Martin's homemade marmalade, organic cereals, yogurts and berries, coffee that'll put hairs on your chest. If you want bacon and eggs etc you need to order it in advance and pay extra. If you're too pooped to go out for dinner Martin is happy to cook for you with a bit of notice. Walk to Batcombe – the village which was so isolated it escaped the Black Death. It's now inhabited by a swathe of old-Etonians and has a nice pub, the Three Horseshoes. Bruton for the Roth Grill is just a seven-minute drive and Frome is 10 minutes in the car for good food shopping at the markets. *Minimum stay: 2 nights.*

Rooms	2 doubles; 1 twin with separate bathroom: £85-£135. Whole house available for reduced rates. Reduced rates for longer stays.
Meals	Full English breakfast £8. Pub 1 mile.
Closed	Rarely.

Martin & Colleen Horsford
Valley View Farm,
Batcombe Park, Bruton, BA4 6AJ

Tel	+44 (0)1749 850943
Mobile	+44 (0)7785 795707
Email	mc@horsford.net

Penny's Mill

The old part of Nunney village, with its small pretty streets, has a shop, a café and Rosie's gorgeous old stone millhouse down in the river valley. You are greeted warmly with tea and biscuits at a large wooden table in the kitchen, or in the drawing room upstairs with family photos, paintings and a big window looking over the millpond. Sunny bedrooms painted in gentle blues and greens have a mix of antique and modern furniture; bathrooms have Molton Brown soaps and white fluffy towels. Rosie's fine breakfasts set you up for a stroll in the woodland, a short walk to Nunney Castle, or a yomp further afield. *Minimum stay: 2 nights at weekends & in high season.*

Rooms	1 double, 1 twin/double with own living room: £95. 1 family room for 4: £165.
Meals	Pub 300 yds.
Closed	Christmas, New Year.

Tel	+44 (0)1373 836210
Email	stay@pennysmill.com
Web	www.stayatpennysmill.com

Rosie Davies
Penny's Mill,
Horn Street, Nunney, Frome, BA11 4NP

Bistro Lotte

Lotte and her team love to make you feel at ease. The bistro hums with happy people, windows are flung open in the summer and comfortable bedrooms above have their own entrance so you can come and go as you please. Step down to the restaurant for a French platter breakfast of zingy juices, croissants, ham, cheese, eggs, sourdough toast and good coffee. Lunches are served until late (everyone loves the buckwheat crêpes) and the convivial vibe continues into the evening with candlelit tables and good-value suppers. Book the atmospheric private dining room upstairs for a special event. Explore Frome with its quirky shops, food and vintage markets, theatre and pretty cobbled streets. Pop back to the bistro for tea and cake in the afternoon, book a table for the evening.

Rooms	6 twin/doubles: £95. Dogs £15 per stay. Futon for children available, £25.
Meals	Lunch from £5. Supper from £13.50. Pubs 10-minute walk.
Closed	Rarely.

Charlotte Evans
Bistro Lotte,
23 Catherine Street,
Frome, BA11 1DB

Tel	+44 (0)1373 300646
Mobile	+44 (0)7828 459696
Email	lottysevans@yahoo.com
Web	www.bistrolottefrome.co.uk

Old Reading Room

Mells is a treasure with its medieval centre and liberal sprinkling of charming cottages. You'll find Vicky and John's attractive house up a lane in the quiet wooded valley on the edge of the village. It's a home with a friendly feel and entertaining hosts. Sleep well in bedrooms in the eaves, listen to the hoot of owls at night and birdsong in the morning and come down for a generous breakfast in the kitchen: delicious local bread, fruit and eggs laid by happy hens within a cockerel's crow of the kitchen. Sit out in the sunny cottage garden, head off on walks from the door. A 10-minute stroll through the village takes you back centuries – thatched houses, a beautiful church (famous for its Munnings equine statue and the graves of Ronnie Knox and Siegfried Sassoon), a tithe barn – and a particularly welcoming, highly recommended coaching inn, The Talbot.

Rooms	2 doubles: £95.
Meals	Pubs/restaurants 5-minute walk.
Closed	Rarely.

Tel	+44 (0)1373 813487
Email	johnmacdonaldm@gmail.com

Vicky & John Macdonald
Old Reading Room,
Mells, Frome, BA11 3QA

The Courtyard at Jericho

Down a long private track surrounded by fields and woodland is your house with a courtyard full of plants and an orchard. Take your morning coffee on the bench that catches the sun just outside your sitting room. Jessica lives next door and delivers a breakfast basket when you want – good coffee and tea, local sourdough, croissants, homemade jam and muesli plus hand-pressed apple juice from the orchard. Cooked breakfast is a little extra – perhaps scrambled eggs and salmon. It's idyllic here: peaceful and secluded, but near some quirky Somerset hubs – Mells is two miles away and Frome's independent cafés, restaurants and shops, plus fab monthly market, are six miles. Return to a glass of wine in the courtyard and relax.

Rooms	1 double: £100-£110. Singles £80-£90. Extra bed/sofabed from £50 per person per night.
Meals	Pub 3 miles.
Closed	Rarely.

Jessica Conway
The Courtyard at Jericho,
Mells, Frome, BA11 2RL

Tel	+44 (0)1373 812090
Email	courtyardatjericho@gmail.com
Web	www.courtyardatjericho.co.uk

Swallow Barn

Views sweep over hills from this eco-friendly barn conversion – join the Macmillan Way from the garden. You have your own entrance to a wing of Penny and Paul's home; each warm bedroom has its own sunny spot outside too. Find tip-top linen on big luxurious beds, espresso machines, Roberts radios and homemade shortbread, smart TVs (with Sky) and comfy seating; swish wet rooms have huge shower heads and Somerset Lavender soaps. Penny brings a delicious continental breakfast to your room – you can take it out to the stunning wild flower meadow in summer. Bath, Frome and Wells are all a hop away: arty haunts, markets and theatre beckon. *Minimum stay: 2 nights.*

Rooms	2 doubles: £115-£125.
Meals	Pub 5-minute walk.
Closed	Rarely.

Mobile	+44 (0)7967 003261/(0)7790 586085
Email	paulpennyreynolds@hotmail.com
Web	www.swallowbarnfrome.com

Penny Reynolds
Swallow Barn,
The Cross, Buckland Dinham,
Frome, BA11 2QS

Park Farm House

Sink into deep well-being here at Katherine's beautiful old Bath stone house with mullion windows. There are bracing walks from the door, a swimming pool and tennis court to make use of, Frome is close for a bit of culture or shopping and there are good pubs and restaurants nearby. Come back to a drawing room with an open fire for chilly evenings and plenty of books and games, bedrooms with squishy pillows and bright white linen, warm bathrooms, soft towels. Breakfast on homemade granola, bacon and sausages from down the road; there are fresh flowers from the garden on the table and always plenty of Italian coffee. *Over 12s welcome.*

Rooms	1 double; 1 double with separate bathroom: £95-£115.
Meals	Pubs/restaurants 1 mile.
Closed	Christmas, New Year & Easter.

Katherine Dabell
Park Farm House,
Lullington, Frome, BA11 2PF

Tel	+44 (0)1373 831402
Mobile	+44 (0)7775 520032
Email	k@dabell.net
Web	www.parkfarm-house.co.uk

The Old Vicarage, Kilmersdon

The vicarage sits at the foot of Jack and Jill's hill in a sleepy Mendip village. Both bedrooms have goose down comfort: one has an antique French bed and limestone wet room; the sunny blue room upstairs has a freestanding roll top. Your hosts are informal and friendly and their home exudes charm: a medieval stone floor in the hall, old flagstones, carpets designed by Lizzy, flowers, wood-burners and a pretty kitchen. Hens potter, carp laze in the canal pond; breakfast when you want on a full English, garden compotes and delicious coffee. National Trust gems and splendid walking on the Colliers Way will keep you busy. *Minimum stay: 2 nights at weekends & in high season.*

Rooms	1 double with sitting room; 1 four-poster with separate wc: £100-£110.
Meals	Pub 100 yds.
Closed	Rarely.

Tel	+44 (0)1761 436926
Email	lizzyashard@gmail.com
Web	www.theoldvicaragesomerset.com

Elizabeth Ashard
The Old Vicarage, Kilmersdon,
Church Street, Kilmersdon,
Radstock, BA3 5TA

Hillview Cottage

Catherine is a wonderful host: warm-spirited, cultured and humorous. She knows the area well, and is happy to show you around Wells Cathedral – she's an official guide. This is a comfy tea-and-cakes family home with rugs on wooden floors and antique quilts. Bedrooms have a French feel, the bathroom an armchair for chatting and there's a friendly sitting room with an open fire. The stunning vaulted breakfast room has huge beams, an old Welsh dresser with hand painted mugs, a cheerful red Aga, a wood-burner to sit by and glorious views; breakfasts are superb. Guests love it here; excellent value too.

Rooms	1 twin/double, 1 twin, sharing bath, let to same party only: £80-£90. Singles £50-£55.
Meals	Pubs 5-minute walk.
Closed	Rarely.

Michael & Catherine Hay
Hillview Cottage,
Paradise Lane, Croscombe, Wells, BA5 3RN

Tel	+44 (0)1749 343526
Mobile	+44 (0)7801 666146
Email	cathyhay@yahoo.co.uk
Web	www.hillviewcottage3.driezendesign.nl

Middle Farm Cottage

David's grandmother bought these two cottages in the 50s. He (ex-TV) and Julie (a Welsh opera singer) have hurled themselves into village life, spruced up the whole place and thrown open their door to guests. You'll be well looked after: breakfast at a pretty walnut table on homemade bread, jams and marmalade, a full Welsh of local bacon, sausages and eggs, good strong coffee. They sometimes do kitchen supper, or it's a short walk to a good pub in the next village. Bedrooms are traditional, peaceful and comfortable – the garden room has its own little outdoor space. Walk to Wells across the fields, get the bus back! *Well-behaved dogs welcome in the Garden Room.*

Rooms	1 twin/double; 2 doubles sharing bathroom, let to same party only: £85. Singles £60.
Meals	Family supper £17. Pubs/restaurants 12-minute walk.
Closed	31 March to 2 April.

Tel	+44 (0)1749 672120
Email	david@costley-white.com

David & Julie Costley-White
Middle Farm Cottage,
Riverside, Dinder, Wells, BA5 3PL

Mount Pleasant Farm

This whitewashed cottage is full of surprises. Daisy has restored it using reclaimed everything – the quirkier the better: painted or gold-leafed pieces, polished boards, beautiful bedheads and Indian banister, clever clothes hooks... Bedrooms, all differently styled, have well-dressed beds and fantastic bathrooms. The breakfast room has separate tables that can all be put together for friends, a snug sofa by the wood-burner, artworks – and pottery for sale; it opens to a sunny terrace. Daisy loves to cook: homemade granola, bread, jams, local bacon, eggs from her parents' smallholding, cakes. Cheddar and Glastonbury are 20 minutes.

Rooms	4 doubles: £95-£115.
Meals	Pubs/restaurants 4-minute walk.
Closed	Christmas & New Year.

Daisy Nicolaou
Mount Pleasant Farm,
Chapel Allerton, Axbridge, BS26 2PP

Tel	+44 (0)1934 710285
Email	mountpleasantfarmsomerset@gmail.com
Web	www.mountpleasantbnb.com

Burrington Farm

High in the Mendips, Ros and Barry's 15th-century longhouse is blissfully rural, yet Bristol, Bath and Wells are close. Their wonderful house glows: rugs and flagstones, books, burnished beams, paintings and fine old furniture. Guests have a cosy sitting room and bedrooms are charming; you'll need to be nimble to negotiate ancient steps and stairs. For those who prefer a bit more privacy there's a lovely family room in a separate green oak barn – stunningly converted and with views over the enchanting garden. Wake for a locally sourced breakfast round a big table. A friendly, relaxed and special place.

Rooms	1 double; 1 twin, 1 double sharing bath, let to same party only: £85-£120. 1 family room for 4: £100-£120. Singles £65.
Meals	Pub 10-minute walk.
Closed	Christmas.

Tel	+44 (0)1761 462127
Mobile	+44 (0)7825 237144
Email	bookings@burringtonfarm.co.uk
Web	www.unwindatburringtonfarm.co.uk

Barry & Ros Smith
Burrington Farm,
Frys Lane, Burrington, BS40 7AD

Coombe Lodge Farm House

Charming Jenny and her energetic Jack Russell Titch welcome you to their comfortable home with tea and homemade cake. You'll be looked after well in this big Victorian house with its huge open fire, antiques in every room, ancestral oil paintings and contemporary art. Inviting bedrooms overlook the gardens; breakfast is at one convivial table and the food is locally sourced and organic as much as possible. If it's sunny you can find your own spot to sit among mature trees, plants and shrubs with views to Blagdon Lake – tawny owls, woodpeckers and birds of prey can often be seen. Bristol and Bath are close, you can walk from the house into the hills or down to the lake. Foodies will love having Michelin-listed restaurants so close. Treat yourself at The Ethicurean in Wrington or The Seymour Arms in Blagdon or the Pony & Trap near Chew Magna. *Pets by arrangement.*

Rooms	2 doubles; 1 twin with separate bathroom: £100-£125. Dinner, B&B £150 per person.
Meals	Pubs/restaurants 10-minute walk.
Closed	Rarely.

Jenny Marks
Coombe Lodge Farm House,
Bourne Lane, Blagdon, BS40 7RF

Tel	+44 (0)1761 462793
Email	jennifer.marks10@me.com

9 Princes Buildings

A super city base in one of Bristol's fine Georgian houses with, without a doubt, the best views in Clifton. Four sunny, traditional bedrooms have a welcoming glass of sherry and homemade cake; one is at the top of the house; the room on the lower ground floor overlooks the large, leafy garden. Simon and Joanna give you a good, leisurely breakfast with a choice of eggs anyway, local sausages and bacon, pancakes, fresh fruit, compotes with star anise, homemade jams and marmalade. Head down the steps and catch a ferry to see the city from the water, walk into Clifton for independent shops and plenty of bustling cafés and restaurants, cross the Suspension Bridge and into Ashton Court for park and woodland walks – and the balloon festival in the summer. Return to the elegant drawing room with its large veranda to take in those views of the Avon Gorge.

Rooms	2 doubles, 1 twin/double; 1 twin/double with separate bath: £105-£125. Singles £75-£79.
Meals	Pub/restaurant 100 yds.
Closed	Rarely.

Tel	+44 (0)117 973 4615
Email	info@9pb.co.uk
Web	www.9princesbuildings.co.uk

Simon & Joanna Fuller
9 Princes Buildings,
Clifton, Bristol, BS8 4LB

The Bristol Wing

It's a hostel, so it's not for those who want hush, posh or privacy but it couldn't have a friendlier vibe. You've a choice of places to sit and work or chat: reception has a busier buzz with folk wandering in and out, probably music and help-yourself coffee and tea; the sitting room is downstairs and quieter with interesting books. Upstairs you'll find eclectic art on the walls, shared dorms, private doubles and family rooms, some en suite and some with shared bathrooms – all dazzlingly white and new. The ethical credentials here are impressive: this is the second brilliant social enterprise scheme initiated by Ben Silvey – the first is where you have your breakfast. Just over a courtyard is The Kitchen, an award-winning café in the old fire station serving fresh local produce. Both businesses are owned and managed by YMCA Bristol, and any profits made are re-invested in supporting young people who are homeless in the city. They don't accept hen or stag parties so the feel is civilised and warm. It will suit single travellers, couples and families equally well and is excellent value – you can even do your washing and drying for free.

Rooms	1 twin/double, 1 twin, 1 twin/double with shared bathroom: £50-£60. 13 family rooms for 3-6, all with shared bathrooms: £54-£102. 1 6-bed male/mixed bunk room, 1 9-bed female/mixed bunk room, 1 12-bed male bunk room: £18.
Meals	Pubs/restaurants 2-minute walk.
Closed	Never.

Ben Silvey
The Bristol Wing,
9 Bridewell Street, BS1 2QD

Tel	+44 (0)117 428 6199
Mobile	+44 (0)7881 244953
Email	enquiries@thebristolwing.co.uk
Web	www.thebristolwing.co.uk

Number 20

Colourful window box, leafy front garden... Jo's terraced Victorian house has an open-door friendliness – chat to her when you arrive over tea and a homemade something. Sleep well in first or top-floor rooms; eat well too, round the sociable kitchen table: proper bread, fresh fruit and yogurt, muesli, good coffee. Borrow maps and explore the city. See a film at Orpheus cinema at the bottom of the road; book a show at the Old Vic or Tobacco Factory; have a day on the harbourside. Stroll out for dinner at nearby Westbury Park pub, Italian Prego or Mesa Tapas; Chandos Road and Whiteladies have lots of good places to eat too. Jo gives you a key, so come and go – return to read in the guest sitting room or out in the suntrap garden under the wisteria.

Rooms	3 doubles: £90-£120. Singles £65-90.
Meals	Pubs/restaurants 2-minute walk.
Closed	Occasionally.

Tel	+44 (0)117 924 3517
Mobile	+44 (0)7929 235647
Email	insidenumber20@yahoo.com
Web	www.number20guesthouse.com

Jo Wookey
Number 20,
Devonshire Road, Bristol, BS6 7NJ

The Curious Cabinet

A typical Victorian terraced house, but step inside and you're in for a surprise. Sadie's an artist and clever magpie, and her home is full of fascinating vintage finds – join her for tea, cake and chat in the kitchen. Everyone sleeps well here. Bedrooms (one downstairs and two in the eaves) are calm retreats with hot water bottles and trays with nice things in jars. Breakfast can be downstairs in the kitchen or a DIY affair in the guest kitchen on the first floor (where you can also heat up supper if you want). Either way it's a continental array of bread, jams, pastries, cold meats, cheeses, fruit salad and yogurt. If you'd like a cooked one head to nearby Porto Lounge, which is open all day. The Bristol to Bath cycle path is nearby or hop on the bus and be in the heart of Bristol in 25 minutes. *Minimum stay: 2 nights.*

Rooms	2 doubles; 2 doubles both with separate bathroom: £89-£145. Reduced rates for longer stays.
Meals	Breakfast from £15. Pubs/restaurants 3-minute walk.
Closed	Christmas.

Sadie Spikes
The Curious Cabinet,
35 Downend Road, Fishponds,
Bristol, BS16 5AR

Tel	+44 (0)117 935 4964
Mobile	+44 (0)7831 381177
Email	sadie_spikes@hotmail.co.uk
Web	www.sadiespikescuriouscabinet.com

Pitfour House

Georgian gentility in a village near Bath. This is where the rector would live in an Austen novel: it's handsome, respectable, and the feel extends inside, where convivial hosts Frances (a keen cook) and Martin (keen gardener) put you at ease in their elegant home. The creamy guest sitting room gleams with period furniture, the dining room is panelled and parqueted, fresh flowers abound. The two bedrooms – one with en suite shower, one with a private bath – are compact but detailed with antiques. Take tea in the neat walled garden, admire the vegetable patch, then taste the spoils in one of Frances's fine dinners. *Minimum stay: 2 nights.*

Rooms	1 twin/double; 1 twin/double with separate bath: £98-£100. Singles £78-£80.
Meals	Dinner, 2-3 courses, £30-£38. Supper £25. Restaurant 1.5 miles.
Closed	Rarely.

Tel	+44 (0)1761 479554
Email	pitfourhouse@btinternet.com
Web	www.pitfourhouse.co.uk

Frances Hardman
Pitfour House,
High Street, Timsbury,
Bath, BA2 0HT

Reeves Barn

Drive under the willow to find a prettily converted studio barn, a gorgeous shepherd's hut and an away-from-it-all feel. The studio comes with limed beams, a romantic bedroom, a simple wet room with scented oils, and a mini kitchen cleverly tucked into a cupboard. Or choose to sleep under the stars in the snug and woody shepherd's hut. You can order dinner for your arrival, and artist Barbette leaves a breakfast hamper for you – wake and eat when you want!

Sit in the sun by pots of flowers, curl up by a wood-burner, enjoy the rustic vibe in the hut. Bath, Wells, Frome and Bruton's Hauser & Wirth are nearby.

Rooms	1 double with sitting room & kitchenette: £115. Shepherd's hut for 2: from £85.
Meals	Dinner, 3 courses for studio guests, £35. Dinner, 2 courses & bottle of prosecco for shepherd's hut guests, £65 for 2.
Closed	Rarely.

Barbette Saunders
Reeves Barn,
17 Whitbourne Springs, Corsley,
Warminster, BA12 7RF

Tel	+44 (0)1373 832106
Mobile	+44 (0)7796 687806
Email	barbettesaunders@gmail.com
Web	www.reevesbarn.com

Oaklands

A spacious townhouse, south-facing garden, two dear dogs and lovely old Silver Cross pram sitting under the stairs. No wonder this delightful, 1880s house has been in the family forever. It was the first house in Warminster to have a bathroom; these have multiplied since and it's a comfortable home filled with fine antiques and attractive furnishings. Andrew and Carolyn, relaxed and charming, serve delicious breakfasts in the large conservatory. Bedrooms are inviting: beds are topped with fine linen, and you have views over churchyard, lawns and trees; bathrooms sparkle – one has a big walk-in shower. Restaurants are a stroll.

Rooms	1 double: £75-£90.
	1 family room for 2-4: £85-£110.
	Singles £55.
Meals	Pub/restaurant 0.5 miles.
Closed	Christmas & occasionally.

Tel	+44 (0)1985 300564
Mobile	+44 (0)7702 587533
Email	apl1944@yahoo.co.uk
Web	www.stayatoaklands.co.uk

Carolyn & Andrew Lewis
Oaklands,
88 Boreham Road,
Warminster, BA12 9JW

Paddock Wood

A great spot for fans of gentle country living, good conversation, art, antiques and romantic gardens. The house, which has 17th-century beginnings, has been added to over the years. It's surprisingly large inside and is surrounded by beautiful gardens with woodland beyond. There's an unhurried, gracious feel to Paddock Wood. Elizabeth and David give you delicious breakfasts in the elegant dining room: full English, home-baked bread, mixed fruits and homemade marmalades and jams. Step out along footpaths you can join from the house; explore the charming village with its ancient church, St Mary's; visit the thriving community shop and post office. There are good local pubs and places to eat; the delightful Deverill villages are close by; it's south to picturesque Shaftesbury; west to Stourton House and Stourhead, north to Longleat.

Rooms	1 double; 1 double with separate bathroom: £85-£95.
Meals	Pub 15-minute walk.
Closed	Christmas.

Elizabeth Gascoyne
Paddock Wood,
Holloway, East Knoyle,
Salisbury, SP3 6AF

Tel	+44 (0)1747 830226
Email	lizzie.gascoyne@mail.com

The Old Rectory

An elegant and much-loved family home set in the picture-postcard village of Ashmore. Its curved yew hedge is topped with magnificent topiary birds, the views across valley and hills almost to the sea are sensational and you arrive to afternoon tea and cake, which Sam serves in the sitting room or out in the sun. Bedrooms are off separate landings and the master has a children's room next door. Settle down to breakfast in a sunny room on the first floor: mixed berries and yogurt, homemade bread, continental or cooked choices. Sam is happy to do family suppers too. Wander around the lovely gardens and down through the woodland, follow the circular two and a half mile walk and spot red kites and buzzards. There are books and games to dip into, and good pubs nearby for dinner.

Rooms	1 double, 1 twin/double: £120-£150. Extra beds available in twin room adjoining twin/double, £50 per person.
Meals	Supper, 2 courses, £25. Pub 3 miles.
Closed	Christmas, New Year & occasional weekends.

Tel	+44 (0)1747 811136
Mobile	+44 (0)7966 225695
Email	sam@lindsayuk.com

Sam Lindsay
The Old Rectory,
Ashmore, Salisbury, SP5 5AG

19 Glenmore Road

An elegant house and a surprising find on the edge of this busy city. Tim (Canadian) and Biddy are a creative pair. Guests have their own sunny yellow sitting room, bedrooms are inviting and you'll find art, antiques, flowers, Tim's photos and beautiful handmade furniture throughout. Breakfast is jam-packed: seasonal fruit from the allotment, greenhouse tomatoes, homemade muesli and marmalade, local market produce – out on the terrace if sunny; the garden is a picture of bluebells in spring. The Cathedral has the tallest spire in the country, Stonehenge is nearby and there are festivals to be enjoyed throughout the year. *Children over 10 welcome.*

Rooms	1 double; 1 twin/double with separate bathroom: £90. Singles £75.
Meals	Pubs/restaurants 20-minute walk.
Closed	Christmas & New Year.

Biddy Walker & Tim Chadsey
19 Glenmore Road,
Salisbury, SP1 3HF

Tel	+44 (0)1722 412077
Mobile	+44 (0)7957 823643
Email	tchadsey@uwclub.net
Web	www.no19bandbsalisbury.com

The Garden Cottage

You'll love the Woodford Valley and this thatched cottage at the edge of the village. It has long views, stacks of character and traditionally decorated rooms: a ground floor twin with roll top bathroom and two cosy doubles upstairs that share a bathroom. Fabrics are flowered, headboards upholstered, mattresses top quality. Or choose to snuggle up by the wood-burner in a charming shepherd's hut and sleep out under the stars – one has a king-sized bed. Breakfast in the kitchen, or pretty garden, on Annie's homemade bread and good things local. Head out to explore Avebury and Stonehenge. *Cash or cheque accepted. Arrivals before 4pm.*

Rooms	2 doubles sharing bathroom, let to same party only; 1 twin with separate bathroom: £90. 2 shepherd's huts for 2 both with shower, sink & wc: £90.
Meals	Pub 0.5 miles.
Closed	November 2019 to February 2020.

Tel	+44 (0)1722 782447
Email	annie747@btinternet.com

Annie Arkwright
The Garden Cottage,
Upper Woodford, Salisbury, SP4 6PA

The Mill House

In a tranquil village next to the river is a house surrounded by water meadows and wilderness garden. Roses ramble, marsh orchids bloom and butterflies shimmer in this 12-acre labour of love. Michael's home, a time-worn 18th-century miller's house, is packed with country clutter – porcelain, foxes' brushes, ancestral photographs above the fire – while bedrooms are quaint, flowery and old-fashioned with firm comfy beds. Breakfasts are served at small tables in the pretty dining room. Visit nearby Stonehenge, wander round historic Salisbury; return to sunny seats in the garden and watch the river Till go by. *Children over 7 welcome.*

Rooms	3 doubles: £100.
	1 family room for 4: £100-£140.
	Singles £75-£80.
Meals	Pub 5-minute walk.
Closed	Rarely.

Michael Mertens
The Mill House,
Berwick St James,
Salisbury, SP3 4TS

Tel	+44 (0)1722 790331
Email	m.mertens@btinternet.com
Web	www.millhouse.org.uk

Great Chalfield Manor

A beautiful National Trust house – a rare example of the English medieval manor complete with 14th-century church and Great Hall but a family home too where you will be treated by smiling Patsy and Robert as a guest not a visitor; history and architecture lovers will adore it. Four-posters are swathed in the warmest colours, bathrooms are deeply old-fashioned (this is not for the power shower brigade, nor those who seek swift internet) and the only sound is bird ballad wafting from the hazy, bloom-filled dreaminess of the garden – which is well worth a wander. Find a structure of neatly clipped yew houses, herbaceous borders, smooth lawns and an orchard, immaculately tended and enhanced by Patsy's love of soft colour and roses. The south-facing terrace brims over with scented pink roses that bloom all summer, ramblers scrabble over old stone walls and the fruit trees in the orchard – and they are not alone; there is honeysuckle in abundance too, rambling hither and thither. Water weaves through the grass in little streams which feed the moats and there is a magical woodland walk bursting with snowdrops in February.

Rooms	2 four-posters both with separate bath: £100-£130. Singles £90.
Meals	Supper £30. Pub/restaurant 1 mile.
Closed	Occasionally.

Tel	+44 (0)1225 782239
Email	patsy@greatchalfield.co.uk
Web	www.greatchalfield.co.uk

Patsy Floyd
Great Chalfield Manor,
Melksham, SN12 8NH

The Moda House

A fine house and a big B&B, but one that retains a deeply homely feel; Duncan and Jo are hugely well-travelled and have filled it with pictures and artefacts from all over the world. Bedrooms differ (three are in a neat annexe) but all are cosy and well decorated with lovely colours, good fabrics, pocket sprung mattresses and bright bathrooms with thick towels. Breakfast – locally sourced, cooked on the Aga and brought to round tables – sets you up for fabulous walks: you are a mile from the Cotswold Way. Return to a basement sitting room with comfy armchairs and lots of books, and a bustling town full of restaurants and shops. *Minimum stay: 2 nights over busy weekends; 3 nights during Badminton.*

Rooms	7 doubles: £87-£105.
	1 single: £67-£75.
Meals	Pubs/restaurants within 100 yards.
Closed	Rarely.

Duncan & Jo MacArthur
The Moda House,
1 High Street,
Chipping Sodbury, BS37 6BA

Tel	+44 (0)1454 312135
Email	enquiries@modahouse.co.uk
Web	www.modahouse.co.uk

Ashley Barn

On the edge of a hamlet... a beautifully restored, traditional converted barn. Huge doorways and floor to ceiling timber-framed windows let the light flood in. You have your own entrance and can come and go as you please. Your suite has good linen, plump pillows, flowers and views onto the garden; the roomy bathroom is gleaming. Walk through for breakfast by a log fire in the huge dining hall in the main barn: local sausages and bacon, eggs from the hens on pretty Poole pottery; Amanda is happy to cook dinner too. Badminton Horse Trials are a hop, Cirencester too; return for a wander round the rose garden, and a snooze by the fire.

Rooms	1 suite for 2: £100-£120. Singles £85.
Meals	Dinner, 3 courses, £25.
	Pub/restaurant 5-minute drive.
Closed	Rarely.

Tel	+44 (0)1666 575156
Mobile	+44 (0)7785 505548
Email	amanda@montgomerie.org
Web	www.ashleybarn.co.uk

Amanda Montgomerie
Ashley Barn,
Ashley, Tetbury, GL8 8SU

Lowfield Farm

Another classic old Cotswold house set in pretty countryside, but with unique character thanks to Giles and Amanda who spent many years in California and have now returned to the family home. Your rooms are on the top floor – both newly done up and neat as a pin with thick cream carpets, heavy floral fabrics, windows with views and comfortable chairs (no guest sitting room). Breakfast is a flexible affair, includes full English with eggs from their own hens and is taken at one long mahogany table. Wander a small wood with mown paths, head off for antiques in Tetbury, gardens at Highgrove, polo at Cirencester. *Minimum stay: 2 nights in high season.*

Rooms	1 double, 1 twin/double: £95-£125. Let to same party only.
Meals	Pubs/restaurants 2 miles.
Closed	Rarely.

Amanda & Giles Preston
Lowfield Farm,
Tetbury, GL8 8AE

Mobile	+44 (0)7876 385441
Email	amanda.lowfield@gmail.com

Well Farm

Perhaps it's the gentle, unstuffy attitude of Kate and Edward. Or the great position of the house with its glorious views across the Slad valley. Whichever, you'll feel comforted and invigorated by your stay. It's a real family home and you get both a fresh, pretty bedroom that feels very private and the use of a comfy, book-filled sitting room opening to a flowery courtyard; Kate is an inspired garden designer. Sleep soundly on the softest of pillows, wake to deep countryside peace and the delicious prospect of eggs from their own hens and good bacon. Friendly dogs Jaffa and Dot add to the charm, the area teems with great walks – lovely pubs too.

Rooms	1 twin/double, with sitting room: £105.
Meals	Dinner from £25. Pubs nearby.
Closed	Rarely.

Tel	+44 (0)1285 760651
Email	kategl@btinternet.com
Web	www.well-farm.co.uk

Kate & Edward Gordon Lennox
Well Farm,
Frampton Mansell, Stroud, GL6 8JB

The Close

Up a hill of pretty Cotswold-stone houses, this large Queen Anne house with handsome sash windows delivers what it promises. Step into a stone-flagged hall with grandfather clock and Georgian oak staircase; take welcoming tea with Karen in the drawing room – all gracious sofas and charming chandelier; then upstairs to three light and airy bedrooms softly furnished with antiques. Window seats, shutters and views over garden or pretty street add to the restful atmosphere. Karen, as gracious and relaxed as her house, serves excellent breakfasts in the polished dining room. An elegantly hospitable base for exploring the Cotswolds. *Minimum stay: 2 nights at weekends.*

Rooms	2 doubles, 1 twin: £95-£105. Singles £75-£85.
Meals	Pubs/restaurants 1-minute walk.
Closed	1 January to 28 February.

Karen Champney
The Close,
Well Hill, Minchinhampton,
Stroud, GL6 9JE

Tel	+44 (0)1453 883338
Email	theclosebnb@gmail.com
Web	www.theclosebnb.co.uk

Woodchester Valley Vineyard Barns

Head up the hill to the vineyard at the top and the Stroud valleys spread out below you. It's an area full of wooded hills, pretty villages, arty events – and inspiring artisans like the Woodchester team. The suites are in a restored barn next to the fields of vines. Each has its own big living room downstairs – watch TV, warm your feet on the underfloor heating or by the gas log-burner. Order a continental basket that includes crumpets, croissants and granola, and rustle up your breakfast when you want. Admire fabulous valley or vineyard views from floor to ceiling windows; sip a Bacchus white or Pinot Rosé on your terrace or balcony after a day's exploring. Taster evenings are on offer and you can book one of their tours, which includes a visit to the winery, learning about the grapes and process and a tasting session. There's a Cellar Door shop too, if you want to call in on your way home. *Minimum stay: 2 nights at weekends.*

Rooms	3 doubles: £120-£165.
Meals	Pubs/restaurants 1.5 miles.
Closed	Never.

Mobile	+44 (0)7808 650883
Email	gail@woodchestervalleyvineyard.co.uk
Web	www.woodchestervalleyvineyard.co.uk

Gail Shiner
Woodchester Valley Vineyard Barns,
Upper Atcombe Farm, Convent Lane,
Woodchester, Stroud, GL5 5HR

Frampton Court

Deep authenticity in this magnificent Grade I-listed house. The manor of Frampton on Severn has been in the Clifford family since the 11th century and although Rollo and Janie manage the estate, it's Tamsin and Owen who greet you on their behalf and look after you. There are exquisite examples of decorative woodwork and, in the hall, a cheerful log fire; perch on the Mouseman fire seat. Bedrooms are traditional with antiques, panelling and long views. Beds have fine linen, one with embroidered Stuart hangings. Stroll around the ornamental canal, soak up the old-master views. An architectural masterpiece. *Children over 10 welcome.*

Rooms	1 double, 1 twin/double, 1 four-poster: £225. Stays of 3 nights: £50 off your 3rd night.
Meals	Occasional dinner £45. Pub across the green. Restaurant 3 miles.
Closed	21 December – 6 February.

Owen McNeir & Tamsin Treverton Jones
Frampton Court,
The Green, Frampton on Severn,
Gloucester, GL2 7EX

Tel	+44 (0)1452 740267
Email	framptoncourt@framptoncourtestate.co.uk
Web	www.framptoncourtestate.co.uk/ framptoncourthomepage.htm

The Grange

The largest green in England and this house is at a leafy corner. Rosanne has that happy knack of making you feel at home. Gibraltarian and keen cook too, her breakfasts come with a continental edge – eggs with chorizo, homemade baked beans; her Spanish soup suppers are hearty. The house has stories – ask about Miss Kickler... Family photos, art, quirky monkeys add warmth, the guest sitting room has original wood panelling with the Clifford Crest, inviting bedrooms are all different; there's an indoor pool, gym, playroom, places to read – dogs Spud and Otto keep you company. Walk to Slimbridge, have fun at Frampton's festivals..

Rooms	1 twin/double; 2 doubles both with separate bathroom): £100-£140. 1 single child's room sharing bath with nearby double: £80-£100.
Meals	Soup with bread, £10. Restaurant and 2 pubs 3 miles.
Closed	Rarely.

Tel	+44 (0)1452 740654
Email	rockape@mac.com
Web	www.atthegrange.com

Rosanne Gaggero-Brodermann
The Grange,
The Green, Frampton on Severn,
Gloucester, GL2 7DX

Legg Barn

Ted and Paddy's barn is a surprise. Tucked off the High Street, it has four acres of garden with space for pigs, chickens, veg, sunny seats, trees – and for collie Bill to chase squirrels. The long hall has a quirky line of antique high chairs, and there's a soaring living space beyond with a big wood-burner and comfy sofas; the white theme throughout contrasts with honey-coloured wood and odd splashes of colour. Bedrooms – one up spiral stairs on the sitting room mezzanine – have lovely linen and piles of pillows. Paddy is a good cook – her generous breakfasts often include their own sausages. Walk from the door into the Forest of Dean.

Rooms	1 double; 2 doubles sharing bathroom, let to same party only: £80-£90.
Meals	Restaurant 2-minute walk; pub 10-minute walk.
Closed	Christmas & occasionally.

Paddy Curtis
Legg Barn,
Church Square,
Blakeney, GL15 4DP

Tel	+44 (0)1594 510408
Email	paddy@leggbarn.co.uk
Web	www.leggbarn.co.uk

Hammonds Farm

This old farmhouse snoozes in its own valley about a mile out of Stroud. It's been restored from top to toe with lots of original features revealed or reinstated. The surrounding 100 acres are home to 100 alpacas and a small flock of black sheep. There's a big wood-burner in the guest sitting room, homemade biscuits and little fridges in smart bedrooms, and flowers in every room. Bea serves breakfast in the sunny dining room at separate tables: avocado on sourdough toast, American pancakes, homemade jams, croissants or a full English. After a wander round to see the animals, head out on one of Bea's recommended walks, visit the humming farmers' market in Stroud or Painswick Rococo Garden (swathes of snowdrops in spring), then have dinner out at one of Nailsworth's starred restaurants. *Over 12s welcome.*

Rooms	3 doubles, 2 twins: £126.
	Extra room and sofabed available.
Meals	Pubs/restaurants 1 mile.
Closed	Rarely.

Mobile	+44 (0)7733 101137
Email	hello@hammonds-farm.co.uk
Web	www.hammonds-farm.co.uk

Bea Hyde
Hammonds Farm,
Wick Street, Stroud, GL6 7QN

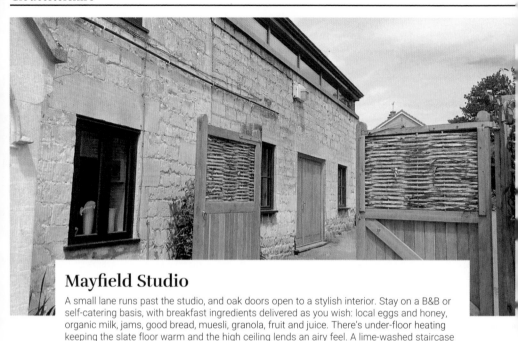

Mayfield Studio

A small lane runs past the studio, and oak doors open to a stylish interior. Stay on a B&B or self-catering basis, with breakfast ingredients delivered as you wish: local eggs and honey, organic milk, jams, good bread, muesli, granola, fruit and juice. There's under-floor heating keeping the slate floor warm and the high ceiling lends an airy feel. A lime-washed staircase leads to a mezzanine bedroom of uncluttered simplicity with views across the valley – and there's a day bed for an extra guest. You don't need a car here – join the Cotswold Way, explore Painswick, work up an appetite by walking the three miles to Laurie Lee's favourite pub, The Woolpack Inn, Slad. In summer open the tri-fold doors and let the sun pour in; in winter relax on the sofa, play games, read or watch one of the many DVDs. *Minimum stay: 2 nights at weekends.*

Rooms	1 double: £120-£140 Extra bed/sofabed £40 per person per night.
Meals	Pubs/restaurants 10-minute walk.
Closed	Rarely.

Sara Kirby
Mayfield Studio,
Vicarage Street, Painswick,
Stroud, GL6 6XP

Tel	+44 (0)1452 814858
Email	sara.kirby@mac.com

The Guest House

Your own timber-framed house with masses of light and space, a sunny terrace, and spectacular valley and woodland views... A peaceful secluded place, it's full of books and mementoes of Sue's treks across the world; the large living room has wooden floors, lovely old oak furniture and French windows onto the rose-filled garden. Sue brims with enthusiasm and is a flexible host: breakfast can be over in her kitchen with delicious farm shop sausages and bacon, or continental in yours at a time to suit you. There's a wet room downstairs, and you hop up the stairs to your charming up-in-the-eaves bedroom with oriental rugs and a big comfy bed. Wonderful! *Minimum stay: 2 nights at weekends Easter-October.*

Rooms	1 double with sitting room & kitchenette: £150-£170.
Meals	Dinner, 2 courses from £17.50; 3 courses from £22.50; 4 courses from £28. Pub 1 mile.
Closed	Christmas.

Tel	+44 (0)1285 831417
Email	sue.bathurst@icloud.com
Web	www.cotswoldguesthouse.co.uk

Sue Bathurst
The Guest House,
Manor Cottage, Bagendon,
Cirencester, GL7 7DU

Calcot Peak House

You feel as if you're visiting old friends when you come to stay with Alexandra and Tom. Nothing is too much trouble and there's always tea and homemade cake waiting for you – or a welcoming tipple if you arrive in the evening. Peaceful bedrooms have garden views; there's a single room too, with a truckle bed for a child. Chickens roam the 19 acres – you'll be offered their eggs at breakfast with bacon, sausage and black pudding from the local butcher, bircher muesli, yogurt and fruit. Sit and chat by the fire, pat Bizzie and Dexie the spaniels, plan your day. Tramp the Salt Way, visit Cheltenham for a festival. On a summer evening take a glass of wine to the bench on the hill for the sunset views, then have dinner down the road at The Wheatsheaf Inn in Northleach. Let the owls hoot you to sleep.

Rooms	1 double, 1 twin, sharing bathroom & drawing room, let to same party only: £110-£120. Children's room available. Singles £75. One-night stay at weekends £120.
Meals	Pub 2 miles.
Closed	Rarely.

Tom & Alexandra Pearson
Calcot Peak House,
Northleach,
Cheltenham, GL54 3QB

Tel	+44 (0)1285 721047
Mobile	+44 (0)7738 468798
Email	pearsonalex5@gmail.com

Clapton Manor

This 16th-century house is as all homes should be: loved and lived-in. And, with three-foot-thick walls, Persian rugs on flagstoned floors, sit-in fireplaces and stone-mullioned windows, it's gorgeous. The garden, enclosed by old stone walls, is full of birdsong and roses. One bedroom has a secret door leading to a duck-egg blue bathroom; the other room, smaller, has a Tudor stone fireplace and wonderful garden views. Unbend in the book-filled sitting room, breakfast by a vast fireplace: homemade bread, award-winning marmalade and eggs from the hens. Karin is vivacious and looks after you beautifully. A charming, down-to-earth place.

Rooms	1 double, 1 twin/double: £125-£130. Singles £110. Extra bed/sofabed £15 per person per night.
Meals	Pub/restaurants within 15-minute drive.
Closed	Rarely.

Tel	+44 (0)1451 810202
Mobile	+44 (0)7967 144416
Email	bandb@claptonmanor.co.uk
Web	www.claptonmanor.co.uk

Karin & James Bolton
Clapton Manor,
Clapton-on-the-Hill, GL54 2LG

Aylworth Manor

Set in a peaceful Cotswolds valley and surrounded by attractive gardens, John and Joanna's gorgeous manor is immaculate. Your hosts have that happy knack of making you feel instantly at home. Find art and family photos, a wood-burner lit on cold nights in a comfy snug and a range of beauty treatments that you can book. Large sunny bedrooms come with garden and valley views, perfect linen on seriously cushy beds, antiques and lavish bathrooms. Wake refreshed for breakfast in the dining room: homemade bread, eggs from the ducks and hens, coffee in a silver pot. The Windrush Way passes the gate at the end of the drive. What a treat! *Over 12s welcome.*

Rooms	1 double; 1 double, 1 twin/double, both with separate bath: £120-£140. Singles £80-£100.
Meals	Pub 1 mile.
Closed	Rarely.

John & Joanna Ireland
Aylworth Manor,
Naunton,
Cheltenham, GL54 3AH

Tel	+44 (0)1451 850850
Mobile	+44 (0)7768 810357
Email	enquiries@aylworthmanor.co.uk
Web	www.aylworthmanor.co.uk

The Courtyard Studio

This smart first-floor studio, attractive in reclaimed red brick, is reached via its own wrought-iron staircase; you are beautifully private. Find a clever, compact, contemporary space with a light and uncluttered living area, a mini window seat opposite two very comfortable boutiquey beds, fine linen, wicker armchair, and a patio area for balmy days. John and Annette live next door, and you stroll over to their friendly home for a tasty, locally sourced breakfast: artisan bread, homemade jams, marmalade and muesli, a traditional full English. It's a 20-minute easy walk to the centre of Cheltenham and you're a quick canter from the races. *Minimum stay: 2 nights*

Rooms	1 twin: £90.
Meals	Restaurants/pubs within 1 mile.
Closed	Christmas, 1 January – 27 February.

Tel	+44 (0)1242 573125
Mobile	+44 (0)7901 978917
Email	courtyardstudio@aol.com

John & Annette Gill
The Courtyard Studio,
1 The Cleevelands Courtyard,
Cleevelands Drive, Cheltenham, GL50 4QF

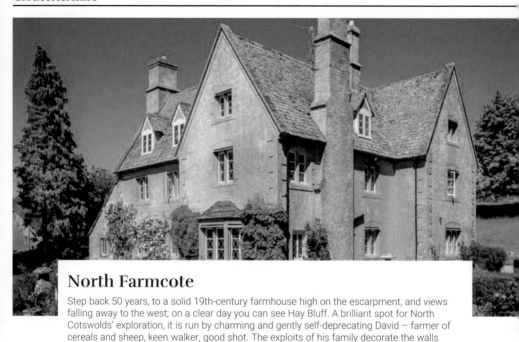

North Farmcote

Step back 50 years, to a solid 19th-century farmhouse high on the escarpment, and views falling away to the west; on a clear day you can see Hay Bluff. A brilliant spot for North Cotswolds' exploration, it is run by charming and gently self-deprecating David – farmer of cereals and sheep, keen walker, good shot. The exploits of his family decorate the walls (racing at Brooklands, hunting in Africa), there's a floral three-piece to sink into, a terrace with outstanding views, and a great pub you can stride to across fields. Bedrooms and bathrooms are old-fashioned, spacious, comfortable and spotless.

Rooms	1 double, 1 twin; 1 twin with separate bath: £100-£110. Singles from £70.
Meals	Pub 2 miles.
Closed	January/February.

David Eayrs
North Farmcote,
Winchcombe,
Cheltenham, GL54 5AU

Tel	+44 (0)1242 602304
Email	davideayrs@yahoo.co.uk
Web	www.northfarmcote.co.uk

Wren House

Barely two miles from Stow-on-the-Wold, this peaceful house sits charmingly on the edge of a tiny hamlet. It was built before the English Civil War and Kiloran spent two years stylishly renovating it; the results are a joy. Downstairs, light-filled, elegant rooms with glowing rugs on pale Cotswold stone; upstairs, delicious bedrooms, spotless bathrooms and a doorway to duck. Breakfast in the vaulted kitchen is locally sourced and organic, where possible, and the well-planted garden, in which you are encouraged to sit, has far-reaching views. Explore rolling valleys and glorious gardens; Kiloran can advise.

Rooms	1 twin/double; 1 twin/double with separate bath, 1 twin/double with separate bath/shower: £120-£135. Singles £110-£135.
Meals	Pubs/restaurants 1 mile.
Closed	Rarely.

Tel	+44 (0)1451 831787
Mobile	+44 (0)7802 676673
Email	enquiries@wrenhouse.net
Web	www.wrenhouse.net

Mrs Kiloran McGrigor
Wren House,
Donnington,
Stow-on-the-Wold, GL56 0XZ

The Old School

So comfortable and filled with understated style is this 1854 Cotswold stone house. Wendy and John are generous, beds are huge, linen is laundered, towels and robes are fluffy. Your own mini fridge is carefully hidden and pretty lamps cast a warm glow. Best of all is the upstairs sitting room: a chic, open-plan space with church style windows letting light flood in and super sofas, good art, lovely fabrics. A wood-burner keeps you toasty, Wendy is a grand cook and all is flexible. A gorgeous, relaxing place to stay – on the A44 but peaceful at night – that positively hums with hospitality. Guests say "even better than home!" *Minimum stay: 2 nights at weekends & in high season. Over 12s welcome.*

Rooms	3 doubles, 1 twin/double: £130-£160. Singles £120-£135. Extra bed/sofabed £30 per person per night.
Meals	Dinner, 3 courses, £32; minimum 4 people.
Closed	Rarely.

Wendy Veale & John Scott-Lee
The Old School,
Little Compton,
Moreton-in-Marsh, GL56 0SL

Tel	+44 (0)1608 674588
Mobile	+44 (0)7831 098271
Email	wendy@theoldschoolbedandbreakfast.com
Web	www.theoldschoolbedandbreakfast.com

Woolmarket House

This listed townhouse is a cosseting place to escape to. Sarah and her team make sure you have everything from slippers, robes and swish beds and baths to a complimentary drink with your evening meal. The Jeremy Houghton artwork displayed throughout is for sale too. Breakfast is a convivial big-table affair with local jams and honey, farmers' market produce, smoked salmon, croissants and more. If you need to head off early, a 'breakfast to go' can be rustled up for you. Find wonderfully buttery biscuits and slices of rich fruit cake (from Huffkins Bakery) under glass domes in your room; 'flowers and fizz' too if you have a celebration in mind; and you can book dinner downstairs in Michael's, the family-owned Mediterranean restaurant. Sit out in the courtyard in summer – made pretty with flowers on tables, climbing roses, fairy lights and lanterns. *Minimum stay: 2 nights at weekends.*

Rooms	2 doubles, 2 twin/doubles: £160-£195.
Meals	Dinner from £15.
	Packed lunches available.
Closed	Christmas.

Tel	+44 (0)1386 840374
Email	info@woolmarkethouse.com
Web	www.woolmarkethouse.com

Sarah Alexiou
Woolmarket House,
High Street,
Chipping Campden, GL55 6AG

Pepper Cottage

Well-travelled Toushy looks after you with warmth – homemade brownies and tea, an elegant drawing room, inviting bedrooms with perfect white linen, and a quiet garden with pretty places to sit in the sun. Her cottage is full of beautiful things: polished antiques, portraits, flowers, lovely old beams. Breakfast is usually in the family room, with doors onto the terrace: eggs and marmalade from friends, fruits, award-winning sausages, continental choices... You're on the edge of the Cotswolds: head out for Bredon Hill walks, Cheltenham's festivals, shops and races, Stow's popular Gypsy Horse Fair. Amiable Raffles the terrier is a treat too. *Minimum stay: 2 nights.*

Rooms	1 double; 1 twin with separate bathroom: £70-£120. Singles £70-£90. Extra bed/sofabed £10 per person per night.
Meals	Pubs/restaurants 10-minute walk.
Closed	Occasionally.

Toushy Squires
Pepper Cottage,
Peppercorn Lane, Kemerton,
Tewkesbury, GL20 7JL

Tel	+44 (0)1386 725644
Email	peppercottage1@gmail.com
Web	www.peppercottage.org

Trevigue, page 47

South East

Uplands House, page 163

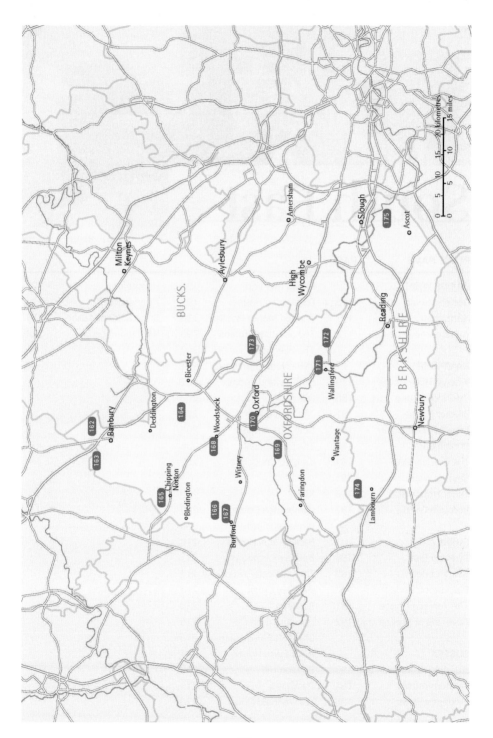

Milton Keynes

Aylesbury

BUCKS.

Amersham

Slough

175 Ascot

High Wycombe

Bicester

173

Reading

BERKSHIRE

172

171 Wallingford

Deddington

164 Woodstock

Oxford

162 Banbury

168

170

OXFORDSHIRE

Newbury

163

Wantage

Chipping Norton

Witney

169

165 Bledington

Faringdon

166 Burford

167

174 Lambourn

20 kilometres

15 miles

South East

The Cloudesley, page 206

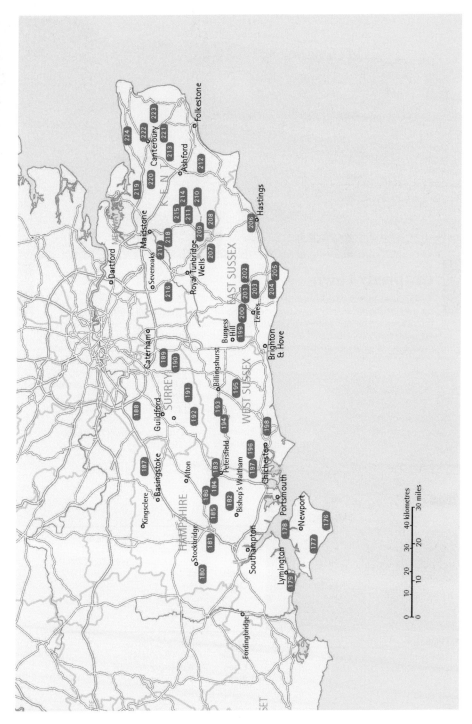

Cropredy Lawn

A long drive leads down to this 1770s house and racing stables – it's all been in Paul's family for generations. Ku welcomes you with tea and cake and you can book a fascinating morning on the gallops with Paul so you'll feel very much at home staying here. Bedrooms are generous and inviting with garden views. The first floor double has a sweet child's room adjoining; hop up more stairs to the atmospheric room in the eaves. Wake for a full English with farm shop sausages and bacon, colourful eggs from the free-range chickens, fruit, yogurt and cereals. Read by the fire in the drawing room, walk on the grass tracks over 200 acres of farmland, sit in the pretty garden. Ku has plenty of pub recommendations – try The Kitchen at Farnborough, just three miles away, or The Red Lion in Culworth, seven miles.

Rooms	1 double; 1 double with separate shower room: £110. Extra bed in adjoining room £50. Singles £108.
Meals	Pubs 3 miles.
Closed	Rarely.

Ku Webber
Cropredy Lawn,
Cropredy, Banbury, OX17 1DR

Tel	+44 (0)1295 750226
Mobile	+44 (0)7766 707421
Email	kuwebber@gmail.com
Web	www.cropredylawn.com

Uplands House

Come to be spoiled at this handsome house, built in 1875 for the Earl of Jersey's farm manager. All is elegant and lavishly furnished; expect large light bedrooms, crisp linen, thick towels and vases of flowers. There are long views from the orangery; relax here with a book as the scents of the pretty garden waft by, or have tea and cake in the drawing room. Poppy will make a delicious dinner – a convivial occasion enjoyed with your hosts. Breakfast is Graham's domain – try smoked salmon with scrambled eggs and red caviar. You're well placed for exploring – Moreton-in-Marsh and Stratford are close, Oxford just under an hour.

Rooms	1 double, 1 twin/double, 1 four-poster: £110-£180. Singles £85-£110; 2-night stay Monday to Thursday.
Meals	Dinner, 2-4 courses, £20-£35. Pub 1.25 miles.
Closed	Rarely.

Tel	+44 (0)1295 678663
Mobile	+44 (0)7836 535538
Email	poppy@cotswolds-uplands.co.uk
Web	www.cotswolds-uplands.co.uk

Poppy Cooksey & Graham Paul
Uplands House,
Upton, Banbury, OX15 6HJ

Heyford House

Old church and handsome house face each other down a village lane – and then the road runs out. In this timeless Oxfordshire valley, the white gate leads into gardens where pathways weave between borders to a kitchen garden and orchards. The house, warm-hearted and well-proportioned, has been in the family for years; your hosts (he a personal trainer, she a chef) live in one wing. Find contemporary art, bright old rugs and open fires – a happy mix of traditional and new. Bedrooms are handsome and comfortable, with excellent bath and shower rooms; Sonja's breakfasts, served by the Aga, are a treat.

Rooms	2 doubles, 2 twin/doubles: £110-£120. Extra bed £30 per person per night.
Meals	Dinner for larger parties, 2 courses from £20; 3 courses from £27; ask about further catering. Picnic from £10. Pubs/restaurants 4 miles.
Closed	Rarely.

Leo Brooke-Little
Heyford House,
Church Lane, Lower Heyford,
Bicester, OX25 5NZ

Tel	+44 (0)1869 349061
Email	info@stayatheyfordhouse.co.uk
Web	www.heyfordhouse.org

Rectory Farm

This big country house has a wonderfully settled, tranquil feel – the family have farmed here for three generations. Find large, light bedrooms, floral and pretty, with bold chintz bed covers, draped dressing tables, thick mattresses and tea trays with delicious chocolate shortbread; all have garden views. Sink into comfortable sofas flanking a huge fireplace in the drawing room, breakfast on local bacon and sausage with free-range eggs, stroll the lovely garden, or grab a rod and try your luck on one of the trout lakes. Elizabeth knows her patch well, walkers can borrow maps and lively market town Chipping Norton is close.

Rooms	1 double, 1 twin/double; 1 twin/double with separate bath: £100-£120. Singles £85-£95.
Meals	Pub/restaurant 1.5 miles.
Closed	December/January.

Tel	+44 (0)1608 643209
Mobile	+44 (0)7866 834208
Email	enquiries@rectoryfarm.info
Web	www.rectoryfarm.info

Elizabeth Colston
Rectory Farm,
Salford, Chipping Norton, OX7 5YY

The Summerhouse

Jacobean Shipton Court has been carefully preserved by the Arathoon family – flats created, outbuildings restored, gardens kept. You stay in Martin and Pauls's Summerhouse – splendid with antiques and china galore. Bedrooms (one ground floor) have well-dressed beds and immaculate shower rooms; step through a 'Narnia' door (cleverly reclaimed old linen press) into the huge second double. Martin rustles up a generous breakfast and the view from your table is a treat: a 300-foot pond with ducks darting between the lilies. Blenheim and Oxford both an easy drive; drinks by the fire in the richly furnished drawing room on your return.

Rooms	2 doubles: £150-£210. Extra double available. Exclusive use for 3 rooms: £400. Short breaks available, £390-£420 midweek. 6-night stay, £740-£810.
Meals	Pubs 5-minute walk.
Closed	Rarely.

Martin Thomas-Jeffreys
The Summerhouse,
High Street, Shipton-under-Wychwood,
Chipping Norton, OX7 6DG

Mobile   +44 (0)7796 615931
Email   martinbandb@hotmail.com
Web   www.shsuw.com

Star Cottage

Classic Cotswolds – from the cottagey stone walls to the flower-bright garden – and swathes of open countryside for cyclists and walkers. Step inside to hand-sewn fabrics, cute lampshades, country furniture, fresh flowers and calm, pretty bedrooms: Sally delights in details. She and Peter, a plant biologist, love their winding stone-walled garden with its herbs, climbers and medlar tree; its jelly appears at breakfast, alongside smoked haddock and local sausages. The pub (yards away) offers dinner, Burford market town is a ten-minute walk, Cheltenham and Oxford a half-hour drive. Or kind Peter will fetch from the station.

Rooms	1 double: £110-£140.
	1 family room for 3; 1 family room for 3 with kitchen: £125-£140.
	Singles £70-£80.
Meals	Pubs/restaurants within walking distance.
Closed	Rarely.

Tel	+44 (0)1993 822032
Email	wyattpeter@btconnect.com
Web	www.burfordbedandbreakfast.co.uk

Peter & Sally Wyatt
Star Cottage,
Meadow Lane, Fulbrook,
Burford, OX18 4BW

Green Close

This trim idyllic village abuts Blenheim Park and the parish church is famous for its medieval wall paintings. The Freelands' old stone house sits on the edge of one of the greens. The feel inside is harmonious and airy: high rafters, polished wood, a hall dining room with light streaming through mullioned windows, a winter fire in the lived-in sitting room, simple spotless bedrooms. Your hosts are easy-going, the retriever is smiley and children are welcome. An Aga breakfast will include compote, yogurt, eggs from the hens, homemade bread and good coffee. Woodstock and Oxford are a hop, and you can walk to supper at the pub. *Pets by arrangement.*

Rooms	2 doubles; 1 twin with separate bath: £95. Singles £65.
Meals	Pubs/restaurants 75 yds.
Closed	Rarely.

Caroline Freeland
Green Close,
West End, Combe, Witney, OX29 8NS

Tel +44 (0)1993 891223
Email julian.freeland@btinternet.com
Web www.greenclose.net

Rectory Farm

Come for the happy relaxed vibe, and Mary Anne's welcome with tea and homemade shortbread. There's a wood-burner in the guest sitting room, and bedrooms have beautiful arched mullion windows. The huge twin with ornate plasterwork overlooks the garden and church, the pretty double is cosier and both have good showers and big fluffy towels. Wake for an excellent Aga breakfast with eggs from the hens, garden and hedgerow compotes, home or locally produced bacon and homemade jams. A herd of Red Ruby Devon cattle are Robert's pride and joy; the family have farmed for generations and you can buy the beef. It's a treat to stay. *Minimum stay: 2 nights at weekends.*

Rooms 1 double, 1 twin: £90–£95. Singles £70.
Meals Pub 2-minute walk.
Closed Christmas & New Year.

Tel +44 (0)1865 300207
Mobile +44 (0)7974 102198
Email enquiries@visitrectoryfarm.co.uk
Web www.visitrectoryfarm.co.uk

Mary Anne Florey
Rectory Farm,
Northmoor, Witney, OX29 5SX

Oxford University

Oxford at your fingertips – at a fair price. In the city's ancient heart are Wadham and Keble; in leafy North Oxford is friendly St Hugh's. Keble's sleeping quarters, functional though a good size, stand in stark contrast to the neo-gothic grandeur of its dining hall – pure Hogwarts! Wadham's hall, 17th century, soaring, is yet more glorious – with top breakfasts. Its student-simple bedrooms are reached via crenellated cloisters and lovely walled gardens; ask for a room facing the beautiful quad. At St Hugh's: three residences (one historic), a student café, 14 acres of romantic gardens and a 15-minute walk into town. *38 colleges in total.*

Rooms	52 doubles, 121 twins: £69-£120. 12 family rooms for 3-4: £100-£165. 1052 singles: £35-£93.
Meals	Breakfast included. Keble: occasional supper £22.50.
Closed	Mid-January to mid-March, May/June, October/November; Christmas. A few rooms available throughout year.
Web	www.universityrooms.com/en-GB/city/oxford/home

University Rooms
Oxford University,
Oxford

Fyfield Manor

A fabulous house in Oxfordshire (once owned by the de Montfort family) with water gardens providing a most romantic setting. The Browns have added solar panels too. Charming bedrooms in your own part of the house have views, slippers and comfy sofas. From the grand wood-panelled hall enter a beamed dining room with high-backed chairs, brass rubbings, wood-burner and pretty 12th-century arch; breakfast is largely locally sourced with organic bacon and eggs and garden fruit. Oxford Park & Ride is nearby, there's walking from the door and delightful Christine has wangled you a free glass of wine in the local pub if you walk to get there! Superb. *Children over 10 welcome.*

Rooms	1 twin/double: £90-£98.1 family room for 4 with sofabed & separate bath: £90-£98; £20-£25 extra per person. Singles £80-£88.
Meals	Pubs within 1 mile.
Closed	Rarely.

Tel	+44 (0)1491 835184
Email	chris_fyfield@hotmail.co.uk
Web	www.fyfieldmanor.co.uk

Christine Brown
Fyfield Manor,
Benson, Wallingford, OX10 6HA

The Old Rectory Swyncombe

Warm, colourful B&B tucked in a valley above Swyncombe House and the 11th-century St Boltoph's Church; the estate runs down to sheep-grazed pastures and footpaths shoot off in all directions. If you come in spring the snowdrops in the church grounds are lovely, and they host afternoon teas. At Lizzie's elegant home you'll be offered homemade cake and tea or a glass of something when you arrive. Breakfast – avocado on toast, bruschetta with basil, homemade granola, sourdough toast with homemade marmalade or local honey – is eaten in the dining room or conservatory overlooking the pretty garden. There's an art-filled living room just for guests and two comfortable bedrooms upstairs. You're on the Ridgeway for superb walking in the Chilterns, try the 11 miles from Watlington to Wallingford if you have the stamina – it's a day's walk – or dip in and out for something more gentle.

Rooms	1 double; 1 double with separate bathroom: £120-£130.
Meals	Dinner, 3 courses, £35. Packed lunch, £8. Pubs 5 miles.
Closed	Christmas, New Year & occasional weekends.

Lizzie Christie-Miller
The Old Rectory Swyncombe,
Swyncombe, Henley-on-Thames, RG9 6EA

Mobile	+44 (0)7721 777222
Email	swyncombe@btinternet.com

Long Crendon Manor

Masses of history and oodles of character at this timbered listed house with high chimneys, dating from 1187... no wonder film companies are keen to get through the arched entrance and into the courtyard! The vast dining room is a dramatic setting for breakfast: sausages from Sue's pigs, home-baked bread and croissants, plum and mulberry jam from the gardens. Windows on both sides bring light into the fire-warmed drawing room with leather sofas, gleaming furniture, family bits and bobs, pictures galore. Sleep soundly in comfortable, country-house style bedrooms (one with gorgeous yellow panelling). The peaceful, pretty village is full of good places to eat.

Rooms	1 double, 1 four-poster; 1 double with extra twin in dressing room: £100-£200. Singles £80-£100.
Meals	Supper £30. Pubs/restaurants 3-minute walk.
Closed	Occasionally.

Tel	+44 (0)1844 201647
Email	sue.soar@longcrendonmanor.co.uk
Web	www.longcrendonmanor.co.uk

Sue Soar
Long Crendon Manor,
Frogmore Lane, Long Crendon,
Aylesbury, HP18 9DZ

Long Acre Farm

You have your own entrance to a converted pigsty and your hosts are charming and generous so join is as much, or as little, as you want. Joanna is in her element creating organic breakfasts: homemade granola, fresh juice from their apples, often home baked bread and a full English if you want it – eat round the family dining table or in the private kitchen. She'll happily rustle up a packed lunch for you so hikers can walk up to White Horse Hill (four miles) or connect with the Ridgeway for 87 miles of glorious downland, secluded valleys and woodland. You're near to elegant Buscot Park and the Faringdon Collection which includes paintings by Rembrandt and Murillo. Bedrooms are sumptuous with underfloor heating, speedy broadband and plenty of books but you can also use the Stable barn with a cosy wood-burner and a telly which can play DVDs. The walled garden is yours to sit in on balmy days, you can walk up to the gallops on the edge of the farm to watch the horses train, and Joanna can give you an organic supper – she is an outstanding cook.

Rooms	2 doubles, 1 twin: £95. Cot available.
Meals	Lunch on request, £5-20. Dinner, 2 courses, £25, 3 courses, £30. Pubs/restaurants 5 miles.
Closed	Christmas & New Year.

Joanna Preston
Long Acre Farm,
Seven Barrows,
Lambourn, RG17 8UH

Mobile +44 (0)7815 782518
Email joannapreston@cheynehouse.com

Monks Walk

You'll feel nicely private here in your own single storey bolthole next to Marion's family home. You have your own sitting room too in the main house where an open fire burns brightly on chilly days. Marion is an excellent cook. She gives you genteel afternoon tea or maybe a glass of wine when you arrive and generous Irish-inspired breakfasts: soda and potato bread if you like, and eggs, honey and apple juice from Royal Farms – she'll also rustle up a picnic lunch for Ascot or Henley. It's a 200-yard stroll down to the Thames where you can hire a boat from Old Windsor's French's Boatyard, or take one of many boat trips. In spite of being so close to London there are plenty of traffic-free bike routes through quiet countryside. *Parking on-site.*

Rooms	1 double with separate shower room: £110-£120.
Meals	Pubs/restaurants 15-minute walk.
Closed	Rarely.

Tel	+44 (0)1753 841202
Mobile	+44 (0)7931 500645
Email	marion.clark@hotmail.com

Marion Clark
Monks Walk,
The Friary, Old Windsor, SL4 2NR

Gotten Manor

Miles from the beaten track and bordered by old stone barns, the guest wing of this Saxon house is charmingly simple. Up steep stone steps (you must be nimble!) and through a low doorway find big bedrooms in laid-back rustic, funky French style: beams, limewashed stone, wooden floors, Persian rugs and a sweet window. Sleep on a rosewood bed and bathe by candlelight – in a roll top tub in your room. Friendly, informal Caroline serves breakfast in the old creamery: homemade yogurts, compotes and organic produce. There's a walled garden and a guest living room with cosy wood-burner.
Over 12s welcome.

Rooms	2 doubles: £80-£115.
Meals	Pub 1.5 miles.
Closed	Rarely.

Caroline Gurney-Champion
Gotten Manor,
Gotten Lane, Chale, PO38 2HQ

Tel	+44 (0)1983 551368
Mobile	+44 (0)7746 453398
Email	caroline@gottenmanor.co.uk
Web	www.gottenmanor.co.uk/bed-breakfast

Northcourt

A Jacobean manor in matchless grounds: 15 acres of terraced gardens, exotica and subtropical flowers. The house is magnificent too; huge but a lived-in home with big comfortable guest bedrooms in one of the wings. The formal dining room has separate tables, where delicious homemade bread and jams, garden fruit, honey and local produce are served. There's a snooker table in the library, a chamber organ in the hall and lovely antiques in every room. Groups are welcome and John offers garden tours. The peaceful village is in lovely downland – and you can walk from the garden to the Needles. *Minimum stay: 2 nights at weekends.*

Rooms	2 twin/doubles: £82-£110.
Meals	Pub 3-minute walk through gardens.
Closed	Rarely.

Tel	+44 (0)1983 740415	**John & Christine Harrison**
Mobile	+44 (0)7955 174699	Northcourt,
Email	christine@northcourt.info	Shorwell, PO30 3JG
Web	www.northcourt.info	

Westbourne House

Watch the yachts go by from this elegant townhouse on the waterfront. A welcoming drink and chat with Richard in the drawing room sets you up well: antiques, oil paintings, a bevy of guitars, family photos – and stunning views. Bedrooms (one downstairs) have WiFi, home-baked biscuits, cosy well-dressed beds. Kate's a marine artist and gives you breakfast looking over the water: lots of choice, homemade marmalade, Bucks Fizz too; if you're an early bird you can help yourself to a continental spread. Between the two main marinas and close to the high street, so shops, bars and restaurants (as well as Southampton ferry) are all a saunter. *Over 13s welcome.*

Rooms	2 doubles: £110-£140.
Meals	Pubs/restaurants 1-minute walk.
Closed	Rarely.

Kate Gough
Westbourne House,
43 Birmingham Road,
Cowes, PO31 7BH

Tel	+44 (0)1983 290009
Email	katec56@gmail.com
Web	www.westbournehousecowes.co.uk

Vinegar Hill Pottery

A sylvan setting, stylish pottery, talented hosts and lively young family. The cobalt blues and rich browns of David's ceramics fill the old stables of a Victorian manor house. Take pottery courses (one day to a long weekend) and be inspired by the warm décor. A narrow staircase spirals up to a modern loft: crisp whites, cathedral ceiling with sunny windows, brilliant shower. The ground-floor garden suite has a patio (with a gorgeous Showman's wagon!), sitting room, painted bed and optional children's beds. Lucy brings a continental breakfast hamper to your room. Stroll to the beach: you can almost touch the Isle of Wight. *Minimum stay: 2 nights at weekends (April-October), 3 on bank holidays.*

Rooms	1 double: £95. 1 suite for 2: £100. 1 wagon for 2 with separate wet room; available in summer: £85. Singles from £60.
Meals	Continental breakfast. Pub/restaurant 0.25 miles.
Closed	Rarely.

Tel	+44 (0)1590 642979
Email	info@vinegarhillpottery.co.uk
Web	www.vinegarhillpottery.co.uk

Lucy Rogers
Vinegar Hill Pottery,
Vinegar Hill,
Milford on Sea, SO41 0RZ

Yew Tree House

Philip and Janet's house is artistic and tranquil. The views, the house and the villagers are said to have inspired Dickens, who escaped London for the peace of the valley. The exquisite red brick house was there 200 years before him; the rare dovecote in the next door churchyard, to which you may have the key, 300 years before that. Thoughtful hosts, interesting to talk to, have created a home of understated elegance: a yellow-ochre bedroom with top quality bed linen, cashmere/silk curtains designed by their son, enchanting garden views, flowers in every room, a welcoming log fire. Breakfast with good coffee is delicious too.

Rooms	1 twin/double: £90.
	Twin by arrangement.
Meals	Pub within 50 yds.
Closed	Rarely.

Philip & Janet Mutton
Yew Tree House,
Broughton, SO20 8AA

| Tel | +44 (0)1794 301227 |
| Email | mutton@mypostoffice.co.uk |

Brymer House

Complete privacy in a B&B is rare. Here you have it, just a 12-minute walk from town, cathedral and water meadows. Relax in your own half of a Victorian townhouse immaculately furnished and decorated, and with a garden to match – all roses and lilac in the spring. Breakfasts are sumptuous, there's a log fire in the guests' sitting room and fresh flowers abound. An 'honesty box' means you may help yourselves to drinks. Bedrooms are small and elegant, with antique mirrors, furniture and bedspreads; bathrooms are warm and spotless. Guy and Fizzy have charmed Special Places guests for many years. *Children over 7 welcome.*

Rooms	1 double, 1 twin: £90-£95. Singles £70-£75. Extra bed/sofabed £25 per person per night.
Meals	Pubs/restaurants nearby.
Closed	Rarely.

Tel	+44 (0)1962 867428
Email	brymerhouse@aol.com
Web	www.brymerhouse.co.uk

Guy & Fizzy Warren
Brymer House,
29-30 St Faith's Road, St Cross,
Winchester, SO23 9QD

Manor House Exton

A magical village setting in the pretty Meon valley for this handsome stone Manor house. Tina gives guests the stable block with its own sitting/kitchen area. Here oak floors, ceiling timbers and whitewashed brick walls give a rustic feel, but two comfy cerise-striped sofas and a flat-screen TV are bang up to date. Sleep deeply in glorious beds with crisp cotton sheets, breakfast heartily in the sunny conservatory: homemade jams, eggs from the happy

hens, local bacon, smoked salmon. Outside is an acre of walled garden, and a woodland area which is carpeted with bulbs: the annual show begins with hellebores, snowdrops and aconites, followed by daffodils. Deep herbaceous borders are packed with colourful cottage garden favourites like delphiniums, sedums, geraniums and salvias. Discover smooth lawns, a beech hedge leading to a secret 'room', box parterres, a veggie patch, and – more formally – a pond and a fountain. Sit for a while on one of the many benches and listen to the birds or find a new aspect of the garden to admire. *Minimum stay: 2 nights at weekends & in high season.*

Rooms	2 doubles, sharing sitting room & kitchenette: £130-£150. Singles £100-£120.
Meals	Pub within walking distance.
Closed	4 December – 4 January.

Tina Blackmore
Manor House Exton,
Church Lane, Exton,
Southampton, SO32 3NU

Tel +44 (0)1489 877529
Email manorhouseexton@gmail.com
Web www.extonbedandbreakfast.com

Dunhill Barn

Arrive for Jan's homemade cake and feel quite at home. Her relaxed, rustic house is full of natural tones, quirky pieces, candles and twinkling wood fires. Bedrooms brim with beamy character; there are four in the main barn, which has the odd steep stair and low bit. Breakfast is in the stunning living area – light streams in through big windows while you tuck into home-baked banana muffins, granola, berries, a full cooked spread. If you fancy independence, the Cartshed is self-catering with doors opening onto a garden area with BBQ firepit. You're in the heart of South Downs National Park; thriving Petersfield and heaps of good pubs are nearby. *Minimum stay: 2 nights at weekends.*

Rooms	3 doubles: £100-£120. 1 single: £80. 1 cartshed for 4, self-catering: £150 per night for 2; extra person £20 per night. Extra futon & cot available.
Meals	Pubs/restaurants 2-minute walk.
Closed	Christmas & New Year. Self-catering Cartshed November to end March.

Tel	+44 (0)1730 268179
Mobile	+44 (0)7789 002342
Email	dunhillbarn@gmail.com
Web	www.dunhillbarn.co.uk

Jan Martin
Dunhill Barn,
Steep, Petersfield, GU32 2DP

The Granary B&B

Vickie runs her own on-site sourdough bakery – she's happy for you to pop in and watch. She leaves you as much bread as you'd like, as well as eggs from their hens, bacon, homemade jam, juice, milk and a laden fruit bowl. Rustle up breakfast when you want. The paintings in the cottage were done by different generations of the family; doors open onto a pretty garden, and there is the world's tiniest wood-burning stove for cosiness. The bedroom looks over the garden and you wake to the smell of the morning's baking. Children fit in well here: a sofabed in the sitting room, fun outside with a trampoline and treehouse, sheep to feed, dogs to pat, chickens maybe popping in to say hello – and learning about dough of course. Explore gardens and woods; follow paths onto the South Downs. Sit by the pond with a sunset G&T on your return.

Rooms	1 double: £110.
	Extra bed/sofabed at no charge.
Meals	Pubs 5-minute drive.
Closed	Rarely.

Vickie Christie
The Granary B&B,
Laundry Cottage, Froxfield,
Petersfield, GU32 1DN

Mobile	+44 (0)7789 962608
Email	vickiechristie@btinternet.com
Web	www.thegranaryfroxfield.co.uk

Shorley Wood

The house looks grand but you'll simply feel like you've gone to stay with friends for the weekend. Alastair is blessed with huge generosity of spirit and gives you proper afternoon tea with scones and cakes and offers of lifts hither and thither – he and Mary just want you to have a happy time. Breakfast is round the huge kitchen table and, if you're hiking that day, will set you up. You get freshly laid eggs from their own hens when they're behaving. The setting is gorgeous: the garden with its sweeping lawns is surrounded by a 50-acre oak wood (a swathe of daffodils in spring) within the 700-acre estate. You can walk straight onto the South Downs Way. Just down the road, you'll find the award-winning Flower Pots Inn and their microbrewery; the attractive village of Alresford (four miles) has plenty of bijou shops, restaurants and another good pub, The Bell. Back at the house there may be a wee dram waiting for you in the guest sitting room and a short walk upstairs to a very comfortable bed.

Rooms	1 double sharing shower room; 1 twin with separate shower room: £85-£100. 1 family room for 5: £115.
Meals	Pub 10-minute walk; pubs/restaurants 4 miles.
Closed	August, Christmas & New Year.

Tel	+44 (0)1962 771275
Email	info@shorleywood.co.uk
Web	www.shorleywood.co.uk

Mary & Alastair Gossage
Shorley Wood,
Cheriton, Alresford, SO24 0NT

Tudor House B&B

Julia couldn't be friendlier and you'll feel at home in her Tudor-style house in the heart of the village. Inside all is beautifully decorated. The drawing room has comfy sofas and chairs and you can settle by the fire with one of the many books. Julia's design flair works its magic upstairs too. Bedrooms have fine linen, an eclectic collection of art, wide South Down country views and swish bathrooms. Wake to a locally sourced full English breakfast, lighter continental choices or 'Mrs Morgan's Omelettata' – served in the pretty garden on sunny days. Explore Winchester with its cathedral, theatre and festivals. *Tea and cake is served till 5.30pm.*

Rooms	2 doubles, sharing bathroom with single: £110. 1 single sharing bathroom with double: £65. Single & double for 2-3 guests, £140-£160. Single & 2 doubles for 3-5 guests, £200-£260.
Meals	Restaurants 4-minute drive.
Closed	Rarely.

Julia Morgan
Tudor House B&B,
Ropley, Alresford, SO24 0DS

Tel	+44 (0)1962 773749
Email	info@tudorhousebandb.com
Web	www.tudorhousebandb.com

Borough Court

Around the core of a medieval timber-framed house, towering chimneys soar skywards and beds face the glorious gardens. Sophie and Ed make you feel at home – snuggle up on sofas around the roaring open fire with a tipple, or sit in the draped window seat with a book. Princess Anne met Mark Phillips in the dining room – it's here you'll be served up scotch pancakes, herb and gruyere omelettes or sausages and bacon from home-reared pigs at a big oak table, also laden with muesli, toast and fruit. Keep your eyes peeled for the bronze deer on your way to the bluebell woods, sit on a stone bench in the garden to drink in the peace, follow a two-mile trail to Alton. This is Jane Austen country; visit her home in nearby Chawton.

Rooms	2 doubles; 1 twin with separate shower room: £120. Z-bed available.
Meals	Pubs/restaurants 1 mile.
Closed	Rarely.

Mobile	+44 (0)7710 056086
Email	boroughcourt@gmail.com
Web	www.boroughcourt.co.uk

Sophie & Edward Bullen
Borough Court,
Borough Court Road,
Hartley Wintney, RG27 8JA

Swallow Barn

A converted squash court, coach house and stables, once belonging to next-door's manor, have become a home of old-fashioned charm. Full of family memories, and run very well by Joan, this B&B is excellently placed for Windsor, Wisley, Brooklands and Hampton Court; close to both airports too. Lovely trees in the garden, fields and woods beyond, a paddock and a swimming pool... total tranquillity, and you can walk to the pub. None of the bedrooms is huge but the beds are firm, the garden views are pretty and the downstairs double has its own sitting room. Breakfasts are both generous and scrumptious. *Children over 8 welcome.*

Rooms	1 double with sitting room, 1 twin; 1 twin with separate shower: £90-£100. Singles £65.
Meals	Pub/restaurant 0.75 miles.
Closed	Rarely.

Joan Carey
Swallow Barn,
Milford Green, Chobham,
Woking, GU24 8AU

Tel	+44 (0)1276 856030
Mobile	+44 (0)7768 972904
Email	info@swallow-barn.co.uk
Web	www.swallow-barn.co.uk

South Lodge

The beautiful Surrey Hills surround this smart home overlooking the village green. Joanna's house gets the sun all day and has a country chic feel. She looks after you well, and gives you tea and cake on arrival, cosy, pretty bedrooms in the eaves and locally sourced and homemade treats at breakfast. Her catering business is run from the house so there are always people coming and going – this is a fun place to stay with a lovely friendly feel. Hop next door for a tasty supper at The Grumpy Mole (popular so you need to book). Near Dorking, and handy for Gatwick, too – it's a 15-minute drive.

Rooms	3 doubles; 1 twin with separate bath: £100-£125. Singles £95. Friday-Sunday: £115 per night; 1-night stay £125.
Meals	Evening meal with wine from £35. Pub next door.
Closed	Christmas.

Tel	+44 (0)1737 843883
Email	bookings@brockhambandb.com
Web	www.brockhambandb.com

Joanna Rowlands
South Lodge,
Brockham Green, Brockham,
Betchworth, RH3 7JS

Blackbrook House

Arriving at this elegant Victorian home surrounded by immaculate lawn, woodland, paddocks and a swing hanging from a huge conifer, you immediately want to explore. Emma and Rae are easy-going, and want you to unwind and feel at home. Bedrooms are spacious and smart with floral fabrics, deep pocket sprung mattresses and good linen; bathrooms are tip-top. Breakfast is a delicious spread: free-range eggs from next door, local bacon and sausages, freshly squeezed apple juice from the orchard. Admire the rose garden, enjoy a game of tennis, head out into the Surrey Hills. Return to a snug sitting room with TV and lots of books. Bliss.

Rooms	1 double: £95-£100.
	1 suite for 2: £105-£115.
	Singles from £60.
Meals	Pub 0.5 miles.
Closed	Christmas & New Year.

Emma & Rae Burdon
Blackbrook House,
Blackbrook, Dorking, RH5 4DS

Tel	+44 (0)1306 888898
Mobile	+44 (0)7880 723512
Email	blackbrookbb@btinternet.com
Web	www.surreybandb.co.uk

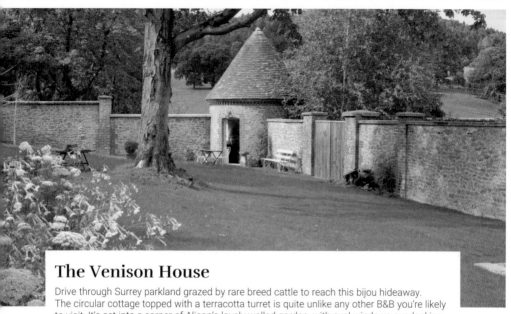

The Venison House

Drive through Surrey parkland grazed by rare breed cattle to reach this bijou hideaway. The circular cottage topped with a terracotta turret is quite unlike any other B&B you're likely to visit. It's set into a corner of Alison's lovely walled garden, with oval windows overlooking the park. Step through the sage green door into a country-chic bedroom with monogrammed pillows and crisp linen. Along a corridor leading to the sparkling shower room, there's a double-fronted cupboard concealing an immaculate kitchen. Alison provides homemade bread, marmalade, bacon, tomatoes and eggs, so guests can make a delicious, DIY breakfast in bed.

Rooms	1 double with separate bathroom & kitchenette: £120-£150.
Meals	Pubs/restaurants 2 miles.
Closed	Rarely.

Tel	+44 (0)1483 200410
Mobile	+44 (0)7768 745765
Email	agmbird@gmail.com

Alison Bird
The Venison House,
Garden Cottage, Park Hatch,
Loxhill, Godalming, GU8 4BL

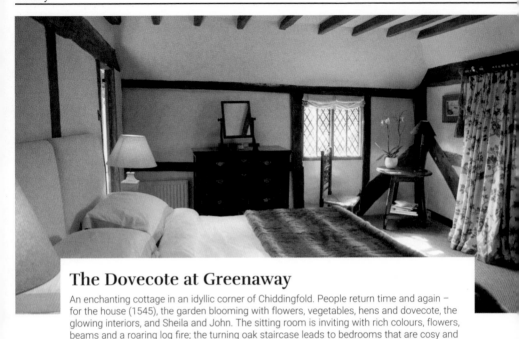

The Dovecote at Greenaway

An enchanting cottage in an idyllic corner of Chiddingfold. People return time and again – for the house (1545), the garden blooming with flowers, vegetables, hens and dovecote, the glowing interiors, and Sheila and John. The sitting room is inviting with rich colours, flowers, beams and a roaring log fire; the turning oak staircase leads to bedrooms that are cosy and sumptuous at the same time, and bathrooms with deep roll top tubs and a pretty armchair. Breakfast is a spread with homemade bread and home-grown tomatoes. Gorgeous countryside, walks on the Greensand Way... who would guess London and the airports were so close? *Pets by arrangement.*

Rooms	1 double; 1 double, 1 twin sharing bath with twin: £115-£135. Singles £95, except weekends. Mid-week prices negotiable.
Meals	Pubs 300 yds.
Closed	Rarely.

Sheila & John Marsh
The Dovecote at Greenaway,
Pickhurst Road, Chiddingfold, GU8 4TS

Tel	+44 (0)1428 682920
Email	jfmarsh@btinternet.com
Web	www.bedandbreakfastchiddingfold.co.uk

Benefold Farmhouse Barn

This 16th-century barn has been renovated with flair by creative hosts. They live in the farmhouse, and the barn is all yours. The living space is open-plan with masses of beautiful beams, sofas by the wood-burner, dining area and well-equipped kitchen. Bedrooms (one down, one mezzanine) are inviting with more honey-coloured wood, natural tones, well-dressed beds and pots of flowers; the double has a striking freestanding bath in the room. Clarissa provides all you need for breakfast – rustle it up when you want. Easy for Goodwood events, Chichester, Arundel; walk the South Downs Way, browse antique shops, spend a day on the beach. *Minimum stay: 2 nights. Stabling for horses by arrangement. Children over 7 welcome.*

Rooms	1 double, 1 twin, let to same party only: £150-£200. Deposit on booking: £100.
Meals	Pubs/restaurants 2 miles.
Closed	Rarely.

Mobile	+44 (0)7796 990660
Email	clarissalangdon@hotmail.com

Clarissa Langdon
Benefold Farmhouse Barn,
Petworth, GU28 9NX

Weston House

Come for Goodwood races and seasonal festivals galore – summer, music and literary. Return to comfortable bedrooms with armchairs, Portmeirion china and spotless en suite bathrooms; the sunny room at the back looks out over pretty garden, fields and the South Downs beyond (you're on the main road but it's surprisingly quiet). Cherry gives you breakfast at a long polished table by the fire in the lovely beamed dining room, or out on the stone terrace if it's summery. You're close to the theatre and sailing in Chichester and the castle in Arundel, Petworth is teeming with antique shops, and you can walk to the pub for a good supper. *Minimum stay: 2 nights in high season.*

Rooms	2 twin/doubles: £90-£100.
Meals	Pubs/restaurants 2-minute walk.
Closed	Rarely.

Cherry Corben
Weston House,
Tillington,
Petworth, GU28 0RA

Tel	+44 (0)1798 344556
Email	westonhousebookings@btinternet.com
Web	www.westonhousetillington.co.uk

Oaklands Farm

Working farm with sheep, geese and chickens deep in the Sussex countryside. Zsa and Stephen's friendly family house is full of books and comfortable places to perch. Close to Gatwick too, so an easy stopover. Your large bedroom gets the morning sun and has a Juliette balcony – little ones can have a grandchild's room if needed. Breakfast includes home-laid eggs, locally grown tomatoes and mushrooms, fruit from the orchard, yogurt and croissants. Eat at the table in the big kitchen or out on the patio when it's balmy. Explore Zsa's brimming garden, which she opens for the NGS; find wild areas, mown paths, veg patch and aviary – tennis courts and trampoline too. Walk across fields to eat at the local pub, or head to Southwater (five miles) for more choice, including a good Indian.

Rooms	1 double: £120-£140.
	Extra bed available for children.
Meals	Pubs 2 miles.
Closed	Christmas.

Tel	+44 (0)1403 741270
Email	zedrog@roggendorff.co.uk

Zsa Roggendorff
Oaklands Farm,
Hooklands Lane, Shipley,
Horsham, RH13 8PX

Crows Hall Farm

The Renwicks are tremendous hosts. Their wonderful flagstone-halled farmhouse in the South Downs National Park is great for walking and cycling and close to Goodwood. Amanda's style is simple and cottagey. Bedrooms are reached by their own staircase; find open brickwork and a big handmade bed in the main one; fantastic views of the walled garden and beyond in the second. In between, the bathroom is fab and fun, with flamingos, freestanding bath and shower (all yours, or shared with your own party). Breakfasts are local, flexible feasts on the terrace or in the quirky rustic kitchen by the wood-burner – comfy sofas here too. Marvellous!

Rooms	2 doubles sharing separate bathroom, let to same party only: £110. Goodwood event prices on request.
Meals	Pubs 1.5 miles.
Closed	Rarely.

Amanda Renwick
Crows Hall Farm,
Chilgrove Road, Lavant,
Chichester, PO18 9HP

Mobile +44 (0)7801 296192
Email amanda@crowshall.com
Web www.crowshallbandb.com

Lordington House

Croquet on the lawn in summer, big log fires in winter, brilliant food all year round. On a sunny slope of the Ems Valley, life ticks by peacefully as it has always done... The house is vast and impressive, a lime avenue links the much-loved garden with the AONB beyond and friendly guard dog Shep looks on. The 17th-century staircase is a glory, the décor is engagingly old-fashioned: Edwardian beds with firm mattresses and floral covers, carpeted Sixties-style bathrooms, toile wallpaper on wardrobe doors.

A privilege to stay in a house of this age and character – bring your woolly jumpers though!
Pets by arrangement.

Rooms	1 double; 1 twin/double with separate bath/shower; 1 double sharing bath/shower with single: £115-£145. 1 single sharing bath/shower with double: £57-£72. Extra bed £20-£25 p.p.p.n..
Meals	Packed lunch from £6. Pub 1 mile.
Closed	Rarely.

Tel	+44 (0)1243 375862
Email	hamiltonjanda@btinternet.com

Mr & Mrs Hamilton
Lordington House,
Lordington, Chichester, PO18 9DX

The Old Manor House

Wild flowers in jugs, old wooden floors and beams, pretty cottagey curtains: Judy's manor house near Chichester has bags of character and she is friendly and kind. Originally constructed round a big central fireplace, the rooms are all refreshingly simple allowing features to shine. Sunny bedrooms up steep stairs have seagrass flooring, limed furniture, gentle colours and warm bathrooms. Enjoy delicious breakfasts by the wood-burner in the dining room: fresh fruit smoothies and an organic full English. Great for horse racing, castle visiting, sailing, theatre and festivals; fantastic walks on the South Downs, too. Lovely. *Minimum stay: 2 nights.*

Rooms	2 doubles: £105.
Meals	Pub/restaurant 500 yds.
Closed	Christmas, New Year.

Judy Wolstenholme
The Old Manor House,
Westergate Street, Westergate,
Chichester, PO20 3QZ

Tel	+44 (0)1243 544489
Email	judy@veryoldmanorhouse.com
Web	www.veryoldmanorhouse.com

The Jointure Studios

A thriving village with an arty heritage. In the centre is your apartment above a lovely big gallery/hall – with piano and wood-burning stove. Find a happy mix of antique and new, a quiet comfy bedroom with leafy views and a cosy sitting room with a kitchen area. Shirley leaves you homemade cakes and breakfast things, and each morning brings over a tray of fruits, yogurt, local artisan bread and eggs for you to cook how you wish. The Ditchling Museum of Art + Craft is inspiring, South Downs National Park is your stomping ground, Brighton and Glyndebourne are close. Return and rustle up supper, or stroll down the road to a good pub. *Minimum stay: 2 nights at weekends, April-September.*

Rooms	1 twin/double with sitting room & kitchen: £115-£130. Singles £100.
Meals	Pubs/restaurants 1-minute walk.
Closed	Rarely.

Tel	+44 (0)1273 841244
Email	thejointurestudios@gmail.com
Web	www.jointurestudiosbandb.co.uk

Shirley Crowther
The Jointure Studios,
11 South Street, Ditchling, BN6 8UQ

The Beeches

Pull the shiny brass bell and step into a wide, welcoming hall. Bedrooms are inviting too with goose down quilts and pillows, striking art and flowers; the guest sitting room below has French windows opening to the garden, more art and comfortable character. Sandy's breakfast by the Aga is a home-produced and local spread, and you eat in a sunny room with pottery on the dresser and an old clock ticking away. Make time to explore the interest-filled garden; there's a willow house by one of the ponds where you can sip wine on summer eves. Find great walks from the door, vineyards and gardens to visit, and Brighton within easy reach.

Rooms	2 doubles: £120-£140.
Meals	Pubs/restaurants 4 miles.
Closed	Rarely.

Sandy Coppen
The Beeches,
Church Road, Barcombe,
Lewes, BN8 5TS

Tel	+44 (0)1273 401339
Email	sand@thebeechesbarcombe.com
Web	www.thebeechesbarcombe.com

Little Norlington Barn

A convivial home with homemade cake at the ready and a fire to settle by – Sandra loves having visitors. She gives you an independent apartment with a private patio, as well as two beamed rooms in the house – one has its own sitting room with a sofabed for an extra guest. Beds are snugly topped with goose down, bathrooms have soft towels and slippers. Wake for a generous breakfast with homemade organic bread and good coffee in the dining room; guests in the Milking Parlour apartment have a continental basket brought over. Glyndebourne is a few minutes' drive, there are masses of great gardens and festivals to dip into and the coast is within easy reach. *Minimum stay: 2 nights at weekends. Apartment minimum stay: 2 nights.*

Rooms	2 doubles: £120-£160.
	1 apartment for 2: £120-£160.
	Sofabed available.
Meals	Pubs/restaurants 1 mile.
Closed	Rarely.

Tel	+44 (0)1273 813321
Email	stay@littlenorlingtonbarn.co.uk
Web	www.littlenorlingtonbarn.co.uk

Sandra Clement
Little Norlington Barn,
Norlington Lane, Ringmer,
Lewes, BN8 5SG

Netherwood Lodge

Garden-lovers will be happy here. Admire brimming borders and pots of colourful flowers, choose a sunny place to sit. Margaret gives you tea and homemade cake on arrival, either on the terrace in fine weather or next to the fire in the sitting room. Ground-floor bedrooms are cosy and quiet. Breakfast is in the dining room overlooking the garden – fresh baked bread, home-grown fruit, homemade muesli and yogurt, and locally sourced eggs and bacon. Margaret is a mine of knowledge about this beautiful corner of East Sussex. Set out on walks, visit National Trust houses and gardens. Glyndebourne is only 10 minutes' drive away, Lewes 20 minutes, and you can stroll to the village pub, The Six Bells, for supper. *Minimum stay: 2 nights on weekdays. Over 16s welcome.*

Rooms	1 twin; 1 double with separate bath: £130-£145.
Meals	Pub/restaurant 0.75 miles.
Closed	Rarely.

Margaret Clarke
Netherwood Lodge,
Muddles Green, Chiddingly,
Lewes, BN8 6HS

Tel	+44 (0)1825 872512
Email	netherwoodlodge@hotmail.com
Web	www.netherwoodlodge.co.uk

Old Whyly

Breakfast in a light-filled, chinoiserie dining room – there's an effortless elegance to this manor house, once home to one of King Charles's Cavaliers. Bedrooms are atmospheric, one in French style. The treats continue outside with a beautiful flower garden annually replenished with 5,000 tulips, a lake and orchard, a swimming pool and a tennis court – fabulous. Dine under the pergola in summer: food is a passion and Sarah's menus are adventurous with a modern slant. Glyndebourne is close so make a party of it and take a divine 'pink' hamper, with blankets or a table and chairs included.

Rooms	2 twin/doubles; 1 double with separate shower; 1 twin/double with separate bath: £98-£150. Singles by arrangement.
Meals	Dinner, 3 courses, £38. Hampers £40. Pub/restaurant 0.5 miles.
Closed	Rarely.

Tel	+44 (0)1825 840216
Email	stay@oldwhyly.co.uk
Web	www.oldwhyly.co.uk

Sarah Burgoyne
Old Whyly,
London Road, East Hoathly, BN8 6EL

The Flint Barns

This pioneering English vineyard sits in the glorious South Downs with views all the way to the sea. Arrive to a glass of wine or pot of tea; there are regular wine nights with talks, and you can book a tour of the vineyard with wine tasting and lunch. Walk straight onto the South Downs Way from the door. More poshtel than hostel, you'll find lots of fresh en suite bedrooms – bring a bunch of friends; one sleeps five (two shower rooms) and those on the

ground floor look over the enclosed garden or the driveway. Breakfast, lovingly cooked and local, is at long tables in the lofty dining room; the innovative dinner and Sunday lunch menus are a treat too – the chef is a keen forager. Spill onto the courtyard for barbecues; settle in to a big communal sitting room made snug with wood-burner, books and games. *Pets by arrangement.*

Rooms	3 doubles, 1 twin: £95-£135. 1 family room for 3, 3 family rooms for 4, 1 family room for 5: £200-£275. 1 single: £85. Dogs £12.50 per night, max 2.
Meals	Packed lunch, £9.50. Dinner, 2 courses, £22.95, 3 courses, £29.95. Pubs 3 miles.
Closed	Sunday-Tuesday except school & bank holidays, weekdays in October.

Adrian Lamb
The Flint Barns,
Rathfinny Wine Estate,
Alfriston, BN26 5TU

Tel   +44 (0)1323 874030
Email flintbarns@rathfinnyestate.com
Web www.rathfinnyestate.com/flint-barns/

Ocklynge Manor

On top of a peaceful hill, a short stroll from Eastbourne, find tip-top B&B in an 18th-century house with an interesting history – ask Wendy! Now it is her home, and you will be treated to home-baked bread, delicious tea time cakes and scrummy jams – on fine days you can take it outside. Creamy carpeted, bright and sunny bedrooms, all with views over the lovely walled garden, create a mood of relaxed indulgence and are full of thoughtful touches: dressing gowns, DVDs, your own fridge. Breakfasts are superb: this is a very spoiling, nurturing place.
Please see owner's website for availability.

Rooms	1 twin; 1 double with separate shower: £100-£120. 1 suite for 3: £120-£130. Singles £60-£110.
Meals	Pub 5-minute walk.
Closed	Rarely.

Tel	+44 (0)1323 734121
Mobile	+44 (0)7979 627172
Email	ocklyngemanor@hotmail.com
Web	www.ocklyngemanor.co.uk/index.html

Wendy Dugdill
Ocklynge Manor,
Mill Road, Eastbourne, BN21 2PG

The Cloudesley

One mile from the sea, a remarkable house full of beautiful things. Shahriar – photographer, holistic therapist, Chelsea gold-medal winner – has created an artistic bolthole: books, African masks, an honesty bar, chic bedrooms and two sitting rooms that double as art galleries. You are looked after with great kindness. Shahriar has a couple of treatment rooms where, in cahoots with local therapists, he offers massage, shiatsu and reiki. You breakfast on exotic fruits, Armagnac omelettes, or the full cooked works; on a bamboo terrace in summer. Don't miss Derek Jarman's cottage at Dungeness or St Clement's for great food. *Minimum stay: 2 nights at weekends. Children over 6 welcome.*

Rooms	3 doubles, 2 twin/doubles: £75-£135. Extra bed £25. Whole house available.
Meals	Pubs/restaurants 5-minute drive.
Closed	Rarely.

Shahriar Mazandi
The Cloudesley,
7 Cloudesley Road,
St Leonards-on-Sea, TN37 6JN

Mobile +44 (0)7507 000148
Email s.mazandi@gmail.com
Web www.thecloudesley.co.uk

King John's Lodge

Deep in the High Weald, down a maze of country lanes, is an enchanting 1650s house in eight acres of heaven: Jill's pride and joy. Inside: oak beams, stone fireplaces, big sofas, and a Jacobean dining room with leaded glass windows, fine setting for a perfect English breakfast. Wing chairs, floral fabrics, dressers with china bowls: the country-house feel extends to the comfortable, carpeted bedrooms. Discover Sissinghurst, Great Dixter, Rye... return to sweeping lawns, wild gardens, ancient apple trees, a woodland walk (spot Titania and Oberon) and a delightful nursery and tea room run by Jill's son. *Minimum stay: 2 nights at weekends & in high season. Broadband unreliable – please ring if you don't get a reply straightaway.*

Rooms	2 doubles, 1 twin: £95-£105. 1 family room for 3: £130-£150. Singles from £75.
Meals	Dinner, 3 courses, £30; minimum 4. Pubs/restaurants 2.5 miles.
Closed	Rarely.

Tel	+44 (0)1580 819232
Email	kingjohnslodge@aol.com

Jill Cunningham
King John's Lodge,
Sheepstreet Lane,
Etchingham, TN19 7AZ

Lamberden Cottage

Down a farm track find two 1780 cottages knocked into one, with flagstone floors, a cheery wood-burner in the guest sitting room and welcoming Beverley and Branton. There's a traditional country-cottage feel with pale walls, thick oak beams, soft carpeting and very comfortable bedrooms (the twin has an adjoining bedroom); views from all are across the Weald of Kent. Find a private spot in the lovely gardens, sip a sundowner on the terrace, relax in the garden room; hearty breakfasts in the family dining room include home-grown fruits, homemade marmalades and yogurts. Near to Sissinghurst, Great Dixter and many other historic places.

Rooms	1 double: £85-£90.
	1 family room for 4: £120.
	Singles from £65.
Meals	Pub 1 mile.
Closed	Christmas & New Year.

Beverley & Branton Screeton
Lamberden Cottage,
Rye Road, Sandhurst,
Cranbrook, TN18 5PH

Tel	+44 (0)1580 850743
Mobile	+44 (0)7768 462070
Email	thewalledgarden@lamberdencottage.co.uk
Web	www.lamberdencottage.co.uk

Ramsden Farm

The views across the Wealds are stunning! These former farm buildings have been renovated with flair, and Sally has created a gorgeous, comfortable home. Unhurried, very good breakfasts are eaten in the huge kitchen by the jaunty lemon Aga, and floor to ceiling glass doors open on to a wooden deck; spill outside on warm days. After a hearty walk you can doze in front of a tree-devouring inglenook. Find lovely sunny bedrooms with more of that view from each, natural colours, tip-top mattresses and the crispest white linen – chocolates too; bathrooms have travertine marble and underfloor heating. Friendly, spoiling and completely peaceful.

Rooms	1 double, 1 twin; 1 double with separate bath: £95-£120. Singles £85-£110.
Meals	Pub 1 mile.
Closed	Rarely.

Tel	+44 (0)1580 240203
Email	sally@ramsdenfarmhouse.co.uk
Web	www.ramsdenfarmhouse.co.uk

Sally Harrington
Ramsden Farm,
Dingleden Lane,
Benenden, TN17 4JT

Beacon Hall House

A family home and Julie truly enjoys having guests. Aga breakfasts are full of delicious homemade, home-grown things; supper too, perhaps cottage pie or Hastings sea bass with veg from the garden. Find sweet herbs on your pillow, home-baked biscuits, flowers and beautiful eclectic furnishings in comfortable bedrooms. Explore seven acres of paddocks, cutting garden and mature elevated terraces, with gorgeous views across rolling Kent and Sussex. Sissinghurst and Great Dixter, castles and pretty villages are close. Return to a sitting room with huge relaxing sofas and fat cushions; Buster and Hetty the spaniels are an added boon.

Rooms	1 double, 2 twin/doubles: £110-£145. Singles £95-£130. Extra bed/sofabed £25 per person per night. Extra bed available in 1 twin/double so can be family room for 3.
Meals	Supper from £20. Pub within 1 mile.
Closed	Christmas, New Year.

Julie Jex
Beacon Hall House,
Rolvenden Road,
Benenden, TN17 4BU

Tel	+44 (0)1580 240434
Email	jjjex@icloud.com
Web	www.beaconhallhouse.co.uk

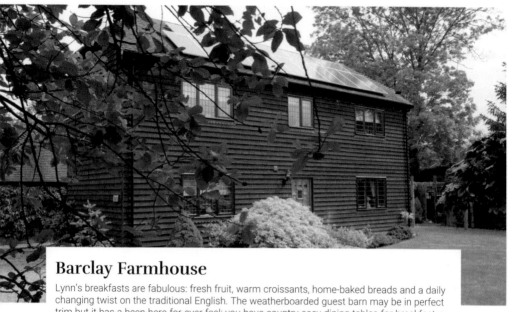

Barclay Farmhouse

Lynn's breakfasts are fabulous: fresh fruit, warm croissants, home-baked breads and a daily changing twist on the traditional English. The weatherboarded guest barn may be in perfect trim but it has a been-here-for-ever feel; you have country-cosy dining tables for breakfast, a patio for summer, a big peaceful garden. Gleaming bedrooms have handmade oak bedheads, chocolates, slippers, discreet fridges, radios, TVs; shower rooms are in perfect order. Couples, honeymooners, garden lovers – many would love it here (but no children: the garden pond is deep). Warm-hearted B&B, and glorious Sissinghurst nearby. *Minimum stay: 2 nights at weekends in high season.*

Rooms	3 doubles: £95. Singles from £70.
Meals	Pubs/restaurants 1 mile.
Closed	Rarely.

Tel	+44 (0)1580 292626
Email	info@barclayfarmhouse.co.uk
Web	www.barclayfarmhouse.co.uk

Lynn Ruse
Barclay Farmhouse,
Woolpack Corner,
Biddenden, TN27 8BQ

The Old Rectory Ruckinge

On a really good day (about once every year) you can see France. But you'll be more than happy to settle for the superb views over Romney Marsh, the Channel in the distance. The big, friendly house, built in 1845, has impeccable, elegant bedrooms and good bathrooms; the large, many-windowed sitting room is full of books, pictures and flowers from the south-facing garden. Marion and David are both charming and can organise transport to the Eurostar for you. It's remarkably peaceful – perfect for walking (right on the Saxon Shore path), cycling and bird watching. *Children over 10 welcome.*

Rooms	1 twin; 1 twin with separate bath/shower: £90. Singles £60.
Meals	Pubs within 4 miles.
Closed	Christmas & New Year.

Marion & David Hanbury
The Old Rectory Ruckinge,
Ruckinge, Ashford, TN26 2PE

Tel	+44 (0)1233 732328
Email	oldrectory@hotmail.com
Web	www.oldrectoryruckinge.co.uk

Handley Cross

This peaceful country house sits in six acres of paddock and flowery gardens. You stay in the charming annexe and have your own entrance. There's a large, sunny living space opening to a terrace, with comfy sofas by the wood-burner, a polished table in the window, a pretty painted dresser. Amanda leaves you a generous continental breakfast – cereals, yogurts, local jams, fresh bread, pastries. Cooked breakfast can be available on request, and Amanda will use freshly laid eggs from her own chickens. Wye has vintage and farmers' markets and you can walk from the door on to the North Downs Way. Further afield are Canterbury, Leeds Castle, Sissinghurst and many stately homes. It's a perfect weekday pad if you're working in the area too. Return to your elegant bedroom upstairs with a king-size double bed and wide countryside views. *Minimum stay: 2 nights at weekends.*

Rooms	1 double with separate bathroom: £80-£95.
Meals	Continental weekday breakfasts & cooked breakfasts at weekends. Pubs/restaurants 1 mile.
Closed	Rarely.

Mobile	+44 (0)7796 332078
Email	ajamiss@outlook.com

Amanda-Jane Amiss
Handley Cross,
Wye, Ashford, TN25 5DL

Romden

Guarded by trees and birds, lording it over meadows and lanes, this rambling 'castle' with its 18th-century tower has a charmingly lived-in feel. Lovely laid-back Miranda and Dominic make you feel at home; help yourself to cereals while they drum up your bacon and eggs, enjoy the flower-filled terrace, play croquet or use their pool and tennis court (by arrangement). Bedrooms, sitting room and hall are decked out with pretty wallpapers, antiques, art, rugs and throws; one of the twins has a tiny shower room; log fires keep things toasty. And if you're hankering after a real castle, Sissinghurst and Leeds are down the road.

Rooms	1 double, 1 twin; 1 twin with separate bath: £70-£100. Singles £55-£75.
Meals	Pubs/restaurants 1.5 miles.
Closed	Rarely.

Miranda Kelly
Romden,
Smarden, Ashford, TN27 8RA

Tel	+44 (0)1233 770687
Email	miranda_kelly@hotmail.com

Hereford Oast

Down the curving drive, past the elegant racehorses in the paddock and the shaded bluebell wood... and arrive to be met with a warm welcome by Suzy who will bring you tea and cake in the garden: sheer heaven in summer. The 1876 oast house, set back from a country road and gazing over fields, has become the loveliest B&B. Downstairs is the dining room, as unique as it is round. Upstairs is the guest room, sunny, fresh and bright, with a rural view; the small bath has an overhead shower. As for the village – white-clapboard cottages, pubs, fine church – it's the prettiest in Kent. Breakfasts of sausages from Pluckley, homemade jams and good coffee set you up for cultured jaunts: Leeds Castle, Sissinghurst, Great Dixter... all nearby. *Minimum stay: 2 nights at weekends.*

Rooms	1 twin/double: £85-£90.
	Singles £50-£55.
Meals	Pubs 1 mile.
Closed	Rarely.

Tel	+44 (0)1233 770541
Email	suzyhereford@gmail.com
Web	www.herefordoast.co.uk

Suzy Hill
Hereford Oast,
Smarden Bell Road, Smarden,
Ashford, TN27 8PA

Charcott Farmhouse

The 1750s farmhouse is rustic and family orientated, and if you don't come expecting an immaculate environment you will enjoy it here. In the old bake house there's a small sitting room with original beams and bread oven, TV and WiFi; relax in here on cooler days, with cats and a dog to keep you company. On sunny days tea is served in the garden. Bedrooms are pretty and comfy with oriental rugs and antique furniture. Nicholas – a tad eccentric for some – is half French and cooks amazing breakfasts on the Aga, while Ginny's great grandfather (Arnold Hills) founded West Ham football team. Come and go as you please.

Rooms	2 twins; 1 twin with separate bath: £90. Singles £60. Extra bed/sofabed £10 per person per night.
Meals	Pub 5-minute walk.
Closed	22–28 December.

Nicholas & Ginny Morris
Charcott Farmhouse,
Charcott, Tonbridge, TN11 8LG

Tel	+44 (0)1892 870024
Mobile	+44 (0)7734 009292
Email	charcottfarmhouse@btinternet.com
Web	www.charcottfarmhouse.com

Rock Farm House

This peaceful 18th-century Kentish farmhouse has ancient beams fashioned from ships' timbers from Chatham dockyard. Bedrooms have garden views and the room in the Victorian extension has two big windows that look eastwards to the glorious Kentish Weald. Sit by the old log fire in the dining room for a breakfast of free-range eggs from the farm, homemade jams and local honey. Well-fuelled you can then join one of the nearby walks that Sue recommends: Greensand Way, Wealden Way and Medway Valley. Sue used to run a well-known nursery at Rock Farm, so knows which plants grow best in these alkaline conditions; her garden is open for the NGS. An evergreen Berberis stenophylla provides a striking backdrop to the herbaceous border – 90-foot long. The bog garden below the house is filled with candelabra primulas, trollius, astilbes, day lilies, gunnera, lythrum, filipendulas and arum lilies. In a further area – around two natural ponds – contrasting conifer foliage interplanted with herbaceous perennials is set against a backdrop of woodland.

Rooms	1 double, 1 twin; 1 twin with separate bath/shower: £100. Singles £50.
Meals	Restaurant within 1 mile.
Closed	Christmas Day.

Tel	+44 (0)1622 812244
Email	susancorfe@btinternet.com
Web	www.rockfarmhousebandb.co.uk

Sue Corfe
Rock Farm House,
Gibbs Hill, Nettlestead,
Maidstone, ME18 5HT

Reason Hill

Brian and Antonia's 200-acre fruit farm is perched on the edge of the Weald of Kent, with stunning views over orchards and oast houses. The farmhouse has 17th-century origins (low ceilings, wonky floors, stone flags) and a conservatory for sunny breakfasts; colours are soft, antiques gleam, the mood is relaxed. Pretty bedrooms have garden views, TVs and magazines; there's a comfy sitting room too. Come in spring for the blossom, in summer for the fruit and veg from the garden; chickens roam free. The Greensand Way runs along the bottom of the farm, you're close to Sissinghurst Castle and 45 minutes from the Channel Tunnel.

Rooms	1 double, 2 twins: £90-£95.
	1 single sharing shower with double, let to same party only: £60.
Meals	Pubs within 1 mile.
Closed	Christmas & New Year.

Brian & Antonia Allfrey
Reason Hill,
Westerhill Road, Coxheath,
Maidstone, ME17 4BT

Tel	+44 (0)1622 743679
Mobile	+44 (0)7775 745580
Email	antonia@allfrey.net
Web	www.reasonhill.co.uk

Dadmans

Once the dower house to Lynsted Park, Dadmans sits on the edge of parkland surrounded by orchards, grazing cattle and sheep. Happy hens provide your breakfast eggs and Amanda sources fantastic local produce for dinner, served in the dining room on gleaming mahogany. There's an elegant drawing room with roaring winter fires and a place to catch the evening summer sun; bedrooms have indulgent beds, views and good bathrooms. Large gardens are pretty too with ancient trees, walled areas, a nuttery, herb gardens – and a swing seat for sitting and admiring. Nearby, find plenty of gardens, castles and cathedrals.
Children over 4 welcome.

Rooms	1 twin/double; 1 double with separate bath: £110. Singles £75.
Meals	Dinner, 4 courses, £35. Supper from £15. Pubs/restaurants 2 miles.
Closed	Rarely.

Tel	+44 (0)1795 521293
Mobile	+44 (0)7931 153253
Email	amandajstrevens@gmail.com
Web	www.dadmans.co.uk

Amanda Strevens
Dadmans,
Lynsted, Sittingbourne, ME9 0JJ

Huntingfield House

This is a joining in sort of place. Children can help feed the hens and meet the ponies in the paddock, while grown-ups can relax. Roses clamber up the walls of this classic Georgian fronted house in open farmland interspersed with woods and orchards. There's a shepherd's hut in the grounds too if you want a quieter spot. Emma is a charming mum and runs a busy kitchen. Not only does she produce local sausages at breakfast, drop-scones from the Aga and honey from the bees, but she whips up children's teas and your suppers too – good honest home cooking. Generosity flows, from free bikes for all to umbrellas on wet days to a fire in the drawing room on winter nights. It's a 30-minute walk to the pub in sleepy little Eastling, 40 to stately Belmont House, and a hop in the car to Faversham, Canterbury and Whitstable. Then it's back home to big traditional bedrooms and owls to hoot you to sleep. *Minimum stay: 2 nights.*

Rooms	1 double, 1 twin: £90-£100. Singles £70-£80. Extra bed/sofabed £30 per person per night.
Meals	Supper, 2 courses, £20. Dinner, 3 courses, £30; children £10. Pubs/restaurants 2 miles.
Closed	Christmas & New Year.

Emma Norwood
Huntingfield House,
Stalisfield Road, Eastling,
Faversham, ME13 0HT

Tel	+44 (0)1795 892138
Email	emma@huntingfieldhouse.co.uk
Web	www.huntingfieldhouse.co.uk

Hornbeams

Rolling hills and woodland, long views and a modern Scandia house brick-built from a Swedish kit. It's brilliant for wheelchair users and altogether easy and comfortable to be in, with floral sofas and chairs and plain reproduction furniture. Alison, a beauty therapist and masseuse, is friendly and gracious. The house is close to Dover so stay here for the night before the ferry. Perfectly designed, brilliantly executed – Alison's garden has come a long way since it was a field. She used to picnic here as a child and dream about living here... Now the garden is bursting with plants. By the front gate is a spring bed, then a purple bed leading to a white-scented border of winter flowering clematis and magnolias. The herbaceous border is a triumph – colours move from pinks, purples and blues through apricots, creams and whites to the 'hot' end. A little waterfall sits in the pond garden and rockery where hostas, ferns, gunnera, bamboo and lilac compete for space. Rejoice in the knowledge that someone who has achieved their dream is so happy to share it with others.

Rooms	1 double; 1 twin with separate bath/shower: £80-£95. 1 single with separate shower: £60-£65. Dinner, B&B £20-£25 per person. Extra bed/sofabed £10-£12 per person per night.
Meals	Occasional dinner £20. Pubs 1 mile.
Closed	Christmas.

Tel	+44 (0)1227 830119
Mobile	+44 (0)7798 601016
Email	hornbeamsbandb@btinternet.com
Web	www.hornbeams.co.uk

Alison Crawley
Hornbeams,
Jesses Hill, Kingston,
Canterbury, CT4 6JD

7 Longport

A delightful, unexpected hideaway bang opposite the site of St Augustine's Abbey and a five-minute walk to the Cathedral. You pass through Ursula and Christopher's elegant Georgian house to emerge in a pretty courtyard, with fig tree and rambling rose, to find your self-contained cottage. Downstairs is a cosy sitting room with pale walls, tiled floors and plenty of books, and a clever, compact wet room with mosaic tiles. Then up steep stairs to a swish bedroom with crisp cotton sheets on a handmade bed and views of the ancient wisteria. You breakfast in the main house or in the courtyard on sunny days. Perfect.

Rooms	1 double with sitting room: £100. Singles £75.
Meals	Restaurants 5-minute walk.
Closed	Rarely.

Ursula & Christopher Wacher
7 Longport,
Canterbury, CT1 1PE

Tel	+44 (0)1227 455367
Email	info@7longport.co.uk
Web	www.7longport.co.uk

Great Selson Manor

A gem of a restoration in a blooming garden. Graham (film maker) and Yolanda's home is one of the earliest Dutch-influenced buildings in east Kent, and you step inside to wonderful features at every turn: a striking brick hall floor, a Jacobean oak staircase, Graham's artwork, oriental musical instruments, an elegant library. Inviting bedrooms, claw foot baths, and cushiony sofas in the sitting room add to the comfortable vibe. Breakfast includes a neighbour's award-winning apple juice, best-sourced sausages, homemade jams, eggs from the hens. Graham and Yolanda exude cheerfulness and interest – it's a treat to stay with them. *Minimum stay: 2 nights at weekends & in high season.*

Rooms	2 doubles: £100-£150.
Meals	Continental breakfast available.
	Pubs/restaurants 2.5 miles away.
Closed	Rarely.

Mobile	+44 (0)7957 160385
Email	g.j3@btinternet.com

Graham Johnston
Great Selson Manor,
Selson Lane, Eastry, Sandwich, CT13 0EF

Northwood Lodge

Emma is happy to share her friendly home. Bedrooms have pretty beds and rugs on painted floors; the huge guest bathroom is gorgeous: freestanding bath, fluffy towels, scented lotions, a jug of flowers. A delicious breakfast with a dish of the day and homemade jam is served in the big, bright kitchen, or outside in the sun. You can settle in the drawing room for a film/dinner night (book beforehand), and there's another sitting room with heaps of books, open fire and large antique mirrors. Head out for seaside walks, Whitstable Oyster Festival and Faversham with its medieval market place; Canterbury and Margate are a short drive too. *Minimum stay: 2 nights on bank holidays & in high season.*

Rooms	2 doubles sharing bathroom: £110. Singles £85.
Meals	Dinner from £25. Dinner & movie from £35. Pubs/restaurants 5 miles.
Closed	Rarely.

Emma Clarke
Northwood Lodge,
Bullockstone Road, Herne Bay, CT6 7NR

Tel	+44 (0)1227 634549
Email	emma@stellarproductions.co.uk

Hay Barton, page 38

Brixton Townhouse, page 239

London

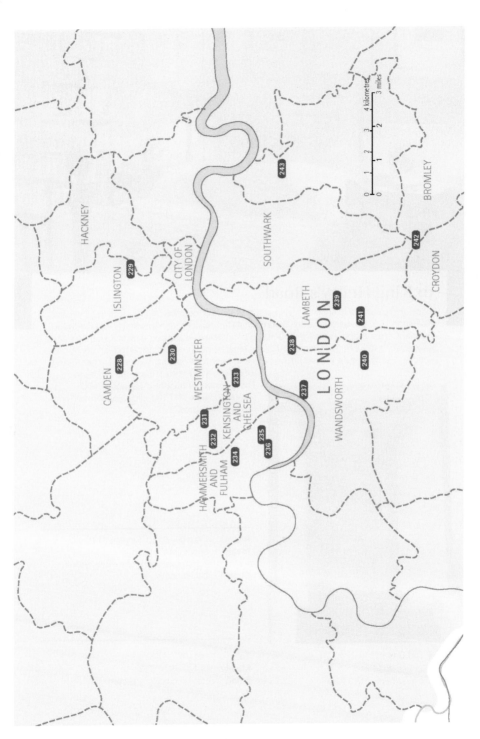

HACKNEY

ISLINGTON

CAMDEN

CITY OF LONDON

WESTMINSTER

HAMMERSMITH AND FULHAM

KENSINGTON AND CHELSEA

SOUTHWARK

LAMBETH

L O N D O N

WANDSWORTH

BROMLEY

CROYDON

228
229
230
231
232
233
234
235
236
237
238
239
240
241
242
243

4 kilometres
3 miles
0 1 2 3
0 1 2 3

30 King Henry's Road

Shops, restaurants and sublime views of Primrose Hill are a five-minute stroll from this interesting 1860s house; walls are covered in a lifetime collection of watercolours, drawings and maps. Your room on the top floor has a comfortable brass bed, a sisal floor, fine pieces of furniture, a wall of books, digital TV and a smart new bathroom. Breakfast on homemade bread and jams, bagels, croissants, yogurts and fresh fruit salad in the large kitchen/dining room with a big open fire and garden views. There's open-air theatre in Regent's Park in summer; Carole and Ted know London well and will happily advise.

Rooms	1 double: £120. Singles £115.
Meals	Continental breakfast.
	Pubs/restaurants 2-minute walk.
Closed	Occasionally.

Carole & Ted Cox
30 King Henry's Road,
Primrose Hill, London, NW3 3RP

Tel	+44 (0)20 7483 2871
Mobile	+44 (0)7976 389350
Email	carole.l.cox@gmail.com

Arlington Avenue

Follow the canal up from Islington to this 1848 townhouse. There's a key safe for late arrivals and then you're given your own key so you can come and go – Thomas will explain the day/night alarm system. Thomas lives at the top of the house and works in the ground floor living room. The first floor is for guests – there's a double and a single, both with views over several gardens to the back. You share the guest bathroom down moderately steep stairs, but if you don't mind that you've struck gold. If you fancy more than cereals, tea, coffee and toast for breakfast you can pick up pastries from Pophams Bakery and eat in the basement kitchen/dining room. Thomas is happy for you to have picnic suppers here too and chill drinks in the fridge; there's a conservatory and a pretty garden beyond.

Rooms	1 double sharing bath with single: £55-£85. 1 single: £45-£65.
Meals	Pubs/restaurants 100 yds.
Closed	Rarely.

Mobile	+44 (0)7711 265183
Email	thomas@arlingtonavenue.co.uk
Web	www.arlingtonavenue.co.uk

Thomas Blaikie
Arlington Avenue,
Islington, London, N1 7AX

22 York Street

A Regency townhouse on a quiet street, a family home for over 60 years. It defies most attempts to pigeonhole it, but we'd say it's a little like staying with an eccentric aunt, who has staff on hand to help. It's a convivial place. A continental breakfast is taken communally at a curved wooden table in the big kitchen/dining room, with guests chatting over coffee and croissants while they plan their day. There's always something to catch your eye, be it the red-lipped oil painting outside the dining room or old riding boots on the landing. A sitting room waits on the first floor with sofas, books, backgammon, and a baby grand piano, which, of course, you are welcome to play; you can also make a cup of tea here. Bedrooms are simple: homely, but comfortable, with good beds, rugs on wood floors and the odd antique; if you're looking for oodles of hotel luxury, this probably isn't for you. However, you're in the middle of Marylebone with good bars and restaurants on your doorstep. Sherlock Holmes lived up the road, Madame Tussauds and Lord's are both close. A very friendly place.

Rooms	5 doubles, 2 twins: £165.
	1 family room for 4: £250.
	3 singles: £99-£125. 1 triple: £195.
Meals	Continental breakfast included.
	Pubs/restaurants nearby.
Closed	Never.

Michael & Liz Callis
22 York Street,
London, W1U 6PX

Tel	+44 (0)20 7224 2990
Email	mc@22yorkstreet.co.uk
Web	www.22yorkstreet.co.uk

1 Peel Street

Step past pots of flowers by the front door to find a friendly home full of fascinating old maps, photos from Susie's world travels, interesting books and objets d'art. Guests love it here. The top floor is all yours: you have a cosy bedroom under the eaves, and there's a second room with bunk beds if you want to bring an extra guest. Breakfast is at a table overlooking the patio or downstairs in the elegant dining room; Susie gives you organic bread, pastries, fruit, yogurt, cereals and excellent coffee. She's happy to help with your itinerary and can tell you the best places to eat nearby. It's just a stroll to tapas, cafés and wine bars, Portobello Market browsing and a surprising number of bookshops. *Second bedroom with bunk beds available for overflow with the same group.*

Rooms	1 double with separate bath/shower: £130. Singles £95.
Meals	Continental breakfast. Pubs/restaurants 2-minute walk.
Closed	Occasionally.

Tel	+44 (0)20 7792 8361
Mobile	+44 (0)7776 140060
Email	susan@susielaws.co.uk

Susan Laws
1 Peel Street,
Kensington, London, W8 7PA

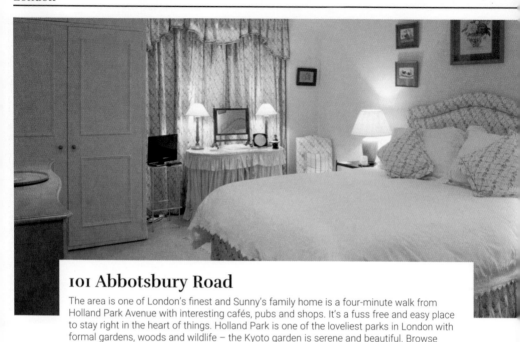

101 Abbotsbury Road

The area is one of London's finest and Sunny's family home is a four-minute walk from Holland Park Avenue with interesting cafés, pubs and shops. It's a fuss free and easy place to stay right in the heart of things. Holland Park is one of the loveliest parks in London with formal gardens, woods and wildlife – the Kyoto garden is serene and beautiful. Browse happily in Daunt Books then treat yourself to supper in Marco Pierre White's Belvedere restaurant. Hop on the tube for Kensington High Street, Notting Hill, Portobello Market and Knightsbridge. Relax, unwind, feel free to come and go but do ask Sunny for tips – she's lived here for more than 40 years. *Children over 6 welcome. Tube: Holland Park, 7-minute walk. Off-street parking sometimes available.*

Rooms	1 double sharing bath with single: £110-£120. 1 single: £65-£75.
Meals	Continental breakfast. Pubs/restaurants 5-minute walk.
Closed	Occasionally.

Sunny Murray
101 Abbotsbury Road,
Holland Park, London, W14 8EP

Tel	+44 (0)20 7602 0179
Mobile	+44 (0)7768 362562
Email	sunny.murray@gmail.com
Web	www.hollandparkbandb.co.uk

37 Trevor Square

A three-minute walk from Hyde Park or Harrods – a fabulous find. The square is peaceful and private, with a well-kept garden in the middle. Margaret is flexible about everything – breakfast and check in times; she will call cabs, arrange collection and really look out for you. A superb full English breakfast is served in the relaxed kitchen/diner; the friendly dachshunds, Jester and Waggy, keep you company. Luxurious bedrooms (one downstairs has an enormous bed and a little patio) have goose down pillows, cashmere duvets, electric blankets and a mini fridge; slip on your robe, listen to some music or watch a DVD – it's all here. *Tube: Knightsbridge. Nearest car park £25 for 24 hrs; closed overnight.*

Rooms	1 double; 1 double sharing shower with single, let to same party only: £200. 1 single: £50-£75.
Meals	Restaurants 200 yds.
Closed	Occasionally.

Tel	+44 (0)20 7823 8186
Email	margaret@37trevorsquare.co.uk
Web	www.37trevorsquare.co.uk

Margaret & Holly Palmer
37 Trevor Square,
Knightsbridge, London, SW7 1DY

31 Rowan Road

Terrific value for money in leafy Brook Green. The two studios are fantastic spaces: one under the eaves (comfy twin beds and armchairs, a deep cast-iron bath from which you can gaze at the birds), the other larger and more contemporary in style, on the lower ground floor, with its own wisteria-clad entrance. All independent with a continental breakfast popped in your fridge. Or join in with family life and stay in the little pink bedroom with books and hats, and take breakfast in the pretty conservatory with Vicky and Edmund. A friendly home with flowers, art, photos and a relaxed vibe – Tiger the terrier and a blossoming garden too. *Tube: Hammersmith. Off-street parking £20 a day.*

Rooms	1 double with separate bath/shower: £75-£90. 2 studios for 2 with kitchenette: £95-£130. Singles £75. Extra bed £20 per person per night.
Meals	Continental breakfast. Pubs/restaurants 2 minutes.
Closed	Occasionally.

Vicky & Edmund Sixsmith
31 Rowan Road,
Brook Green, Hammersmith,
London, W6 7DT

Tel	+44 (0)20 8748 0930
Mobile	+44 (0)7966 829359
Email	vickysixsmith@me.com
Web	www.abetterwaytostay.co.uk

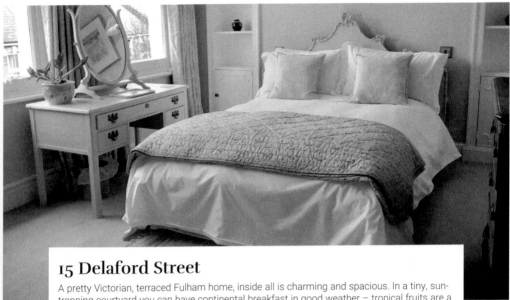

15 Delaford Street

A pretty Victorian, terraced Fulham home, inside all is charming and spacious. In a tiny, sun-trapping courtyard you can have continental breakfast in good weather – tropical fruits are a favourite and the coffee is very good; a second miniature garden bursts with life at the back. The bedroom, up a wide spiral staircase, is nicely private on the second floor. Expect perfectly ironed sheets on a comfy bed, a big sofa, TV and books, a sunny bathroom and fluffy white towels. The tennis at Queen's is in June and on your doorstep. Tim and Margot – she's from Melbourne – are fun, friendly and happy to pick you up from the nearest tube. *Tube: West Brompton. Parking free eves & weekends; otherwise pay & display. 74 bus to West End nearby.*

Rooms	1 double: £100-£105. Sofabed suitable for a child available; extra room too. Singles £80-£85.
Meals	Restaurants nearby.
Closed	Occasionally.

Tel	+44 (0)20 7385 9671
Email	woodsmargot@hotmail.co.uk

Margot & Tim Woods
15 Delaford Street,
Fulham, London, SW6 7LT

29 Bronsart Road

Caroline's generosity of spirit makes the house feel like home and she's steeped in her community so can tell you about all the best haunts. There's a fuss-free feel: lovely things to look at, spotless spaces filled with light. Your bedroom, up in the eaves, has rooftop views and a neat little bathroom next door. Plan your days in the chintzy living room, doors flung open onto the secret rooftop patio filled with potted tubs and trellises where you can perch on the bench and drink a glass of something chilled among the chimneys. You'll breakfast on fruit and croissants in the informal kitchen. Central London is close: explore South Ken's museums, shop on the King's Road or pop in to an exhibition. Boris bikes can be found two streets away, buses are frequent and there's much to see and do. It's quiet back here though and there's a very good pizzeria on the corner. *Children over 8 welcome. Parking by permit only 9am-5pm during weekdays; free on Sundays.*

Rooms	1 double: £110-£130.
Meals	Continental breakfast available. Restaurants 2-minute walk.
Closed	Rarely.

Caroline Docker
29 Bronsart Road,
Fulham, London, SW6 6AJ

Tel	+44 (0)20 8616 9595
Mobile	+44 (0)7767 436487
Email	dockercaroline@gmail.com
Web	www.londonfulhambnb.com

Ara

Jenny and Henry's Belgian Spitz barge was originally used for shipping grain, but they've transformed it single-handedly into an utterly unique home. They'll be on hand to greet you on arrival, along with Moose, their friendly Newfoundland dog. There's a wonderful feeling of space, and two rooms at a time are given over to guests unless you're a group. Settle in the guest sitting room by the wood-burner, hop up a ladder into a little wheelhouse library and look out onto the river from the chaise longue. Sunbathe on the two decks and lap up the to-ing and fro-ing of passing boats, herons and cormorants. Jenny loves to cook, so breakfast is a treat: good coffee, croissants, eggs Benedict or a full English – it's a convivial affair at a long table on the upstairs level. You can take the Thames Clipper river bus into central London and there are plenty of restaurants and shops close by.

Rooms	3 doubles; 1 double with separate wc: £130-£300.
Meals	Pubs/restaurants 2-minute walk.
Closed	Occasionally.

Mobile	+44 (0)7921 764634
Email	jennifersforrester@gmail.com

Jennifer Forrester
Ara,
Battersea, London, SW11 3TN

Battersea B&B

Come to retreat from the frenzy of city life. In the 1890 Victorian cottage all is peaceful and calm and Barbara looks after you beautifully. The dining room, with the odd oriental piece from past travels, is where you have your full English breakfast – unusual for London – and across the hall is the elegant sitting room, with gilt-framed mirrors, sumptuous curtains, and a piano which you are welcome to play. Upstairs is a bright, restful bedroom with pretty linen and a cloud of goose down. The large bathroom next door is all yours – fabulous. Nothing has been overlooked and the tiny courtyard garden is a summer oasis. *Train: 6-min Waterloo, 3-min Victoria. Bus: 137, 452 (Sloane Sq) & 156 (Vauxhall). Tube: 10 min. Parking: £2.90/hour or £10/day permit; weekends free.*

Rooms	1 double with separate bath & shower: £110-£115. Singles £80-£85.
Meals	Pubs/restaurants 200 yds.
Closed	Occasionally.

Barbara Graham
Battersea B&B,
Battersea, London, SW8 3SL

Tel   +44 (0)20 7622 5547
Email batterseabedandbreakfast@gmail.com
Web   www.batterseabandb.co.uk

Brixton Townhouse

You're separated from busy Brixton Hill by a large communal garden so it's tranquil here, and Anne and Ian give you a whole floor of their house along with an elegant sitting room with a wood-burner. Breakfast is in the garden room – excellent coffee, sourdough toast, homemade jams and fruit compotes. Head off to explore – you'll find lots of maps and guide books in the house or ask your hosts who are locals. The tube is a ten-minute walk, or you can hop on a bus to get there in five. In summer explore the back garden – enormous for London with secret paths, a greenhouse, herb garden, veg patch and fruit trees. Walk out to a huge choice of all kinds of food and some independent shops including Anne and Ian's 'Cornercopia' which sells useful, beautiful and curious things for the home and garden; you get 10% off. *Minimum stay: 2 nights. Over 12s welcome.*

Rooms	3 doubles, 1 twin, all with separate bathrooms: £90-£110.
Meals	Pubs/restaurants 5-minute walk.
Closed	Christmas.

Mobile	+44 (0)7803 528739
Email	anne.fairbrother@gmail.com

Anne Fairbrother
Brixton Townhouse,
17 Raleigh Gardens,
Brixton, London, SW2 1AD

The Coach House

A rare privacy: you have your own coach house, separated from the Notts' home by a stylish terracotta-potted courtyard with Indian sandstone paving and various fruit trees (peach, pear, nectarine). Breakfast in your own sunny kitchen, or let Meena treat you to a full English in hers (she makes great porridge, too). The lovely big attic bedroom has beams, cream curtains, rugs on polished wood floors; the brick-walled ground-floor twin is pleasant and airy; both look over the peaceful garden. Urban but bucolic – just perfect as a romantic retreat, or a family getaway. *Minimum stay: 3 nights; 2 nights January & February. Tube: Balham Station to Leicester Square & Oxford Street or train to Victoria.*

Rooms	1 family room for 3: £125-£210. 1 twin with separate shower, same-party bookings only: £125-£210. £210 for the whole Coach House.
Meals	Pub/restaurant 200 yds.
Closed	Occasionally.

Meena & Harley Nott
The Coach House,
2 Tunley Road, Balham,
London, SW17 7QJ

Tel	+44 (0)20 8772 1939
Email	coachhouse@chslondon.com
Web	www.coachhouse.chslondon.com

38 Killieser Avenue

You can be in central London in 15 minutes from this Victorian townhouse on a quiet leafy street. Philip and Winkle have brought country-house elegance and the fruits of far-flung travels to South London, and their home is an oasis from the hustle and bustle. Bedrooms are at the top of the house; there's space for an extra bed in the single room. Come down to an airy, art-filled kitchen for breakfast: continental or full English (mainly organic) with interesting breads, nuts and seeds and fruit salads. Winkle is good humoured and has masses of advice on what to visit and where to eat. Return and relax in her award-winning garden with its parterre, arbour, brimming borders and secluded seats. *Minimum stay: 2 nights at weekends. Parking restricted 10am-12 noon; free from 12 noon-10am.*

Rooms	1 twin: £110-£115.
	1 single with separate bath: £90-£95.
Meals	Dinner £35.
	Afternoon tea on request, £25.
Closed	Occasionally.

Tel	+44 (0)20 8671 4196
Email	winklehaworth@hotmail.com
Web	www.thegardenbedandbreakfast.com

Winkle Haworth
38 Killieser Avenue,
Streatham Hill, London, SW2 4NT

24 Fox Hill

This part of London is full of sky, trees and wildlife; Pissarro captured on canvas the view up the hill in 1870 (the painting is in the National Gallery). There's good stuff everywhere – things hang off walls and peep over the tops of dressers; bedrooms are stunning, with antiques, textiles, paintings and big, firm beds. Sue, a graduate from Chelsea Art College, employs humour and intelligence to put guests at ease and has created a special garden too.

Tim often helps with breakfasts: eggs to order, good coffee. Owls hoot at night, woodpeckers wake you in the morning, in this lofty, peaceful retreat. *Train: Crystal Palace. Underground: East London line. Collection possible. Good buses to West End & Westminster. Victoria 20 min by train.*

Rooms	1 twin/double; 1 double, 1 twin, sharing shower: £90-£120. Singles £60. Extra bed £30 per person per night; sofabed £50 per night.
Meals	Dinner £35. Pubs/restaurants 5-minute walk.
Closed	Rarely.

Sue & Tim Haigh
24 Fox Hill,
Crystal Palace, London, SE19 2XE

Tel +44 (0)20 8768 0059
Email suehaigh@hotmail.co.uk
Web www.foxhill-bandb.co.uk

113 Pepys Road

This Victorian terraced house overlooks the first landscaped park of its kind in south-east London; the pretty garden, designed by David's father, is graced with majestic magnolias. Find a quirky mix of classic British furniture and oriental antiques. Picking up from his Chinese mother Anne, David has now taken on the B&B (helped by his housekeeper) and breakfast can be English or oriental. It's a convivial, lived-in home full of family portraits, batiks and books; the Chinese 'Peony' room downstairs has a huge bed, bamboo blinds, kimonos for the bathroom. A short walk to buses and tubes... and blissfully quiet for London.

Rooms	1 double, 1 twin/double; 1 twin with separate bath: £110. Singles £85.
Meals	Restaurant 0.5 miles.
Closed	Rarely.

Tel	+44 (0)20 7639 1060
Email	davidmarten@pepysroad.com
Web	www.pepysroad.com

David Marten
113 Pepys Road,
New Cross, London, SE14 5SE

East of England

Meadow House, page 281

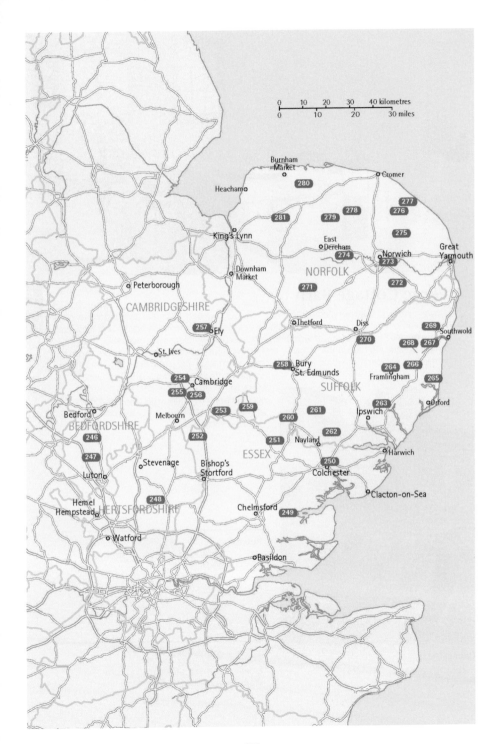

Forge Cottage Barn

A sweet pea and lavender-clad pergola leads to your own barn... Carmel and David give you a fresh bedroom with tip-top linen and cheerful bedspread on a seriously comfy bed; they have an interesting library that you're welcome to browse too. Breakfast is a moveable feast – have it outside the barn in the sun, over in the main house or on the deck by a stream; tuck into locally sourced everything with homemade marmalade and jams. Masses to do nearby – gardens, cycling, rowing on the river Ouse, walks on the Greensand Ridge. Return to explore the pretty cottage garden, and then curl up with a book on the sofa in your room.
Pets by arrangement.

Rooms	1 double: £85. Friday & Saturday: £90. Extra child's bed and travel cot available.
Meals	Pub 3-minute walk.
Closed	Christmas.

Carmel Golding
Forge Cottage Barn,
Forge Cottage, The Knoll,
Maulden, Bedford, MK45 2DB

Tel	+44 (0)1525 840485
Email	carmel@dandcgolding.com
Web	www.forgecottagebarn.co.uk

Harlington Manor

Charles II may have stayed, and his bedroom has changed little... Off a busy street yet an ancient dream of a manor house, David's home is a dramatic trove of antiques, art, rich colour, grand piano, rose carvings, gorgeous bedrooms – be swept along by his enthusiasm and generosity, marvel at the attention to detail. Breakfast is served in the magnificent Tudor dining room at one long table: continental with compotes and yogurt, home-baking, tea in heirloom china. David's a good cook, and dinner with the family might include a harpsichord recital. A pretty garden, guided local tours... hop on a train from St Pancras and arrive in time for drinks. *Public transport 2-minute walk.*

Rooms	2 doubles; 1 double with separate bathroom: £88-£120. Singles from £60.
Meals	Continental breakfast on weekdays, cooked breakfast at weekends. Dinner, 4 courses with glass of champagne & port, £40. Restaurants 2-minute walk.
Closed	Rarely.

Mobile	+44 (0)7788 742209
Email	blakeman.david1@gmail.com
Web	www.harlingtonmanor.com

David Blakeman
Harlington Manor,
Westoning Road, Harlington, LU5 6PB

Number One

It's worth hopping out of bed for Annie's breakfast: luxury continental with raspberry brioche or the full delicious Monty. Her house is a sparkling Aladdin's cave of mirrors, bunches of white twigs with birds atop, candles, cherubs, painted wooden floors, big open fires and generous bunches of roses. Bedrooms are lavishly done; nifty bathrooms have Italian tiles – and more roses! Close to the centre, this good-looking Georgian terrace house featured in Pevsner's guide to Hertfordshire, and the market town is busy with theatre, shops and galleries. Return for a gourmet dinner in the magical courtyard garden – when the sun is shining! *Over 12s welcome.*

Rooms	2 twin/doubles; 1 double with separate bath/shower: £130-£160.
Meals	Dinner £45; minimum 6 people. Pubs/restaurants 5-minute walk.
Closed	Rarely.

Annie Rowley
Number One,
1 Port Hill, Hertford, SG14 1PJ

Tel	+44 (0)1992 587350
Mobile	+44 (0)7770 914070
Email	annie@numberoneporthill.co.uk
Web	www.numberoneporthill.co.uk

32 The Hythe

The Thames barge in all her glory: the Gibbs' garden runs almost into the river Blackwater where these majestic old craft are moored and the mudflats are a bird watcher's dream. Summer breakfast on the deck – local smoked kippers and free-range eggs – watching the barges sail up the river is a rare treat. Beneath wide limpid skies this sensitively extended fisherman's cottage looks out to 12th-century St Mary's at the back where Kim and Gerry ring the Sunday bells. It's immaculate and comfortable inside, an inspired mix of modern and antique lit by myriad candles, among other romantic touches. *Over 14s welcome.*

Rooms	2 doubles: £110. Singles £90.
Meals	Pub 100 yds.
Closed	Christmas & Boxing Day.

Tel	+44 (0)1621 859435
Mobile	+44 (0)7753 135108
Email	gibbsie@live.co.uk
Web	www.thehythemaldon.co.uk

Kim & Gerry Gibbs
32 The Hythe,
Maldon, CM9 5HN

Baye House

You're in the old Dutch Quarter – calm and secluded but right in the middle of town. This is a very interesting house, some parts of it Tudor with original beams. Anne, delightfully easy-going, will welcome you with a refreshing drink. Breakfasts are fabulous: often home baked granola and breads, Welsh scones and pancakes, unusual options for vegetarians. All is served at a convivial table either in Anne's kitchen or the dining room. There's a guest kitchen too and a chef can be summoned for big groups at weekends who want supper. Wander out to the walled garden which is wild enough to get lost in and hides hammocks and benches in quiet corners. You can walk to the High Street for shops, restaurants and much more history. A lovely, relaxing place to stay. *Minimum stay: 2 nights in high season.*

Rooms	4 doubles all with separate bathrooms: £88-£117. 1 family room for 3, 1 triple both with separate bathrooms: £108-£117. Singles £59. Whole house available to let from £2688 per week.
Meals	Pubs/restaurants 2-minute walk.
Closed	Rarely.

Anne Minns	**Mobile**	+44 (0)7737 533879
Baye House,	**Email**	anneminns@googlemail.com
Colchester, C01 1HE	**Web**	www.bayehouse.com

The Old Pottery

Tubs of flowers at the door, Twiglet the dog to pat and a friendly feel throughout. Jacky moved from London to this charming village house and has restored and decorated with natural style: new oak floors, stripped beams, polished antique pieces. Bedrooms have well-dressed beds and thick curtains; the extra little room is just right for a child. Jacky is a good cook, so hop downstairs for a delicious breakfast – the best sausages and bacon or continental with home-baked ham; she's happy to do light suppers, and makes Christmas puds to sell. There are fun events at the Norman motte-and-bailey castle; thriving Long Melford and Clare are close. *Children over 8 welcome. Parking available on lane next to house.*

Rooms	1 twin/double; 1 double with separate bathroom: £90-£110. 1 single sharing bathroom with double, let to same party only: £60-£65.
Meals	Light supper from £20. Pubs/restaurants 2-minute walk.
Closed	Rarely.

Tel	+44 (0)1787 582168
Email	jackyshort@outlook.com
Web	www.hedinghamoldpottery.com

Jacky Short
The Old Pottery,
37 St James Street, Castle Hedingham,
Halstead, CO9 3EW

Elmdon Lee

Take the London train to Audley End (55 minutes), and this Georgian farmhouse retreat is then just a five-minute drive. It's on the top of a hill with farmland all around and has been in the Duke family for over 100 years. Bedrooms all have views of the pretty gardens full of mature trees and wildlife; there are stairs down to one of the bathrooms. Wake to birdsong and hop down for breakfast next to the Aga in the family kitchen; Kate gives you a full English with local produce (veggie options too). In the evenings settle by the fire with a book in the guest drawing room. You're on the border of Essex, Cambridgeshire and Hertfordshire, with heaps of history and culture to dip into; walkers can join the Icknield Way, which passes near the house. Back here explore the garden, meadow and bluebell woods, or sign up to one of the wellbeing sessions (including yoga and meditation), and bushcraft events for children and parents, which are held down by the lake (check what's available first). *Minimum stay: 2 nights.*

Rooms	1 double; 1 double with separate bathroom: £95-£105. 1 family room for 4 with separate bathroom: £125-£165 Singles £85-£95.
Meals	Pubs/restaurants 4 miles.
Closed	Rarely.

Kate Duke
Elmdon Lee,
Littlebury Green,
Saffron Walden, CB11 4XB

Tel	+44 (0)1763 838237
Mobile	+44 (0)7813 709593
Email	kate.duke@btopenworld.com
Web	www.elmdonlee.co.uk

Springfield House

The former school house hugs the bend of a river, its French windows opening to delightful rambling gardens with scented roses... and a yew garden, and a mulberry tree that provides fruit for breakfast. It's an elegant home reminiscent of another age, with fascinating history on the walls and big comfortable bedrooms for guests; one is reached by narrow stairs and has steps out to the garden. The conservatory, draped with a huge mimosa, is an exceptional spot for summer breakfasts, and the breakfasts are rather delicious. Good value and peaceful, yet close to Cambridge, of which Judith is a fund of knowledge.

Rooms	2 doubles; 1 twin/double with separate bath: £70-£90. Extra bed £15-£30 per person per night.
Meals	Pubs 150 yds.
Closed	Rarely.

Tel	+44 (0)1223 891383
Email	springfieldhouselinton@gmail.com
Web	www.springfieldhouselinton.com

Judith Rossiter
Springfield House,
14-16 Horn Lane, Linton, CB21 4HT

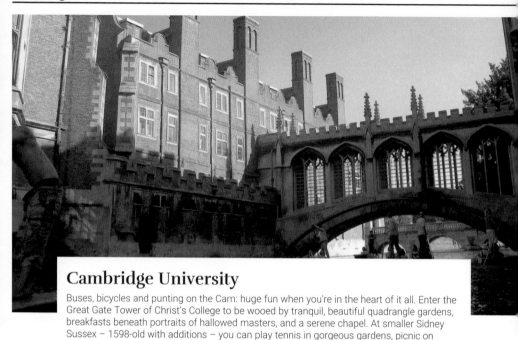

Cambridge University

Buses, bicycles and punting on the Cam: huge fun when you're in the heart of it all. Enter the Great Gate Tower of Christ's College to be wooed by tranquil, beautiful quadrangle gardens, breakfasts beneath portraits of hallowed masters, and a serene chapel. At smaller Sidney Sussex – 1598-old with additions – you can play tennis in gorgeous gardens, picnic on perfect lawns and start the day with rare-breed sausages. Churchill has a great gym, Downing has Quentin Blake paintings on the walls, St Catharine's has a candlelit chapel. Bedrooms (some shared showers) and lounges are functional; well-informed porters are your first port of call. *Rooms spread across 23 colleges.*

Rooms	60 doubles, 206 twins: £75-£128. 804 singles: £49-£79. 3 apartments for 2-3: £85-£150.
Meals	Breakfast included. Some colleges offer dinner from £7. See website for details.
Closed	Mid-January to mid-March, May/June, October/November; Christmas. A few rooms available throughout year.

University Rooms
Cambridge University,
Cambridge

Web	www.universityrooms.com/en-GB/city/cambridge/home

Duke House

Opposite Christ's Pieces, one of the city's oldest green spaces, and right in the centre: perfect! This house has been refurbished from top to toe and all is gleaming and generous. Settle into the guest sitting room (chandelier, Regency style furniture, calm colours) and sleep soundly under Irish goose down in beautiful bedrooms all named after dukes; top-floor's Cambridge suite has a romantic balcony. The lovely breakfast room has separate tables with fabric-backed chairs overlooking a little plant-filled courtyard; Liz serves an excellent organic and homemade spread. Shops, botanical garden, restaurants... a happy stroll. *Minimum stay: 2 nights at weekends. Children over 10 welcome.*

Rooms	4 doubles: £140-£170.
	1 suite for 2: £160-£250.
	Singles £125-£160.
Meals	Pubs/restaurants 5-minute walk.
Closed	Rarely.

Tel	+44 (0)1223 314773
Email	info@dukehousecambridge.co.uk
Web	www.dukehousecambridge.co.uk

Liz Cameron
Duke House,
1 Victoria Street, Cambridge, CB1 1JP

5 Chapel Street

Exemplary! Where: in a lovely, comfortable, refurbed Georgian house 20 minutes' walk from Cambridge centre. How: with warmth, pleasure, intelligence and local knowledge. Bedrooms have good quality mattresses, bedding and towels. Characterful pieces too – antique brass bed, freestanding bath, oriental rugs on polished floors – with flowers and garden views. The breakfasts are delicious, largely organic and local: fresh fruit salad, kedgeree with smoked Norfolk haddock, home baking (three types of bread; gluten free, no problem). If you'd like to swing a cat book the biggest room; borrow vintage bikes and thoroughly enjoy your break. *Minimum stay: 2 nights. Children over 11 welcome.*

Rooms	2 doubles, 1 twin: £100-£140. Singles £90-£130.
Meals	Pubs/restaurants 5-minute walk.
Closed	Rarely.

Christine Ulyyan
5 Chapel Street,
Cambridge, CB4 1DY

Tel	+44 (0)1223 514856
Email	info@5chapelstreet.co.uk
Web	www.5chapelstreet.co.uk

Peacocks Fine B&B

Above their delightful riverside tearoom in the heart of Ely, George and Rachel have created two suites. Each bedroom has its own sitting room stocked with books and squashy sofas. Brewery House has a fireplace and river views; Cottage is cosy and pretty with flowery wallpaper. Both have goose down duvets and tea trays. Enjoy breakfast by the Aga: perhaps savoury crumpets, omelette or delicious Croque Madame. Browse the nearby antique centre, visit the cathedral, stroll out for dinner or explore Cambridge and the Fens; but make sure to leave time for tea – there are 70 kinds! The Peacocks are friendly and funny – lovely hosts.

Rooms	1 suite for 2; 1 suite for 2 with separate bathroom & wc: £135-£160. Singles £110-£135. Extra bed/sofabed £50-£70 per person per night.
Meals	Pubs/restaurants 3-minute walk. Tearoom closed Monday & Tuesday.
Closed	Rarely.

Mobile	+44 (0)7900 666161	**Rachel Peacock**
Email	peacockbookings65@gmail.com	Peacocks Fine B&B,
Web	www.peacockstearoom.co.uk	65 Waterside, Ely, CB7 4AU

The Old Stable

A rural ramble brings you to a flint and brick bolthole – tucked into the courtyard of the main house. Joanna has restored her stables with a blend of old and new: beams, lime washed walls, rustic window sills, modern log-burner, swish new bathrooms. Bedrooms ('Hayloft' up, 'Coach House' down) are fresh and comfy – one has a double sofabed for extra guests. Wide French windows in the big dining/sitting room open to the pool – have a dip on summer mornings; dahlias and roses fill the garden. Joanna brings over breakfast: homemade jams, home-buzzed honey, a full English spread. Walk from the door; hop on a bike and discover nearby Bury. *Over 13s welcome.*

Rooms	1 twin/double; 1 twin with separate bathroom: £95-£115. Singles £70-£80. Extra bed £25 per person per night.
Meals	Occasional supper from £15. Packed lunch £7.50. Pubs/restaurants within 3 miles.
Closed	Occasionally.

Joanna Mayer
The Old Stable,
Cattishall Farmhouse, Great Barton,
Bury St Edmunds, IP31 2QT

Tel	+44 (0)1284 787340
Mobile	+44 (0)7738 936496
Email	joannamayer42@googlemail.com
Web	www.theoldstablebandb.co.uk

The Old Vicarage

Up the avenue of fine white horse chestnut trees to find just what you'd expect from an old vicarage: a Pembroke table in the flagstoned hall, a refectory table sporting copies of *The Field*, a piano guests can play, silver pheasants, winter log fires in the breakfast and drawing rooms and homemade cake on arrival. The house is magnificent, with huge rooms and passageways. Comfy beds are dressed in old-fashioned counterpanes; the twin has stunning far-reaching views. Weave your way through the branches of the huge copper beech to Jane's colourful garden; she grows her own vegetables, keeps hens, makes jams and cooks delicious breakfasts. *Children over 7 welcome.*

Rooms	1 twin/double with separate bath; single room available, let to same party only; 1 twin with separate bath: £80-£90. Singles £50.
Meals	Packed lunch £6. Pub 1 mile.
Closed	Christmas.

Tel	+44 (0)1440 783209
Mobile	+44 (0)7887 717429
Email	s.j.sheppard@hotmail.co.uk
Web	www.thurlowvicarage.co.uk

Jane Sheppard
The Old Vicarage,
Great Thurlow, Newmarket, CB9 7LE

The Mill

Your comfort is Paul and Clare's priority. They'll happily run you and the kayaks up to Sudbury for a day on the river, or lend you bikes and give advice about where to cycle. There are wonderful walks straight from the door too – return to chocolates and fruit cake in your room. Attention has been lavished on the guest bedrooms in the converted cottage by the front gate. The Melford room has views over the Tudor turrets of Melford Hall and a great brass bath. The Garden room has its own log-burner and a private walled garden. Everything under the old beams is bespoke, interesting, immaculate. Ask your hosts about the rich history of the house and its most famous occupant, the WWI poet Edmund Blunden – they'll show you his first editions. You have a generous and relaxed breakfast in the main house conservatory; forget the car and spend days enjoying the village treasures and shops; stroll out to a different place to eat each evening. *Minimum stay: 2 nights at bank holidays & in high season.*

Rooms	2 doubles: £135-£145. Singles £110-£120.
Meals	Pub 1-minute walk.
Closed	Rarely.

Paul Jarrett & Clare Livens
The Mill,
Hall Mill House, Hall Street,
Long Melford, CO10 9DY

Tel	+44 (0)1787 378035
Mobile	+44 (0)7791 532531
Email	contact@themill-longmelford.com
Web	www.themill-longmelford.com

The Old Rectory

A handsome house surrounded by large gardens and sheep-dotted fields. Maggie's home is filled with beautiful things: old family china, prints, portraits, blue and white decorated lamps, polished wood – a piano you can play too. Bedrooms are peaceful and pretty; 'Rose' is reached up a few steps. Breakfast is well worth waking up for: granola, compote, homemade jams, home-buzzed honey, sausages and bacon from their own pigs; sourcing local food is a passion and Maggie loves to cook, so dinner will be equally good. Set off for Constable country, charming old wool town Lavenham, antiques in Long Melford, the coast... it's a fascinating spot.

Rooms	1 twin/double; 1 double with separate bathroom: £100-£125. Extra bed £25 per person per night. 1-night bookings accepted on Saturdays; 2+ nights including Saturday: 25% discount.
Meals	Dinner, 2-3 courses with wine, £20-£30. Pubs/restaurants 2 miles.
Closed	Rarely.

Tel	+44 (0)1449 740400
Email	theoldrectorykettlebaston@gmail.com
Web	www.theoldrectorykettlebaston.co.uk

Maggie Lawrence
The Old Rectory,
Kettlebaston, Ipswich, IP7 7QD

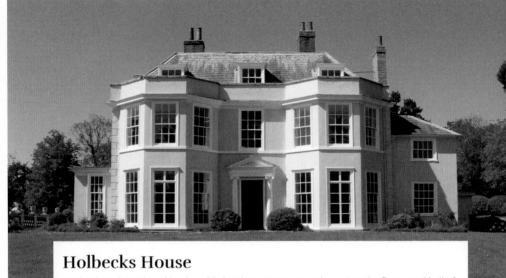

Holbecks House

Up the drive through parkland studded with ancient trees and step into the flagstoned hall of this 18th–century house. Find gracious rooms, soft colours, Persian rugs, antiques, hunting prints and books to browse. Perry is delightful and looks after you well; settle into big peaceful bedrooms with good beds, chocolates and long rural views. Just beyond the market town of Hadleigh, the house snoozes on a hill with acres of garden, orchard, croquet lawn, rose walk and pond. Explore Constable Country, visit the Munnings Art Museum in Dedham, Gainsborough House in Sudbury and the cathedral city of Bury St Edmunds. *Minimum stay: 2 nights at weekends.*

Rooms	2 twin/doubles; 1 twin/double with separate bath: £105-£145. 1 suite for 4 sharing bathroom: £209-£245.
Meals	Pubs/restaurants 0.5 miles.
Closed	Christmas.

Perry Coysh
Holbecks House,
Holbecks Lane, Hadleigh,
Ipswich, IP7 5PE

Tel	+44 (0)1473 823211
Mobile	+44 (0)7875 167771
Email	perry.coysh@gmail.com
Web	www.holbecks.com

Church House

A short hop from riverside Woodbridge and musical Snape Maltings, between a conservation churchyard and a history-rich field, is something different and unusual: a customised house of gentle colours and textures, home to an architect and a designer. From the hand-carved oak porch to the lovely wildlife garden, there's a feeling of warmth and delight. Under the eaves: two jewel-bright and comfortable bedrooms full of books and fresh flowers. In the kitchen: a big farmhouse table laid for breakfasts with homemade bread (locally ground flour from the family farm), granola and marmalade. And, a short walk away, an excellent village pub. *Minimum stay: 2 nights at weekends. Children over 6 welcome.*

Rooms	1 twin/double; 1 twin/double with separate bath/shower: £80-£85. Singles £65-£70.
Meals	Pub 1 mile.
Closed	Rarely.

Tel	+44 (0)1473 735350
Email	sallypirkis@gmail.com
Web	www.churchhousebandbsuffolk.co.uk

Sally & Richard Pirkis
Church House,
Clopton, Woodbridge, IP13 6QB

Abbey House

A spectacular arrival. A handsome, Grade II listed, Dutch-gabled house (1846) fronted by an impressive fishpond upon which black swans glide. On land, the peacocks lord it over the chickens. Sue welcomes you easily, her bedrooms are simple and comfortable, each with a couple of armchairs and garden or pond views. Settle down in front of the fire in the guest drawing room, or wander out to the shrub walk. Fine old trees – oaks, limes, beeches and weeping willows – dignify the mature garden and meadowland. Early flowering yellow banksia climbs the front of the house, fighting for the limelight with the *Clematis montana* that tumbles around the door. The heated pool (just ask) lies enclosed in a suntrap surrounded by trellises of honeysuckle and jasmine. This is a thoroughly peaceful space to amble around: sit and contemplate a game of croquet under the magnificent copper beech, admire the swans and ducks in the lovely pond lined with flag irises – best viewed from a picturesque arched wooden bridge. *Children over 6 welcome.*

Rooms	2 doubles; 1 twin with separate bath: £80-£100. Singles £40-£50.
Meals	Pubs 2.5 miles.
Closed	Christmas & New Year.

Sue Bagnall
Abbey House,
Monk Soham,
Framlingham, IP13 7EN

Tel	+44 (0)1728 685225
Email	sue@abbey-house.net
Web	www.abbeyhousesuffolk.co.uk

Five Acre Barn

David and Bruce's home in the village of Aldringham is set back from the road, and with no neighbours visible, and surrounded by woodland and fields, it feels tranquil and secluded. They'll greet you warmly with tea and freshly baked cake, and Lola and Ruby the dogs give a gentle welcome too. A guest sitting room, large breakfast table and open-plan kitchen run the length of the old barn, with steps at one end leading down to an award-winning cedar-clad guest wing perfectly in keeping with its surroundings. Bedrooms are bright with vaulted ceilings, comfy chairs, ottomans for an extra guest and French windows onto a furnished deck with garden and woodland views beyond. Four of the rooms have mezzanine sleeping areas. Leisurely, sociable breakfasts include locally sourced and home-baked products. You can walk to the local pub, the Parrot, and you're five minutes' drive from Aldeburgh and Thorpeness, which between them have nine pubs and restaurants. The coast has miles of beaches from Slaughden to Southwold and beyond. *Minimum stay: 2 nights at weekends. Over 12s welcome.*

Rooms	4 doubles: 100-£130. 1 suite: £120-£160. Singles from £90. Extra guests £30 per person.
Meals	Pub 10-minute walk. Pubs/restaurants 5-minute drive.
Closed	Rarely.

Mobile	+44 (0)7788 424642/ +44 (0)7595 328529
Email	contactus@fiveacrebarn.co.uk
Web	www.fiveacrebarn.co.uk

Bruce & David
Five Acre Barn,
Aldeburgh Road, Aldringham, IP16 4QH

Willow Tree Cottage

Seductively near RSPB Minsmere, medieval castles and the glorious Heritage coast. The evening sun pours into the back of this contemporary cottage with butter yellow walls; you are on the edge of the village so all is quiet with an orchard behind and a bird-filled garden for tea and cake. No sitting room, but easy chairs in your pretty bedroom face views. Caroline is a good cook and breakfast is delicious (try her kedgeree and homemade jams). Snape Maltings for music, Southwold for the famous pier, Aldeburgh with its shingle beach, boats, fun shops and good places to eat – all are close by. Holly the labrador adds to the charm. *Minimum stay: 2 nights at weekends.*

Rooms	1 double: £80-£85. Singles £55-£65.
Meals	Pub/restaurant 1.5 miles.
Closed	Rarely.

Caroline Youngson
Willow Tree Cottage,
3 Belvedere Close, Kelsale,
Saxmundham, IP17 2RS

Tel	+44 (0)1728 602161
Mobile	+44 (0)7747 624139
Email	cy@willowtreecottage.me.uk
Web	www.willowtreecottage.me.uk

Trustans Barn

Ancient oak beams have been carefully kept in this smart Suffolk barn conversion. It's a family affair here: friendly sisters Sally and Rosie give you contemporary bedrooms with artistic touches, king-sized beds, sleek bathrooms and drench showers. Breakfast is served at two scrubbed pine tables in the airy slate-floored breakfast room; a big blackboard lists tasty choices – everything from home-laid eggs and local sausages to home-grown tomatoes and muesli. Masses to do nearby: Snape Maltings music, wonderful old churches, summer festivals, the Heritage Coast... A great place for a peaceful holiday with a group of friends. *Minimum stay: 2 nights in high season.*

Rooms	5 doubles, 1 twin/double: £100-£140.
Meals	Pubs less than a mile away.
Closed	Christmas.

Tel	+44 (0)1728 668684
Email	sallyandrosie@trustansbarn.co.uk
Web	www.trustansbarn.co.uk

Sally Prime
Trustans Barn,
Westleton Road, Darsham,
Saxmundham, IP17 3BP

Oak Tree Farm

A magnificent ancient oak tree stands guard over this 300-year old Georgian-fronted farmhouse. John and Julian love all things Art Nouveau/Art Deco and their home is filled with pieces from those periods, including china with masses of different patterns; fine books galore too, and peaceful bedrooms with smart white linen. Breakfast is a moveable feast: in the conservatory in summer, or by the fire in the dining room in winter; the bird feeders get moved too so you're kept entertained while you tuck in! You can wander the five-acre garden and meadows, pretty Yoxford village has antique shops to browse, and Snape Maltings is a hop. *Minimum stay: 2 nights at weekends.*

Rooms	3 twin/doubles: £90. Singles £70.
Meals	Pubs/restaurants 5-minute walk.
Closed	1 November – 28 February.

Julian Lock & John McMinn
Oak Tree Farm,
Little Street, Yoxford,
Saxmundham, IP17 3JN

Tel	+44 (0)1728 668651
Mobile	+44 (0)7969 459261
Email	oaktreefarmyoxford@gmail.com
Web	www.oaktreefarmyoxford.co.uk

Church Farmhouse

This Elizabethan farmhouse is by the ancient thatched church in a little hamlet close to Southwold. Minsmere RSPB bird sanctuary, Snape Maltings and the coast are nearby for lovely days out. Sarah, characterful, well-travelled and entertaining, is also an excellent cook, so breakfast will be a treat with bowls of fruit, Suffolk bacon and free-range eggs; occasional candle-lit dinners are worth staying in for, too. Bedrooms have supremely comfy beds well-dressed in pure cotton. Although there is no sitting room, you can enjoy tea and cake and linger in the garden, there are flowers in every room and books galore. *Over 12s welcome.*

Rooms	1 double, 1 twin/double; 1 double with separate bath: £110-£115. Singles £70-£80.
Meals	Dinner £28. Pubs/restaurants within 4 miles.
Closed	Christmas.

Tel	+44 (0)1502 578532
Mobile	+44 (0)7748 801418
Email	sarahlentaigne@btinternet.com
Web	www.churchfarmhousesuffolk.co.uk

Sarah Lentaigne
Church Farmhouse,
Uggeshall, Southwold, NR34 8BD

Camomile Cottage

Aly and Tim's 16th-century longhouse is a feast of old beams, kilims, antiques and art. They give you homemade cake on arrival; relax in the garden or the guest lounge, kick off your shoes and enjoy a glass of wine by the log fire. Beamed bedrooms have period furnishings, goose down duvets, luxury linen, flowers and handmade chocolates; bathrooms have Molton Brown toiletries. Aly will also bring you tea in bed! Breakfast is in the garden room: cornbread toast, eggs from the hens, croissants and all sorts of cooked choices. Eye is an attractive old market town; Southwold, Bury St Edmunds and Snape Maltings are all close. *Minimum stay: 2 nights at weekends.*

Rooms	2 doubles: £99-£110. Singles £85.
Meals	Pubs/restaurants 0.5 miles.
Closed	Rarely.

Aly Kahane
Camomile Cottage,
Brome Avenue, Eye, IP23 7HW

Tel	+44 (0)1379 873528
Email	aly@camomilecottage.co.uk
Web	www.camomilecottage.co.uk

College Farm

Katharine is a natural at making guests feel like friends. Her beautiful farmhouse tucks itself away on the edge of the village and the big friendly kitchen is filled with delicious smells of home baking. Meals are served by the large wood-burner in the grand Jacobean dining room, filled with good antiques, period furnishings and cosy places to sit; food is home-grown, seasonal and local. Sleep well in charming bedrooms with smooth linen, pretty furniture and garden views; bathrooms are small and simple.

A fascinating area teeming with pingos, wildlife, old churches... and glorious antique shops.

Over 12s welcome.

Rooms	3 twin/doubles: £100-£125. Singles £60.
Meals	Dinner from £20. Pub 1 mile.
Closed	Christmas.

Tel	+44 (0)1953 483318
Email	info@collegefarmnorfolk.co.uk
Web	www.collegefarmnorfolk.co.uk

Katharine Wolstenholme
College Farm,
Thompson, Thetford, IP24 1QG

Washingford House

Tall octagonal chimney stacks and a Georgian façade give the house a stately air. In fact, it's the friendliest of places to stay and Paris gives you a delicious, locally sourced breakfast including plenty of fresh fruit. The house, originally Tudor, is a delightful mix of old and new. Large light-filled bedrooms have loads of good books and views over the four-acre garden, a favourite haunt for local birds. Bergh Apton is a conservation village seven miles from Norwich and you are in the heart of it; perfect for cycling, boat trips on the Norfolk Broads and the twelve Wherryman's Way circular walks.

Rooms	1 twin/double; 1 twin/double with separate bath & shower: £80-£95. 1 single with separate bath: £45-£60.
Meals	Pubs/restaurants 4-6 miles.
Closed	Christmas.

Paris & Nigel Back
Washingford House,
Cookes Road, Bergh Apton,
Norwich, NR15 1AA

Tel	+44 (0)1508 550924
Mobile	+44 (0)7900 683617
Email	parisb@waitrose.com
Web	www.washingford.com

Gothic House

Silver tea and coffee pots and Portmeirion china, pictures and prints from far-flung places, and an unexpected peace in the centre of the city – welcome to Gothic House. The building is listed and Regency and your host, enthusiastic, charming, knows the history. As for breakfast, it is fresh, lavish and locally sourced; in short, a treat. Bedrooms are stylish and spacious with a strong period feel, the double and the two bathrooms on the first floor, and the twin above. Norwich is blessed with culture, character and pubs, and a cathedral with the second tallest spire in England. Fabulous! *Parking space available.*

Rooms	1 double with separate bathroom; 1 twin with separate bathroom & wc: £105. Singles £75.
Meals	Pubs/restaurants 5-minute walk.
Closed	Rarely.

Tel	+44 (0)1603 631879
Email	gothic.house.norwich@gmail.com
Web	www.gothic-house-norwich.com

Clive Harvey
Gothic House,
King's Head Yard, 42 Magdalen Street,
Norwich, NR3 1JE

The Buttery

Down a farm track, a treasure: your own thatch-and-flint octagonal dairy house perfectly restored by local craftsmen and as snug as can be. You get a jacuzzi bath, a little kitchen and a fridge stocked with delicious bacon and ground coffee so you can breakfast when you want; take it to the sun terrace in good weather. The sitting room is terracotta-tiled and has a music system, a warming fire and a sofabed for those who don't want to tackle the steep wooden stair to the cosy bedroom on the mezzanine. You can play a game of tennis, and walk from the door into peaceful parkland and woods. Lovely! *Minimum stay: 2 nights at weekends.*

Rooms	1 double with sitting room & small kitchen: £90-£110.
Meals	Pub 10-minute walk.
Closed	Rarely.

Deborah Meynell
The Buttery,
Berry Hall, Honingham,
Norwich, NR9 5AX

Tel	+44 (0)1603 880541
Email	thebuttery@paston.co.uk
Web	www.thebuttery.biz

Hoveton Hall

A Regency house snoozing in beautiful parkland and gardens. Formal and grand, yet comfortably friendly, Harry and Rachel's home brims with wonderful woodwork, decorated ceilings, art old and new. Their children are keen to play with visiting young ones, there's a lovely collection of hare sculptures up the stairs and the views over the 620 acres are stunning. Airy bedrooms have well-dressed beds, tea trays, biscuits and flowers. Morning sun lights up the panelled library/sitting room where you have breakfast, shelves are crammed with books and there's a large fire to sit by. Explore the estate, head off for beaches and the Broads. *Minimum stay: 2 nights at weekends & in high season.*

Rooms	1 double: £130.
	1 family room for 4: £160.
Meals	Pubs/restaurants 1 mile.
Closed	Rarely.

Tel	+44 (0)1603 784297
Email	rachel@hovetonhallestate.co.uk
Web	www.hovetonhallestate.co.uk

Rachel Buxton
Hoveton Hall,
Hoveton Hall Estate, Hoveton,
Norwich, NR12 8RJ

The Old Rectory

Conservation farmland all around; acres of wild heathland busy with woodpeckers and owls; the coast two miles away. Relax in the big drawing room of this 17th-century rectory and friendly family home, set in mature gardens full of trees. Fiona loves to cook and bakes her bread daily; food is delicious, seasonal and locally sourced, jams are homemade. Comfortable bedrooms have *objets* from diplomatic postings and the suite comes with mahogany furniture and armchairs so you can settle in with a book. Super views, friendly dogs, tennis in the garden and masses of space. If you fancy self-catering then opt for an independent break in the Garden Room. *Dogs welcome downstairs only.*

Rooms	1 double with kitchenette & separate bath/shower: £80-£100.
	1 suite for 2: £80-£100. Singles £50.
Meals	Pubs 2 miles.
Closed	Rarely.

Peter & Fiona Black
The Old Rectory,
Ridlington, NR28 9NZ

Tel	+44 (0)1692 650247
Mobile	+44 (0)7774 599911
Email	ridlingtonoldrectory@gmail.com
Web	www.oldrectorynorthnorfolk.co.uk

Primrose Cottage

Karen's a B&B veteran and has thought of everything: peaceful spaces for reading, sweets, always fresh flowers on the table. It would be lovely for friends or couples together; the two bedrooms have views for miles, both with short private staircases and generous tea trays. Breakfasts are hearty: homemade jams, cereals and a full English, served in the quarry-tiled dining room. The big, comfortable sitting room is packed with books, music, games and a TV, so if it pours you can light the wood-burner and batten down the hatches for the day, grab a handful of leaflets from the porch and plan your next outing. The countryside is good for walking and cycling and the coast is close, with Walcott and Happisburgh beaches within two miles and Cromer 30 minutes' drive, or you could mess about on the Broads with boat trips and pub lunches by the water.

Rooms	1 twin/double; 1 double with separate bathroom: £95.
Meals	Pubs 1.5 miles.
Closed	Christmas.

Mobile	+44 (0)7979 982613
Email	mkelliott2@aol.com
Web	www.primrosecottage-norfolk.co.uk

Karen Elliott
Primrose Cottage,
Old Lane, Walcott, NR12 0PA

Stable Cottage

Sarah's home is set in the grounds of Heydon Hall, one of Norfolk's finest Elizabethan houses. In the Dutch-gabled stable block, fronted by Cromwell's Oak, is her cottage – fresh, sunny and enchanting. Each room is touched by her warm personality and love of beautiful things: seagrass floors, crisp linen and pretty china; the cosy sitting room is set with tea and biscuits for your arrival. Bedrooms are cottagey and immaculate; bathrooms have baskets of treats. Sarah serves a delicious breakfast with golden eggs from her hens, homemade marmalade and garden fruit. Thursford is close and you're 20 minutes from the coast. *Minimum stay: 2 nights at weekends.*

Rooms	2 twin/doubles: £100. Singles £80.
Meals	Pub 1 mile.
Closed	Christmas.

Sarah Bulwer-Long
Stable Cottage,
Heydon, Norwich, NR11 6RE

Tel	+44 (0)1263 587343
Mobile	+44 (0)7780 998742
Email	sjblong@icloud.com
Web	www.heydon-cottages.co.uk

Stables & Coach House

You stay in converted outbuildings in the back garden of this Georgian house in the centre of the village. Both have a separate entrance and look out on to the vegetable patch and gardens. Karena has thought of everything. You have your own kitchenette and dining/sitting area, a large comfortable bedroom and drench shower above and use of the garden. A continental breakfast is left for you: homemade bread, fruit, yogurt and muesli.

Take your morning coffee outside to a suntrap bench and plan your days – Karena has heaps of information about the area. Join the Marriott's Way, take a trip to the coast, hunt for antiques in Holt. Return to your cosy bolthole for tea and biscuits and walk to The Queen's Head for supper. *Minimum stay: 2 nights.*

Rooms	1 double, 1 twin/double: £78-£120.
Meals	Pub 2-minute walk.
Closed	Rarely.

Tel	+44 (0)1362 683241
Email	stablesandcoachouse@gmail.com
Web	www.norfolkbandb.co.uk

Karena Taylor
Stables & Coach House,
1 Hindolveston Road, Foulsham, NR20 5RX

The Control Tower

A unique slice of history. This iconic landmark on the former RAF North Creake airfield was built in the 1940s to command 199 and 171 Squadrons. The restoration has been a labour of love and Ni and Claire's attention to detail is remarkable: modernism and Art Deco design in full flow. Be greeted with tea or locally roasted coffee in the art-filled sitting room; sink into goose down in bright bedrooms; enjoy shiny bathrooms with period fittings and lavender soaps. Vegetarian breakfasts are good! House tours include the open roof deck; you can lunch al fresco in the wild flower garden; Wells-next-the-Sea and Blakeney seal trips are close.

Rooms	3 doubles: £110-£130.
	1 suite for 2: £140. Extra bed/sofabed
	£30 per person per night.
Meals	Restaurants 3 miles.
Closed	Rarely.

Claire Nugent & Nigel Morter
The Control Tower,
Bunkers Hill, Egmere,
Walsingham, NR22 6AZ

Tel	+44 (0)1328 821574
Email	mail@controltowerstays.com
Web	www.controltowerstays.com

Meadow House

A beautifully traditional new-build with handmade oak banisters and period furniture. Step into a large drawing room, where you find a warm, sociable atmosphere with squashy sofas and comfy chairs. Breakfast is served in here or in the conservatory. One bedroom is cosy and chintzy, the other is larger and more neutral; brand-new bathrooms gleam. Amanda looks after you well; she's lived in Norfolk most of her life and is delighted to advise. There are footpaths from the door and plenty to see, starting with Walpole's Houghton Hall, a short walk. A bucolic setting for a profoundly comfortable stay, perfect for country enthusiasts.

Rooms	2 twin/doubles: £70-£85.
	Singles £40-£50.
Meals	Packed lunch £5-£7.
	Pub 9-minute walk.
Closed	Rarely.

Tel	+44 (0)1485 520240
Mobile	+44 (0)7890 037134
Email	amandacase@amandacase.plus.com
Web	www.meadowhousebandb.co.uk

Amanda Case
Meadow House,
Harpley, King's Lynn, PE31 6TU

East Midlands

The Old Vicarage Wetton, page 304

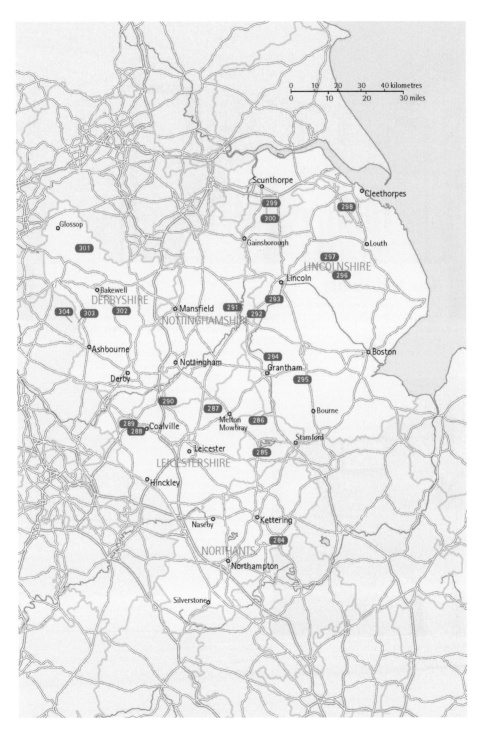

The Old House

Northamptonshire is the county of spires and squires. And here, on the through-road of this fascinating medieval town, is a listed squire's house – once home to a merchant who traded in the marketplace opposite. Enter the heavy oak door and step back 400 years. William, courteous, hospitable and upgrading with aplomb, is forever tweaking the ambience. Facing the courtyard at the back (furnished for summery breakfasts and aperitifs) are the quietest rooms; all have sumptuous fabrics and wallpapers, dramatic touches and divine beds. Delightfully quirky, spanking new bathrooms with power showers are as special as all the rest.

Rooms	4 doubles, 1 twin/double: £85. Singles £65.
Meals	Pubs/restaurants 150 yds.
Closed	Rarely.

William Evans
The Old House,
5 Market Square, Higham Ferrers,
Rushden, NN10 8BP

Tel	+44 (0)1933 314006
Email	theoldhousehighamferrers@gmail.com
Web	www.theoldhousehighamferrers.co.uk

Pear Tree Cottage

Have tea and cake on the patio when you arrive, accompanied by birdsong and the odd baa from sheep in the field beyond. From the garden there are magnificent views across the valley. Both cosy rooms are en suite – the twin has the garden view. Anne gives you a generous breakfast with eggs from the farm at the bottom of the hill, Oakham butcher bacon and sausages, mushrooms, beans, fruit, porridge, cereals... Walk to Rutland Water where you can kayak, windsurf or hop on the Rutland Belle Paddle Steamer. Dinner is just a stroll – at the award-winning Horse & Jockey pub; their lunchtime baguettes are legendary fuel too for hungry cyclists who have completed the 20 or so miles of the Rutland Water circuit.

Rooms	1 double, 1 twin: £80-£85. Singles £70.
Meals	Pubs/restaurants 5-minute drive.
Closed	Rarely.

Tel	+44 (0)1572 737810
Mobile	+44 (0)7770 881966
Email	abutlerbrookfarm@aol.com
Web	www.peartreecottagemanton.co.uk

Anne Butler
Pear Tree Cottage,
10 Wing Road, Manton,
Oakham, LE15 8SZ

Old Rectory

Guests love it here and Jane Austen fans are especially happy. This elegant 1740s village house was used as Mr Collins's 'humble abode' by the BBC: you breakfast in the beautiful dining room that was 'Mr Collins's hall', and you can sleep in 'Miss Bennett's bedroom'.Victoria is wonderful – feisty, fun and gregarious – and loves having people to stay. She looks after you beautifully with White Company linen in chintzy old-fashioned bedrooms and a log fire in the drawing room. Breakfast, cooked on the Aga, includes artisan bread, bacon and sausages from a local butcher, home-grown tomatoes, garden fruit and homemade jams and marmalade. Children can let off steam on the slide, swing and trampoline, it's good walking/riding country and lively Oakham, with its Wednesday and Saturday markets, is well worth a browse.

Rooms	1 double, 1 twin: £90. Singles £50.
Meals	Pubs within 3 miles.
Closed	Rarely.

Victoria Owen
Old Rectory,
Teigh, Oakham, LE15 7RT

Tel	+44 (0)1572 787681
Mobile	+44 (0)7484 600721
Email	torowen@btinternet.com
Web	www.teighbedandbreakfast.co.uk

The Gorse House

Passing cars are less frequent than passing horses – this is a peaceful spot in a pretty village. Lyn and Richard's 17th-century cottage has a feeling of lightness and space; there's a fine collection of paintings and furniture, and oak doors lead from dining room to guest sitting room. Country style bedrooms have green views and are simply done. The garden has sunny places to sit, you can bring your horse (there's plenty of stabling) and it's a stroll to a good pub for dinner. The house is filled with laughter, breakfasts with home-grown fruits are tasty and the Cowdells are terrific hosts who love having guests to stay. *Pets by arrangement (not in the house).*

Rooms	1 double: £80.
	1 family room for 4: £80-£130.
	1 triple with kitchenette: £80-£120.
	Singles £50.
Meals	Packed lunch £5.
	Pub 75yds, closed on Sun eves.
Closed	Rarely.

Tel	+44 (0)1664 813537
Mobile	+44 (0)7780 600792
Email	cowdell@gorsehouse.co.uk
Web	www.gorsehouse.co.uk

Lyn & Richard Cowdell
The Gorse House,
33 Main Street, Grimston,
Melton Mowbray, LE14 3BZ

Ravenstone Hall

Drive through the large double gates and arrive at Ravenstone – a fabulous house where Jemima welcomes you with tea and cake – or a glass of wine if you come later. Guests have the west wing so you'll feel nicely private and views are over the garden or woodland. Breakfast is served at one large antique table – bacon and sausages from a local butcher, eggs from Jemima's hens, local honey, and homemade marmalade and crab apple jelly.

Wander the gardens and lake, have a dip in the swimming pool, go and see the resident alpacas, rheas, guinea fowl and hens – Raven the black Labrador might keep you company. The elegant drawing rooms, Blue Room and the Ballroom, have huge open fires and brimming bookcases – lovely spaces to sit and read.

Rooms	2 doubles: £130-£140.
Meals	Pubs 5-minute drive.
Closed	Christmas & New Year.

Jemima Wade
Ravenstone Hall,
Ashby Road,
Ravenstone, LE67 2AA

Mobile +44 (0)7976 302260
Email jemimawade@hotmail.com

The Old Stables Packington

The barn dates from the early 1800s and is one of four set around a large courtyard. You have your own private wing; children will love their inter-connected room with bunk beds and lots of toys and books. Julie has good local knowledge and goes the extra mile for her guests – she'll babysit too given a bit of notice. You'll be greeted with a freshly-baked cake from the café in the village, and breakfast is the best of regional stuff: local bread, pastries, cold meats and cheeses, a boiled egg cooked to order and cereals, jam and honey. Sit out in the garden with a glass of wine, stroll to The Bull and Lion for a drink or drive five minutes for shops and restaurants in Ashby-de-la-Zouch. Packington is in the middle of The National Forest, a regeneration project with activities, festivals, cycle trails and walks for all ages.

Rooms	1 family room for 4: £70-£100. Bunk room available, £20 per child.
Meals	Pub 5-minute walk.
Closed	Rarely.

Mobile	+44 (0)7980 281329
Email	pritchard74@hotmail.co.uk

Julie Pritchard
The Old Stables Packington,
Mill Street, Packington,
Ashby-de-la-Zouch, LE65 1WN

St Anne's House

A Georgian house in the middle of pretty Sutton Bonington. Choose a garden spot and listen to the birds while your hosts bring you a pot of tea. Breakfast is in the orangery – you're surrounded by a forest of greenery with banana and orange trees, ferns and a deliciously scented lemon verbena which tumbles out of a window. Chris and Janine give you a full English cooked on the Aga with tomatoes and herbs from the garden, local bacon, sausages and honey, homemade jams. Wander the colourful gardens, read by the fire in the snug, dip into magazines and board games, help yourself to a sherry or port nightcap. There's an arts and crafts gallery in the village with a café and you don't have to go far for dinner – the King's Head is a three-minute walk. You can also walk to the University campus in ten minutes; return to comfortable bedrooms named after flowers.

Rooms	1 double; 1 double, 1 twin both with separate bathroom: £80-£90.
Meals	Dinner, 2 courses, £20.
Closed	Rarely.

Chris & Janine Bone
St Anne's House,
12 St Anne's Lane,
Sutton Bonington, LE12 5NJ

Mobile	+44 (0)7769 748415
Email	stanneshouse@btinternet.com
Web	www.stanneshouse.co.uk

Willoughby House

A tall village house with an air of smart comfort. Step in to a warming log fire, antiques, quirky collections, art and lively colours. Bedrooms have tea, coffee and homemade flapjacks, fine linen and comfy sofas; Harry's and Bobby's are in the main house, Arthur's Stable and Top Barn are over the cobbles in Granary Annexe. Suzannah runs the family fruit farm and turns the produce into jams and juices; she and Marcus make scrumptious breakfasts. Norwell is on the edge of the Dukeries; head out for Sherwood Forest and the famous Major Oak, Lincoln and its cathedral, historic Newark and Southwell. Walk to the village pub for supper.

Rooms	2 twin/doubles; 1 double with separate bathroom: £120-£130. 1 suite for 3: £180. 1 family room for 4: £250. Singles £80-£90. Extra beds £60. Dogs £20.
Meals	Pub 3-minute walk.
Closed	Rarely.

Tel	+44 (0)1636 636266
Mobile	+44 (0)7780 996981
Email	willoughbyhousebandb@gmail.com
Web	www.willoughbyhousebandb.co.uk

Suzannah & Marcus Edwards-Jones
Willoughby House,
Main Street, Norwell,
Newark, NG23 6JN

Brills Farm

Sophie and Charles' Georgian farmhouse is at the top of one of Lincolnshire's rare hills with far-reaching views over to Belvoir Castle and Newark. Sophie's great grandfather was involved in the creation of the RAF and a life-size replica of a Lancaster Bomber is going to be sited on the hilltop – guests will be offered a personal tour. Flower-filled drawing and dining rooms overlook the valley. Breakfast is an event – cereals, fruit salad and yogurts followed by Lincolnshire sausages, home bacon, eggs and marmalade, field mushrooms and locally baked bread. On sunny days eat under the old oak tree – one set of guests were entertained by a visiting family of Little Owls. Sit in the garden, walk to the lake and woodland beyond; then sleep well in large bedrooms made inviting with gowns, slippers, biscuits and drinks. *Over 12s welcome.*

Rooms	2 doubles, 1 twin/double: £110. Singles £55-£60.
Meals	Supper £20. Dinner £30. Packed lunch £10. Pubs 5-minute drive.
Closed	Christmas & New Year.

Sophie White
Brills Farm,
Brills Hill,
Norton Disney, Lincoln, LN6 9JN

Tel +44 (0)1636 892311
Email admin@brillsfarm-bedandbreakfast.co.uk
Web www.brillsfarm-bedandbreakfast.co.uk

Lut's B&B

You'd be hard pressed to find as warm as welcome as you will at this 18th-century farmhouse. Set in a rural spot by a livery yard, it's had great care poured into it by lovely Lut and Bruce, who've kept the original features but given it a fresh feel. Bedrooms have well-dressed beds and flowers (hop up to the attic for the single); bathrooms are spotless. Anglo-Belgian breakfasts are plentiful and eaten at one large table. There's plenty to do: historic Lincoln nearby, bikes to borrow and walks from the door. Return to a stroll in the beautiful garden, an inviting sitting room and a tasty veggie meal – make sure to book ahead. *Minimum stay: 2 nights at weekends.*

Rooms	1 double; 1 double sharing shower/bathr with single, let to same party only: £85-£125. 1 single sharing shower/bath with double, let to same party only: £60-£75.
Meals	Dinner £25. BYO. Pubs/restaurants 2 miles.
Closed	Rarely.

Tel	+44 (0)1522 306215
Mobile	+44 (0)7793 034734
Email	lut@lutsbandb.co.uk
Web	www.lutsbandb.co.uk

Lut Dierckx
Lut's B&B,
Grange Farm, Mill Lane,
North Hykeham, Lincoln, LN6 9PB

Kelling House

Dating from 1785, three old cottages are now a long, low, rose-covered house of gentle rubble masonry with a pantile roof, a pretty painted gate edged with lolling hollyhocks and a super garden. Well-proportioned rooms have good English furniture and interesting paintings. Bedrooms are softly coloured with a pretty mix of checks, stripes and plain white cotton. Sue is delightful and looks after you without fuss; breakfast will set you up for the day. When she arrived in 1999 she kept only a few shrubs and mature trees; the rest of the garden she bulldozed. Now French windows and doors lead directly onto the generous flagged terrace with its young box-edged parterre filled with herbs. Clumps of lavender, rosemary and sage give a Mediterranean feel and scent the house and it is also a lovely place to sit and admire the rest – in particular, the wide bed of summer-flowering perennials: sweet-scented white phlox, elegant perovskia with its lavender blue spikes and grey foliage, and dramatic acanthus. This is a charming, well planted garden with good lawns and unexpected surprises.

Rooms	1 double; 1 double with separate bath: £85-£90. 1 single sharing bath with double, let to same party only: £45-£55.
Meals	Dinner £25. Packed lunch £7.50. Pubs/restaurants 3-minute walk.
Closed	Rarely.

Sue Evans
Kelling House,
17 West Street, Barkston,
Grantham, NG32 2NL

Tel	+44 (0)1400 251440
Mobile	+44 (0)7771 761251
Email	sue@kellinghouse.co.uk
Web	www.kellinghouse.co.uk

The Barn

Surrounded by meadows this 17th-century barn is in a quiet spot in a conservation village. Step in to a light-filled home with old beams and good antiques; a fireplace glows and heated floors keep toes warm. Above the high-raftered main living/dining room is a comfy, good-sized double; two adjoining rooms share a shower and are perfect for family or friends sharing; the single has an antique brass bed. Jane is helpful and friendly, there are endless extras and nothing is too much trouble; her delicious breakfasts and suppers are entirely local or home-grown. Views are to sheep-dotted fields and the village is on a 25-mile cycle trail. *Pets by arrangement.*

Rooms	1 twin/double; 2 twin/doubles sharing shower: £60-£80. 1 single with separate bath/shower: £55-£60.
Meals	Supper, 2 courses, £17.50. Dinner, 3 courses, £25. BYO. Pubs in village & 2 miles.
Closed	Rarely.

Tel	+44 (0)1529 497199
Mobile	+44 (0)7876 363292
Email	sjwright@farming.co.uk
Web	www.thebarnspringlane.co.uk

Jane Wright
The Barn,
Spring Lane, Folkingham,
Sleaford, NG34 0SJ

Baumber Park

Lincoln red cows and Longwool sheep surround this attractive rosy-brick farmhouse – once a stud that bred a Derby winner. The old watering pond is now a haven for frogs, newts and toads; birds sing lustily. Maran hens conjure delicious eggs, and charming Clare, a botanist, is hugely knowledgeable about the area. Bedrooms are light and traditional with mahogany furniture; two have heart-stopping views. Guests have their own wisteria-covered entrance, sitting room with an open fire, dining room with local books and the lovely garden to roam. This is good walking, riding and cycling country; seals and rare birds on the coast. *Minimum stay: usually 2 nights at weekends in high season.*

Rooms	2 doubles; 1 twin with separate shower: £72-£85. Singles £45-£70. Extra bed £15-£25 per person per night.
Meals	Pubs 1.5 miles.
Closed	Christmas & New Year.

Clare Harrison
Baumber Park,
Baumber, Horncastle, LN9 5NE

Tel +44 (0)1507 578235
Mobile +44 (0)7977 722776
Email mail@baumberpark.com
Web www.baumberpark.com

The Grange

Wide open farmland and an award-winning farm on the edge of the Lincolnshire Wolds. This immaculately kept farm has been in the family for generations; Sarah and Jonathan are delightful and make you feel instantly at home. Find acres of farmland and a two-mile farm trail to explore, a trout lake to picnic by and an open fire to warm you in an elegant drawing room with Georgian windows. Sarah gives you delicious homemade cake on arrival and huge Aga breakfasts with home-laid eggs and local produce. Comfortable bedrooms have TVs, tea trays and gleaming bathrooms. Fabulous views stretch to Lincoln Cathedral and the walks are superb.

Rooms	2 doubles: £82-£85. Singles £60-£65.
Meals	Pub/restaurant 1 mile.
Closed	Christmas & New Year.

Tel	+44 (0)1673 858670
Mobile	+44 (0)7951 079474
Email	sarahstamp@myfwi.co.uk
Web	www.thegrange-lincolnshire.co.uk

Sarah & Jonathan Stamp
The Grange,
Torrington Lane,
East Barkwith, LN8 5RY

The Old Farm House

You will feel at home in this rambling, quirky house – Nicola loves having guests to stay. The house is 300 years old and it's said that Dick Turpin, on the run, once hid in the roof. Read the papers by a winter fire, flop into worn leather chairs, sip an evening glass of wine in the garden, sleep soundly on a fine brass bed. Rooms are named after the men of the extended family – King Henry, George and James – and all are colourful, comfortable and cushioned. There are cycle routes, walks and golf courses galore (Nicola has all the info), racing at Market Rasen, quaint churches to visit and an annual classic car rally.

Rooms	2 doubles: £85. 1 family room for 4: £80 for 2, £90 for 3, £120 for 4. Singles £55.
Meals	Pub 2.5 miles.
Closed	Christmas, New Year & occasionally.

Nicola Clarke
The Old Farm House,
Low Road, Hatcliffe,
Grimsby, DN37 0SH

Tel	+44 (0)1472 824455
Mobile	+44 (0)7818 272523
Email	clarky.hatcliffe@btinternet.com
Web	www.oldfarmhousebandbgrimsby.com

The Manor House

At the end of a neatly raked gravel drive, a new manor house with wide views and stunning sunsets over the peaceful Trent valley. The Days have farmed in the village since 1898 and look after you with friendly ease. They give you a bedroom in the main house, or an annexe with its own entrance hall and sunny patio; find period furniture, a comfy sofa or two and rural art. The beautiful gardens are awash with roses, ducks on the pond, horses in the paddock. Shooting can be arranged and you can fish for carp in the lake, or play golf nearby; there are music and art festivals, antique fairs and walks in abundance too.

Rooms	1 double, 1 twin/double with kitchenette: £75-£80. Singles £55.
Meals	Pub/restaurant 3.5 miles.
Closed	Christmas & New Year.

Tel	+44 (0)1652 649508
Mobile	+44 (0)7712 766347
Email	hobbsmanton@gmail.com
Web	www.manorhousebedandbreakfast.co.uk

Judy Day
The Manor House,
Manton, Kirton Lindsey,
Gainsborough, DN21 4JT

Grayingham Lodge

An attractive stone farmhouse surrounded by fields. Jane and Peter's house is a working sheep farm, and you arrive to a welcoming cup from a silver teapot and delicious cake by the fire. If you're peckish later too, there are homemade flapjacks in pretty, very comfortable bedrooms. In the morning, the sideboard holds an impressive spread: homemade marmalade, fruit salad, compote, cereals – and a tasty cooked breakfast to follow. Have a day sightseeing in Lincoln – the Cathedral is magnificent and the castle has a copy of the Magna Carta; explore the Lincolnshire Wolds and coast; head off early for some exciting racing at Blyton Park.

Rooms	3 doubles: £60-£85. Singles £60.
Meals	Pubs/restaurants 3 miles.
Closed	Rarely.

Jane Summers
Grayingham Lodge,
Gainsborough Road, Northorpe,
Gainsborough, DN21 4AN

Tel	+44 (0)1652 648544
Email	janesummers@btinternet.com
Web	www.grayinghamlodge.co.uk

Underleigh House

A Derbyshire longhouse in Charlotte Brontë's *Jane Eyre* country built by a man called George Eyre. The position is unbeatable – field, river, hill, sky – but the stars of the show are Philip and Vivienne, dab hands at spoiling guests rotten. There's a big sitting room with maps for walkers, a dining room hall for hearty breakfasts, and tables and chairs scattered about the garden. Back inside, bedrooms vary in size, but all have super beds, goose down duvets and stunning views; a couple have doors onto the garden, the suites have proper sitting rooms. Fantastic walks start from the front door, Castleton Caves are on the doorstep and Chatsworth is close. *Over 12s welcome.*

Rooms	1 double: £100–£110. 3 suites for 2: £120–£130. Singles £80–£110. Extra bed/sofabed £20 per person per night.
Meals	Packed lunches £6. Pubs/restaurants 0.5 miles.
Closed	Christmas, New Year, 1 January – 7 February.

Tel	+44 (0)1433 621372
Email	underleigh.house@btconnect.com
Web	www.underleighhouse.co.uk

Philip & Vivienne Taylor
Underleigh House,
Lose Hill Lane, Hope,
Hope Valley, S33 6AF

Manor Farm

Between two small dales, close to great houses (Chatsworth, Hardwick Hall, Haddon Hall), lies this peaceful cluster of three ancient farms and a church; welcome to the 16th century! Simon and Gilly, warm, delightful and fascinated by the history, have restored the east wing to create big, beamy rooms in the old hayloft and a pretty garden room on the ground floor. Wake to a choice of scrumptious breakfasts with local and organic produce – served in the cavernous Elizabethan kitchen. There's a lovely garden with sweeping views across Derwent Valley and distant hills, walks from the doorstep and the Peak District to explore. *Minimum stay: 2 nights at weekends. Children over 5 welcome. The Garden Room (twin) is open March-October only.*

Rooms	3 twin/doubles, 1 twin: £85-£99. Singles £65-£85.
Meals	Pubs 10-minute walk, restaurants 10-minute drive.
Closed	Rarely.

Simon & Gilly Groom
Manor Farm,
Dethick, Matlock, DE4 5GG

Tel	+44 (0)1629 534302
Mobile	+44 (0)7944 660814
Email	gilly.groom@w3z.co.uk
Web	www.manorfarmdethick.co.uk

Alstonefield Manor

Country manor house definitely, but delightfully understated and cleverly designed to look natural. This family home, sitting in walled gardens, is high in the hills above Dovedale. Local girl Jo spoils you with homemade scones and tea when you arrive, served on the lawns or by the fire in the elegant drawing room. Beautiful bedrooms have antiques, flowers, lovely fabrics, painted floors and garden views; wood panelled bathrooms have showers or a roll top tub. Wake to birdsong – and a candlelit breakfast with local bacon and Staffordshire oatcakes. After a great walk, stroll across the village green for supper at The George. A joy. *Minimum stay: 2 nights. Over 12s welcome.*

Rooms	1 double; 2 doubles each with separate bathroom: £130-£170. Singles £100.
Meals	Pub 100 yds.
Closed	Christmas.

Tel	+44 (0)1335 310393
Email	stay@alstonefieldmanor.com
Web	www.alstonefieldmanor.com

Robert & Jo Wood
Alstonefield Manor,
Alstonefield, Ashbourne, DE6 2FX

The Old Vicarage Wetton

Wind through pretty Wetton, park under the big tree and find a front door with a cheery bell and a box of slippers waiting the other side. You're looked after well and the house has a convivial air. Bedrooms have well-dressed beds; the dining room encourages you to linger: flowers, garden views, open fire, books and maps. Nicky gives you lots of breakfast choices including eggs from the hens and homemade jams from her organic plot. There are benches for sitting outside on sunny days, the colourful garden is full of birds and the White Peak is on the doorstep – Nicky, super-friendly and a keen walker, will happily direct you.

Nicola Drummond
The Old Vicarage Wetton,
Wetton, Ashbourne, DE6 2AF

Rooms	2 doubles, 1 twin/double: £100-£127. Extra Z-bed available £28 per person per night.
Meals	Packed lunch £7.50. Pubs/restaurants 1 mile.
Closed	Never.

Tel	+44 (0)1335 310296
Mobile	+44 (0)7854 456678
Email	nicola@oldvicaragewetton.co.uk
Web	www.oldvicaragewetton.co.uk

PUBLIC FOOTPATH

West Midlands

The Old Manor House Halford, page 314

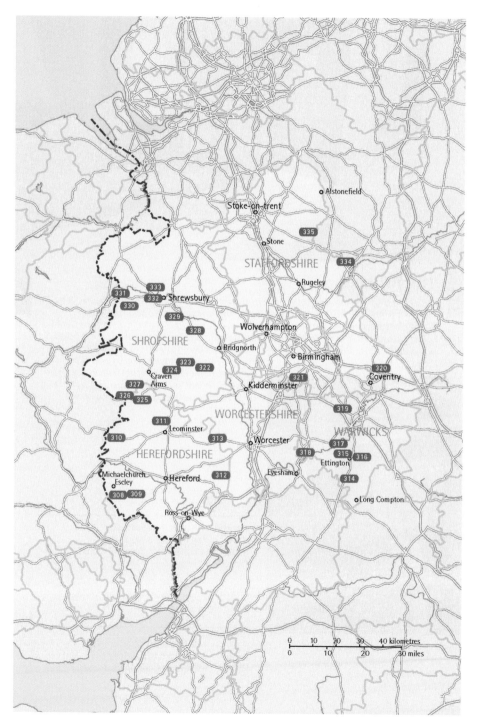

The Bridge Inn

Getting here is huge fun. The 16th-century inn (with a pretty garden) and farmhouse sit by the river beneath the Black Hill of Bruce Chatwin fame and willows line the footbridge. Walkers descend, as do local farmers and shooting parties, and Glyn is a great host. Comfy country bedrooms lie in the farmhouse; find antiques, flagstone floors and a dark panelled sitting room below. Breakfast on the best bacon and local eggs in the huge farmhouse kitchen, visit Hay for bookshops, yomp in the Beacons. Return to a piping hot bath then wander down to the pub for a tasty supper and a pint of Butty Bach (small friend) by the wood-burner.

Rooms	1 double, 2 twin/doubles: £95-£110. Hay Festival price: £165.
Meals	Lunch £8-£22. Dinner £12-£22.
Closed	Rarely.

Glyn Bufton & Gisela Vargas
The Bridge Inn,
Michaelchurch Escley,
Hereford, HR2 0JW

Tel	+44 (0)1981 510646
Email	thebridgeinn@hotmail.com
Web	www.thebridgeinnmichaelchurch.co.uk

Rock Cottage

Birds, books and beautiful Black Mountain views highlighted by morning sun, turning to an inky black line at dusk; the cottage glows. There's an instant feeling of warmth and friendliness as you step into the snug hall; find rich autumnal colours, old rugs, a big wood-burner and comfy sitting rooms. Local art and photos line the walls, bedrooms have sumptuous beds, perfect linen and garden posies. You eat (very well) en famille at the communal oak table, or out on the pretty terrace. Thoughtful Chris and Sue will take you to hear the dawn chorus and there are food and literary festivals, bookshops and walks galore.

Rooms	2 doubles: £70-£110. Singles £70-£90. Extra bed £10 per person per night.
Meals	Packed lunch £6. Dinner, 2-3 courses, £20. Pub/restaurant 4 miles.
Closed	Christmas & New Year.

Tel	+44 (0)1981 510360
Email	robinsrockcottage@googlemail.com
Web	www.rockcottagebandb.co.uk

Chris & Sue Robinson
Rock Cottage,
Newton St Margarets,
Hereford, HR2 0QW

Castle Hill House

Start the day with a big breakfast and a gorgeous green view. This grand old townhouse, with a landscaped garden, a brook and a weir, combines a 'top of the town' position with a delightfully rural feel. Hetan and Silvia spoil you rotten and know the best places to go. Welsh border country is famously wild so order a picnic and set off on the Offa's Dyke Path which runs past the door – it's one of the most beautiful stretches and views from Hergest Ridge

stretch for miles. The Mortimer Trail can be joined from the house too. Return to a luxurious soak or drenching shower, perhaps an in-room massage, and then relax in the guest sitting room. You can trot down the hill to one of several pubs and restaurants. Or drive to the Stagg Inn at Titley, four miles away, where the kitchen has been winning awards for 20 years. *Minimum stay: 2 nights on weekends in high season. Massages available.*

Rooms	3 doubles, 1 twin: £90-£110.
Meals	Pubs/restaurants 5-minute walk.
Closed	Rarely.

Hetan & Silvia Patel
Castle Hill House,
5 Church Road, Kington, HR5 3AG

Tel	+44 (0)1544 209066
Mobile	+44 (0)7714 204080
Email	info@castlehillhousekington.co.uk
Web	www.castlehillhousekington.co.uk

Bunns Croft

The timbers of this medieval yeoman's house are quite possibly a thousand years old. Little of the structure has ever been altered and it is sheer delight. Stone floors, rich colours, a piano, books, cosy chairs, friendly dog – all give a homely, lived-in warm feel. Cruck-beamed bedrooms are snugly small, the stairs are steep, and the twin's bathroom has its own sweet fireplace. The countryside is 'pure', too, with 1,500 acres of National Trust land a short hop away. Anita is charming, loves to look after her guests, grows her own fruit and vegetables and cooks fabulous dinners. Just mind your head!

Rooms	1 twin; 1 double sharing bath with 3 singles, let to same party only: £85-£95. 3 singles: £43.
Meals	Dinner, 3 courses, £25. BYO. Pub 7 miles.
Closed	Rarely.

Tel	+44 (0)1568 615836
Email	anitasyersg2@gmail.com

Anita Syers-Gibson
Bunns Croft,
Moreton Eye, Leominster, HR6 0DP

Old Country Farm & The Lighthouse

Ella's passion for this tranquil place – and conservation of its wildlife – is infectious. She's keen on home-grown and local food too so breakfast is delicious. Dating from the 1400s, the farm is a delightful rambling medley: russet stone and colour-washed brick, huge convivial round table by the Aga, rugs on polished floors. The sitting room has wood-burner, piano and books, and you sleep soundly in pretty, cottagey bedrooms: lovely linen, garden flowers. In winter you stay in The Lighthouse, down the lane: an inspired green-oak retreat with soaring beams, snug library, comfy downstairs bedrooms and roses in the garden. Magical. *Minimum stay: 2 nights.*

Rooms	1 double; 1 double with separate bath, 1 double with separate shower: £70-£105. Singles £45-£65.
Meals	Pubs/restaurants 3 miles.
Closed	Rarely.

Ella Grace Quincy
Old Country Farm & The Lighthouse,
Mathon, Malvern, WR13 5PS

Tel	+44 (0)1886 880867
Email	ella@oldcountryhouse.co.uk
Web	www.oldcountryhouse.co.uk

Huntlands Farm

Deep in the rural shires Lucy (who runs inspiring upholstery courses) and Stephen give you delightful B&B on a working farm. They've lovingly coaxed this 15th-century house back to life: huge rooms, two with four-posters, are hugely comfortable with patterned rugs on wide floorboards, reclaimed wardrobes and views over the orchard or farm. You get roll top tubs to wallow in, fluffy towels and local soaps. Breakfast in the convivial dining room on eggs from the hens, sausages from the pigs and homemade preserves. There's dinner too, roasts and stews or traditional Caribbean fare. The Malvern showground is nearby. *Minimum stay: 2 nights. Children over 10 welcome.*

Rooms	2 doubles, 1 twin/double: £85-£100. 1 suite for 2: £100-£105. 1 family room for 4 with sofabed & separate bathroom: £70-£95.
Meals	Dinner, 3 courses, £24.50. Pubs/restaurants 0.5 miles.
Closed	Rarely.

Tel	+44 (0)1886 821955
Mobile	+44 (0)7828 286360
Email	lucy@huntlandsfarm.co.uk
Web	www.huntlandsfarm.co.uk

Lucy Brodie
Huntlands Farm,
Gaines Road, Whitbourne,
Worcester, WR6 5RD

The Old Manor House Halford

An attractive 16th-century manor house with peaceful landscaped gardens sweeping down to the river Stour. The beamed double has oak furniture and a big bathroom; the fresh twin rooms (one in a private wing) are simply lovely. There is a large and elegant drawing and dining room for visitors to share, with antiques, contemporary art and an open fire. Jane prepares first-class breakfasts, and in warm weather you can have tea on the terrace: enjoy the pots of tulips in spring, old scented roses in summer, the meadow land beyond. A comfortable, lived-in family house with Stratford and the theatre close by. Guests love it here. *Minimum stay: 2 nights at weekends after Easter.*

Rooms	1 double, 2 twin/doubles all with separate bath: £95. Singles £85.
Meals	Dinner, 3 courses, from £35. Restaurants nearby.
Closed	22 December to 1 March.

Jane Pusey
The Old Manor House Halford,
Halford,
Shipston-on-Stour, CV36 5BT

Tel   +44 (0)1789 740264
Mobile +44 (0)7786 467916
Email   oldmanorhalford@btinternet.com
Web   www.oldmanor-halford.co.uk

Stamford Hall

Soft hills and lines of poplars bring you to the high, pretty red-brick Georgian house with a smart hornbeam hedge. James, whose art decorates the walls, and Alice look after you impeccably but without fuss. You have a generous sitting room overlooking the garden, with gleaming furniture, early estate and garden etchings, and pastel blue sofas. Peaceful bedrooms are on the second floor and both have charm: soft wool tartan rugs on comfy beds, calming colours, attractive fabrics, restful outlooks. Wake to a delicious full English breakfast; walk it off in open countryside or a day out exploring Stratford.

Rooms	1 double, 1 twin: £85. Singles £60.
Meals	Pub 1 mile.
Closed	Christmas & occasionally.

Tel	+44 (0)1789 740239
Email	stamfordhall@gmail.com
Web	www.stamfordhall.co.uk

James & Alice Kerr
Stamford Hall,
Fosse Way, Ettington,
Stratford-upon-Avon, CV37 7PA

Grove Farm

Down quiet lanes to the house that Charlie was born in – her young family are the third generation to live here. Bright bedrooms up in the eaves have oak beams, gingham armchairs and comfy beds; small bathrooms, recently revamped. Hop down for homelaid eggs, homemade bread, sausages, bacon and black pudding from down the road – outside when the sun shines, or by the fire in the dining room. Children will love it: dogs, rabbits, hens all happy to have a pat, a swing, log cabin, dens and Flappy the cockerel too. Roses and gangs of cheerful hollyhocks dot the gardens, you can roam the woodland and owls hoot you to sleep. Charming.

Rooms	2 doubles: £85-£90.
	1 family room for 5: £120-£180.
	Singles £60. Extra bed available.
Meals	Pubs/restaurants 1.5 miles.
Closed	Rarely.

Charlie Coldicott
Grove Farm,
Stratford Road, Ettington,
Stratford-upon-Avon, CV37 7NX

Mobile	+44 (0)7774 776682
Email	grovefarmbb@btconnect.com

Sequoia House

A riverside stroll along the old tramway path brings you to the centre of Stratford. Step into the handsome hallway of this impeccable Victorian house to find high ceilings, deep bays, generous landings and a homely sitting room. The Evanses downsized from the hotel they used to run here, and are happy to treat just a few guests: trouser presses (yes!) and piles of towels mingle with fine old furniture in immaculate bedrooms; two have Swan Theatre views. Hotel touches, a lovely warm welcome, Jean's cake on arrival and homemade preserves at breakfast. Park off road – or leave the car at home. *Minimum stay: 2 nights at weekends.*

Rooms	4 doubles: £125-£135.
	1 single: £95-£110.
Meals	Pub/restaurant 100 yds.
Closed	Christmas & New Year.

Tel	+44 (0)1789 268852
Mobile	+44 (0)7833 727914
Email	info@sequoia-house.co.uk
Web	www.sequoia-house.co.uk

Jean & Philip Evans
Sequoia House,
51 Shipston Road,
Stratford-upon-Avon, CV37 7LN

Salford Farm House

Beautiful within, handsome without. Subtle colours, oak beams and lovely old pieces: Jane has achieved a seductive combination of comfort and style. A flagstoned hallway and an old rocking horse, ticking clocks, beeswax and fresh flowers speak of a much-loved house. Dinners are superb: meat and game from the Ragley Estate, delicious fruits in season. Bedrooms have a soft, warm elegance and garden views while bathrooms are spotless. It's all wholly delightful and worth a serious detour as is the enchanting garden that flows from one space to another, studded with rare and interesting plants. It is also divided by a wing of the house, so you pass under an open-sided brick and timber barn to cross from one side to the other. Beautiful arrangements of plants in pots and a square, formal pond reveal Jane's artistic talents. There is always another corner to peek around and plenty of height: a pretty gazebo covered in wisteria, weathered deer-fencing screens, a large pergola the length of one wall. Green-fingered Richard is MD of nearby Hillers, an award-winning fruit farm, café, shop and display garden.

Rooms	2 twin/doubles: £100. Singles £75.
Meals	Dinner £30. Restaurant 2.5 miles.
Closed	Rarely.

Jane & Richard Beach
Salford Farm House,
Salford Priors, Evesham, WR11 8XN

Tel	+44 (0)1386 870000
Mobile	+44 (0)7798 820713
Email	salfordfarmhouse@aol.com
Web	www.salfordfarmhouse.co.uk

Shrewley Pools Farm

A charming, eccentric home and fabulous for families, with space to play and animals to see: sheep, bantams and pigs. A fragrant, romantic garden with a blossoming orchard and a fascinating house (1640), all low ceilings, aged floors and steep stairs. Timbered passages lead to large, pretty, sunny bedrooms (all with electric blankets) with leaded windows and polished wooden floors and a family room with everything needed for a baby. In a farmhouse dining room Cathy serves sausages, bacon, and eggs from the farm, can do gluten-free breakfasts and is happy to do teas for children. Buy a day ticket and fish in the lake.

Rooms	1 twin: £75. 1 family room for 4: £79. Singles £55-£65. Extra bed/sofabed £20-£30 per person per night. Cot available £10.
Meals	Packed lunch £7. Child's high tea £7. Pub/restaurant 1.5 miles.
Closed	Christmas.

Tel	+44 (0)1926 484315
Mobile	+44 (0)7818 280681
Email	cathydodd@hotmail.co.uk
Web	www.shrewleypoolsfarm.co.uk

Cathy Dodd
Shrewley Pools Farm,
Five Ways Road, Haseley,
Warwick, CV35 7HB

Park Farm House

Fronted by a circular drive, the warm red-brick farmhouse is listed and old – it dates from 1655. Linda is friendly and welcoming, a genuine B&B pro, giving you an immaculate guest sitting room filled with pretty family pieces. The bedrooms sport comfortable mattresses, mahogany or brass beds, blankets on request, bathrobes, flowers and magazines; bathrooms are traditional but spotless. A haven of rest from the motorway (morning hum only) this is in the heart of a working farm yet hugely convenient for Birmingham, Warwick, Stratford and Coventry. You may get their own beef at dinner and the vegetables are home-grown.

Rooms	1 double, 1 twin: £89. Singles from £58.
Meals	Dinner, 3 courses, from £25.
	Supper £19. Pub/restaurant 1.5 miles.
Closed	Rarely.

Linda Grindal
Park Farm House,
Spring Road, Barnacle Shilton,
Coventry, CV7 9LG

Tel	+44 (0)2476 612628
Email	richgrinfarm@btconnect.com
Web	www.parkfarmguesthouse.co.uk

Woodbrooke

A pleasure to find ten tranquil acres (woodlands, lawns, lake and walled garden) so close to the centre of Birmingham – run by such special people. This impressive Georgian mansion was donated by George Cadbury to the Quakers in 1903, as a place for study and contemplation. And so it remains. There are corridors aplenty and public rooms big and small: a library, a silent room, a lovely new garden lounge, and a dining hall where organic buffet meals feature fruit and veg from the grounds. Bedrooms, spread over several buildings, are carpeted, comfortable, light and airy, and most have en suite showers. Welcoming, nurturing, historic. *Please note the reception is not open 24hrs*

Rooms	5 doubles, 7 twins, mostly en suite: £69-£99. 1 family room for 5, 1 family room for 6: £135-£179. 53 singles, mostly en suite: £49-£79. 2 triples: £95-£119.
Meals	Breakfast included. Lunch & dinner £11. Pubs/restaurants 15-minute walk.
Closed	Christmas & Boxing Day.

Tel	+44 (0)121 472 5171
Email	enquiries@woodbrooke.org.uk
Web	www.woodbrooke.org.uk

Woodbrooke Reservations
Woodbrooke,
1046 Bristol Road, Selly Oak,
Birmingham, B29 6LJ

The Old Rectory

With its own spring water, horses, dogs and slow pace this Georgian rectory is comfortable country living at its best. Izzy and Andy are charming and interesting and give you scones and tea by the fire in a drawing room full of family photos, plump sofas and books. Elegant bedrooms have fluffy hot water bottles; smart bathrooms have scented lotions in pretty bottles, robes and slippers. Candlelit dinner will often be fish or game with garden vegetables; breakfast is local and leisurely with homemade granola and jams. There's a bootroom for muddy feet and paws, stabling and seven acres to roam. *Pets welcome, sleeping in bootroom.*

Rooms	1 double, 1 twin/double; 1 double with separate bathroom: £85-£125. Singles £70-£110.
Meals	Dinner, 3 courses with coffee, drinks & canapés, £35. Supper tray, soup & sandwich, £10. Pubs 1.25-4 miles.
Closed	Rarely.

Isabel Barnard
The Old Rectory,
Wheathill, Ludlow, WV16 6QT

Tel	+44 (0)1746 787209
Email	enquiries@theoldrectorywheathill.com
Web	www.theoldrectorywheathill.com

Timberstone Bed & Breakfast

The house is engaging – as are Tracey and Alex. Bedrooms are inviting – two snug under the eaves, two in the smart oak-floored extension – roll top baths, pretty fabrics, thick white cotton, beams galore... Or you can decamp to The Retreat, a wooden cabin in the garden warmed with a wood-burner. Tracey, once in catering, is a reflexologist – book a session, or sauna, in the garden studios; ask about 'gadget-free breaks' too. In the guest sitting/dining room find art, books, comfy sofas and doors onto the terrace. Breakfasts are good with croissants and local eggs and bacon; dinners are delicious too, or you can head off to Ludlow and its clutch of Michelin stars.

Rooms	3 doubles: £100-£150. 1 family room for 4: £110-£120. 1 cabin for 2: £100-£150. Singles £75-£98.
Meals	Dinner, 3 courses, £25. Pubs/restaurants 5 miles.
Closed	Rarely.

Tel	+44 (0)1584 823519
Mobile	+44 (0)7905 967263
Email	timberstone1@hotmail.com
Web	www.timberstoneludlow.co.uk

Tracey Baylis & Alex Read
Timberstone Bed & Breakfast,
Clee Stanton, Ludlow, SY8 3EL

Crow Leasow Farm

A pretty 1600s Dutch brick house with the famous Crow Leasow Oak (over a thousand years old) gracing the garden and a cockerel strutting about with his hens; there's much history here and Sally will be happy to tell you all about it over tea. If you're a group you may get to stay in for supper too – good English cooking from great ingredients and masses of vegetables. Sally likes to make people happy, so breakfast is a convivial affair around a big table: eggs from her hens, sourdough bread baked by a friend, homemade compote, bacon and sausages from the butcher in Ludlow, Peruvian coffee, homemade marmalade and jams. She'll make you a picnic and pack it up in a basket too. Head out for the wonderful, untrammelled Shropshire Hills, an AONB with many footpaths. Wild swim in rivers, watch salmon leaping in spring and visit castles and churches. Ludlow is three miles for food markets and independent shops. *Minimum stay: 2 nights at weekends. Pets by arrangement.*

Rooms	1 double: £105-£125. 1 twin: £95-£120. 1 suite: £110-£135. Singles £95-£110. Reduced rates for larger groups.
Meals	Supper from £25, cold platter for late arrivals from £15. Picnic basket from £17.50 per person.
Closed	Rarely.

Sally Kellard
Crow Leasow Farm,
Middleton, Ludlow, SY8 3EE

Mobile +44 (0)7812 602122
Email   sally@wickton.co.uk

Walford Court

Come for a break from clock-watching and a spot of Shropshire air. Large bedrooms delight with the comfiest mattresses on king-size beds, scented candles, antiques, books, games and double-end roll top baths – one under a west facing window. Debbie and Craig's Aga-cooked breakfasts have won awards and include eggs from 'the ladies of the orchard'. Wander through the apple, plum and pear trees, find a motte and bailey, strike out for a long, leafy hike. Craig and Debbie are thoughtful and hugely keen on wildlife (you get binoculars) and this is the perfect place to bring a special person – and a bottle of champagne. *Minimum stay: 2 nights.*

Rooms	1 double; 2 doubles each with sitting room: £95-£105. Extra bed/sofabed £30 per person per night.
Meals	Room platter of local pâté, cheeses, ham & homemade pickles & chutney. Packed lunch. Pubs/restaurants 1-3 miles.
Closed	Christmas & Boxing Day.

Tel	+44 (0)1547 540570
Email	info@romanticbreak.com
Web	www.romanticbreak.com

Debbie & Craig Fraser
Walford Court,
Walford, Leintwardine,
Ludlow, SY7 0JT

The Hall

Matt and Juliet have breathed new life into this attractive old house close to the Welsh border. They love welcoming guests and your stay starts with a home-baked something and hot drinks – and a tour of the cellar if you'd like with its salting tables and the remains of huge old cider barrels. Bedrooms in airy vaulted spaces come with sofas and flowers. Wake for imaginative breakfasts: homemade bread, rhubarb and ginger jam, buckwheat granola and apple juice, porridge with cream and whisky, spicy Mexican beans on toast, Ludlow sausages, poached home-laid eggs with avocado on sourdough topped with tomato, garlic and chilli... Join the Heart of Wales Line Trail, have a foodie day in Ludlow, catch the evening sun from a pretty garden spot, finish off with a Moroccan rose oil bath before bed.

Rooms	2 doubles: £120.
Meals	Pub 5-minute walk, restaurants 20-minute drive.
Closed	Christmas, New Year & occasionally.

Matt Bellamy & Juliet Earp
The Hall,
Bucknell, SY7 0AA

Mobile +44 (0)7905 503039
Email info@thehallbucknell.com
Web www.thehallbucknell.com

Hopton House

Karen looks after you very well – she's such an expert on B&B she runs courses on how to do it. And how to do it beautifully: unwind in this fresh converted granary with old beams, high ceilings and a sun-filled dining/sitting room overlooking the hills. You sleep over in the barn: choose between two bedrooms – one up, one down – each with its own entrance. Find beautifully dressed beds, silent fridges, good lighting, homemade cakes. Bathrooms have deep baths (and showers) – from one you can lie back and gaze at the stars. Karen's breakfasts promise Ludlow sausages, home-laid eggs, fine jams and homemade marmalade. *Minimum stay: 2 nights. Over 16s welcome. Check owner's website for availability calendar & booking engine.*

Rooms	2 doubles: £125-£135.
Meals	Restaurant 3 miles.
Closed	19-27 December.

Tel	+44 (0)1547 530885
Email	info@shropshirebreakfast.co.uk
Web	www.shropshirebreakfast.co.uk

Karen Thorne
Hopton House,
Hopton Heath, Craven Arms, SY7 0QD

5 Wilmore Street

Clare delights in making her home glow. Passionate about interior décor, she's designed an immaculate house crammed with creative touches and Georgian elegance; inviting sitting and breakfast rooms have comfy sofas, a wood-burner and refectory tables. An experienced cook too, so expect good breakfasts and dinners: homemade treats, eggs from a friend's hens, fish from the market. Soak in a slipper bath; sleep in a charming bedroom – both have armchairs, hand-painted antiques and pictures; church bells keep time. The historic town is rich in timbered buildings, monastic ruins, arty festivals and award-winning independent shops.

Rooms	2 doubles: £110. Singles £85.
Meals	Lunch & dinner by arrangement. Pubs/restaurants 5-minute walk.
Closed	Rarely.

Richard & Clare Wozniak
5 Wilmore Street,
Much Wenlock, TF13 6HR

Tel	+44 (0)1952 727268
Mobile	+44 (0)7530 779568
Email	5wilmorestreet@gmail.com
Web	www.5wilmorestreet.co.uk

North Farm

Peaceful green Shropshire and a stunning garden surround this classic white farmhouse. Chickens, ducks and geese are happily dotted about and the veg patch blooms. Tess and family look after you well. Bedrooms have flowery fabrics, tip-top linen, Lloyd Loom chairs and pretty tea trays. Wake for a delicious breakfast served on Portmeirion china: homemade marmalade, compotes, eggs from the hens, bacon and sausages from home-reared pigs. Lots to do close by: historic Shrewsbury, Ironbridge, Ludlow, Powis Castle – and the walks are a treat. Settle by the log-burner on your return: books to browse, a glass of wine... lovely.

Rooms	1 double, 1 twin; 1 double with separate bath: £90. Singles £60.
Meals	Pubs/restaurants 4-minute drive.
Closed	Rarely.

Tel	+44 (0)1743 761031
Mobile	+44 (0)7956 817705
Email	tessbromley@ymail.com
Web	www.northfarm.co.uk

Tess Bromley
North Farm,
Eaton Mascott, Cross Houses,
Shrewsbury, SY5 6HF

Whitton Hall

Down a long private drive with fields on either side is a lovely 18th-century farmhouse, elegant but not intimidating, with a sense of timelessness. A large open hallway and a cosy sitting room where tea and a drinks tray are provided are peaceful spaces for relaxing with a book. You breakfast in the dining room, on local muesli, bread, marmalades and jams, milk from their Jersey cows, soft fruit from their garden, sausages and bacon from down the road. Peaceful, light and large bedrooms in an adjacent wing have modern bathrooms, country house furniture and long views to glorious gardens. Unwind in the peace. *Children over 10 welcome. Self-catering option in family room*

Rooms	1 double with separate bathroom; 1 twin/double with separate shower: £100-£110. 1 family room for 4 with separate bathroom: £110-£140. Singles £70.
Meals	Supper in dining room £25 for 4+. Cold supper tray in room/garden £15 for 1, £20 for 2. Pub 10-minute drive.
Closed	Christmas, New Year & Easter.

Christopher & Gill Halliday & Kate Boscawen
Whitton Hall,
Westbury, Shrewsbury, SY5 9RD

Tel	+44 (0)1743 884270
Mobile	+44 (0)7974 689629
Email	kate@whittonhall.com
Web	www.whittonhall.co.uk

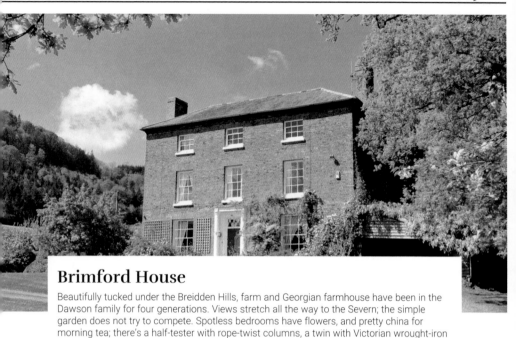

Brimford House

Beautifully tucked under the Breidden Hills, farm and Georgian farmhouse have been in the Dawson family for four generations. Views stretch all the way to the Severn; the simple garden does not try to compete. Spotless bedrooms have flowers, and pretty china for morning tea; there's a half-tester with rope-twist columns, a twin with Victorian wrought-iron bedsteads, a double with a brass bed, a big bathroom with a roll top bath. Liz serves you farm eggs and homemade preserves at breakfast, and there's a food pub just down the road.
Sheep and cattle outdoors, a lovely black lab in, and wildlife walks from the door. Good value.
Pets by arrangement.

Rooms	2 doubles, 1 twin: £80-£90. Singles £50-£60. Extra bed/sofabed £20 per person per night.
Meals	Packed lunch £4.50. Pub 3-minute walk.
Closed	Rarely.

Tel	+44 (0)1938 570235
Mobile	+44 (0)7801 100848
Email	info@brimford.co.uk
Web	www.brimford.co.uk

Liz Dawson
Brimford House,
Criggion, Shrewsbury, SY5 9AU

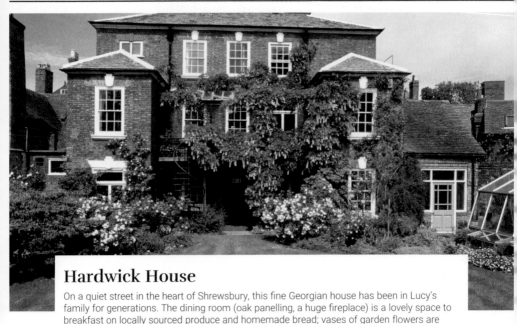

Hardwick House

On a quiet street in the heart of Shrewsbury, this fine Georgian house has been in Lucy's family for generations. The dining room (oak panelling, a huge fireplace) is a lovely space to breakfast on locally sourced produce and homemade bread; vases of garden flowers are dotted all around this cheerful family home. Bedrooms are traditional and comfortable with pretty china tea cups; bathrooms are old-fashioned. The walled garden is fabulous; take tea in an 18th-century summerhouse. Birthplace of Darwin, this is a fascinating historic town; walk to the abbey, castle, theatre, festivals and great shops. Lucy is delightful. *Luggage can be stored post check out on request*

Rooms	2 twin/doubles, one with adjoining room can form a large suite: £95–£105. Singles £70–£80.
Meals	Pubs/restaurants 150 yds.
Closed	Christmas & New Year.

Lucy Whitaker
Hardwick House,
12 St John's Hill, Shrewsbury, SY1 1JJ

Tel	+44 (0)1743 350165
Email	gilesandlucy@btinternet.com
Web	www.hardwickhouseshrewsbury.co.uk

The Isle

History buffs and nature lovers rejoice. You drive through lion-topped stone pillars to a house built in 1682 (then extended) that stands in 800 acres enfolded by the river Severn. Charming Ros and Edward are down-to-earth and hands-on: eggs, bacon, ham, vegetables, and logs, all come from the estate. Flop in front of a huge fire in the drawing room, homely with family antiques, big rug, magazines strewn on large tables. Peaceful bedrooms are large and light with pocket-sprung memory mattresses and snazzy upmarket bathrooms. Walk, fish, ride (there's a livery stable on site) and lap up the views – they're sublime.

Rooms	3 doubles, 1 twin: £80-£100.
	1 family room for 4: £90-£145.
	Singles £50-£70.
Meals	Packed lunch £5. Dinner £15-£20.
	Pub/restaurant 4.3 miles.
Closed	Rarely.

Mobile	+44 (0)7776 257286
Email	ros@isleestate.co.uk
Web	www.the-isle-estate.co.uk

Ros & Edward Tate
The Isle,
Bicton, Shrewsbury, SY3 8EE

Westmorland Cottage

The pretty village has hanging baskets decorating shops and riverside, and Tim and Caroline's house was built in the arboretum of Oswald Mosley's former family seat. Comfy sitting rooms have heaps of books, art, a log fire; bedrooms (one in the studio) have tip-top linen, garden views and shortbread. Wake for a generous Aga breakfast: homemade granola, Tim's bread, local bacon – or continental with croissants. You're on the edge of the Peak District National Park – head out for walks, cycling, National Trust houses galore. Return to the stunning garden for afternoon tea and cake: unusual trees, Italianate pond, sunny spots...

Rooms	1 double; 1 double with separate bathroom: £75-£85. 1 studio for 2: £95. Singles £65.
Meals	Pubs/restaurants 5-minute walk.
Closed	Rarely.

Caroline Bucknall
Westmorland Cottage,
Hall Grounds, Rolleston-on-Dove,
Burton-on-Trent, DE13 9BS

Tel	+44 (0)1283 813336
Mobile	+44 (0)7814 849211
Email	bucknalltandc@gmail.com
Web	www.westmorlandcottage.co.uk

Manor House Farm

A working rare-breed farm in an area of great beauty, a Jacobean farmhouse with oodles of history. Behind mullioned windows is a glorious interior crammed with curios and family pieces, panelled walls and wonky floors... hurl a log on the fire and watch it roar. Rooms with views have four-posters; one bathroom flaunts rich red antique fabrics. Chris and Margaret are passionate hosts who serve perfect breakfasts (eggs from their own hens, sausages and bacon from their pigs and home-grown tomatoes) and give you the run of a garden resplendent with plants, vistas, tennis, croquet, two springer spaniels and one purring cat. Heaven. *Minimum stay: 2 nights at weekends during high season.*

Rooms	1 double, 2 four-posters: £74-£80.
	1 family room for 4: £85-£110.
	Singles £45-£50.
Meals	Pub/restaurant 1.5 miles.
Closed	Christmas.

Tel	+44 (0)1889 590415
Mobile	+44 (0)7976 767629
Email	cmball@manorhousefarm.co.uk
Web	www.manorhousefarm.co.uk

Chris & Margaret Ball
Manor House Farm,
Prestwood, Denstone,
Uttoxeter, ST14 5DD

North West

Wood House, page 349

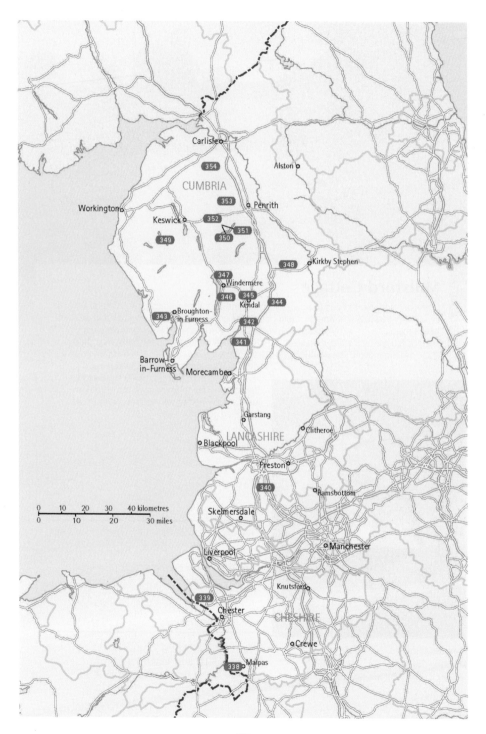

Carlisle

354

CUMBRIA

353 Penrith

Workington

Keswick 352

349 350 351

348 Kirkby Stephen

347

346 Windermere

343 345 344

Broughton-in-Furness Kendal

342

341

Barrow-in-Furness

Morecambe

Alston

Garstang

LANCASHIRE

Clitheroe

Blackpool

Preston

340

Ramsbottom

| 0 | 10 | 20 | 30 | 40 kilometres |
| 0 | 10 | 20 | 30 miles |

Skelmersdale

Manchester

Liverpool

Knutsford

339

Chester

CHESHIRE

Crewe

338 Malpas

Mulsford Cottage

Delicious! Not just the food (Kate's a pro chef) but the sweet whitewashed cottage with its sunny conservatory and vintage interiors, and the green Cheshire countryside that bubble-wraps the place in rural peace. Chat – and laugh – the evening away over Kate's superb dinners, lounge by the fire, then sleep deeply in comfy bedrooms: cane beds, a bright red chair, a vintage desk. The double has a roll top bath, the family room a tiny shower-with-a-view. Wake for local bacon, sausages and honey and just-laid bantam eggs. Walk the 34-mile Sandstone Trail to Shropshire; Wales starts just past the hammock, at the bottom of the bird-filled garden.

Rooms	1 double: £90. 1 family room for 3 with separate bath/shower: £90-£115. Singles £65.
Meals	Dinner from £18. Pub 1.5 miles.
Closed	Rarely.

Kate Dewhurst
Mulsford Cottage,
Mulsford, Sarn, Malpas, SY14 7LP

Tel   +44 (0)1948 770414
Email   katedewhurst4@gmail.com
Web   www.mulsfordcottage.co.uk

Trustwood

Small and pretty and wrapped in beautiful country, Trustwood stands in peaceful gardens that are open through the NGS with National Trust woods at the end of the lane. Outside, sweetpeas flourish to the front, while lawns run down behind to a copse where bluebells thrive in spring. Inside, warm, fresh, contemporary interiors are just the ticket: super bedrooms, fabulous bathrooms, and a wood-burner and sofas in the sitting room. Free-range hens provide eggs for delicious breakfasts, Lin accounts for the lovely scones. As for the Wirral, much more beautiful than you probably imagine; coastal walks, botanic gardens and the spectacular Dee estuary all wait.

Rooms	2 doubles: £80. Singles £55.
Meals	Restaurants 2 miles.
Closed	Occasionally.

Tel	+44 (0)151 336 7118
Mobile	+44 (0)7550 012462
Email	lin@trustwoodbnb.uk
Web	www.trustwoodbnb.uk

Lin & Peter Friend
Trustwood,
Vicarage Lane, Burton,
Neston, CH64 5TJ

The Ridges

John and Barbara look after you well in a lovely old mill-owner's house built in the 1700s. Traditional bedrooms have patterned walls and wrought-iron beds; breakfast is in a cosy room overlooking the garden, with a log-burner for chilly mornings. Both garden and welcome will delight you. The story of the garden starts in the 1970s when Barbara used to help her mother with their garden centre. The more she learned, the more her interest grew; by the time her children had flown she was hooked and began restoring and developing. The old apple trees lining the path were pruned, but not much else is recognisable now; instead, dense cottage garden planting demonstrates Barbara's eye for combinations of colour, form and foliage. This shelter protects tender plants and is a great setting for a Victorian-style glass house used for entertaining. In a natural looking stream garden damp-loving plants such as rodgersia and gunnera grow down towards a pool, while a 'Paul's Himalayan Musk' runs rampant over trellis and trees. Let Barbara take you on a tour: the history is fascinating.

Rooms	2 doubles; 1 twin/double sharing bath with 1 single: £80-£90. 1 single sharing bath with 1 twin/double: £50-£55. Singles £50.
Meals	Pub within walking distance.
Closed	Christmas & New Year.

John & Barbara Barlow
The Ridges,
Weavers Brow, Limbrick,
Chorley, PR6 9EB

Tel	+44 (0)1257 279981
Email	barbara@barlowridges.co.uk
Web	www.bedbreakfast-gardenvisits.com

Challan Hall

The wind in the trees, the boom of a bittern and birdsong. That's as noisy as it gets. On the edge of the village, delightful Charlotte's former farmhouse overlooks woods and Haweswater Reservoir; deer, squirrels and Leighton Moss Nature Reserve are your neighbours. The Cassons are well-travelled and the house, filled with a colourful collection of mementos, is happily and comfortably traditional. Expect a sofa-strewn sitting room, a smart red and polished-wood dining room and two freshly floral bedrooms (one with a tiny shower room). Morecambe Bay and the Lakes are on the doorstep – come home to lovely views and stunning sunsets.

Rooms	1 twin/double; 1 twin/double with separate bath: £75. 2 nights or more: £70 (Mon-Fri). Singles from £50.
Meals	Dinner, 2 courses, £25. Packed lunch available. Pubs 1 mile.
Closed	Rarely.

Tel	+44 (0)1524 701054
Mobile	+44 (0)7790 360776
Email	cassons@btopenworld.com
Web	www.challanhall.co.uk

Charlotte Casson
Challan Hall,
Silverdale, LA5 0UH

Viver Water Mill

Dianne and Ian have spent years renovating their attractive Lakeland stone water mill. Mentioned in the Domesday Book, it dates from the 13th-century and one of the grinding stones is set in the traditional sitting room. Arrive to afternoon tea next to the fire, or by the summerhouse overlooking the mill stream and pretty valley. Fresh bedrooms have comfy beds and coordinating fabrics. Wake to home-grown fruits, homemade jams and eggs from the hens; Dianne is happy to do supper too. Wander the beautiful garden, visit historic homes and market town Kirkby Lonsdale; great walking and cycling, and close to the A590 so a good Scotland stop-over.

Rooms	1 double; 1 double with separate bathroom: £70–£80.
Meals	Supper £10. Dinner, 2 courses, £17. Pubs/restaurants 3 miles.
Closed	Rarely.

Dianne Woof
Viver Water Mill,
Viver Lane, Hincaster, LA7 7NF

Tel	+44 (0)1539 561017
Email	info@viverwatermill.co.uk
Web	www.viverwatermill.co.uk

Broadgate

Through stone pillars is a lovely Georgian house with stunning views to the sea. Vivid blue hydrangeas make a startling contrast to its white façade and smooth green lawns. Find large elegant bedrooms with comfortable beds and antique furniture, a cosy sitting room with a wood-burner, and a beautifully laid table in the dining room. Diana, an accomplished cook, treats you to home-produced vegetables and fruits, local sausages, cakes and scones. Her walled garden, surrounded by woodland, is full of old roses, wide borders and places to sit. Head out for castles, gardens, Beatrix Potter's house, Coniston Water sailing and great walks. *Children over 10 welcome.*

Rooms	2 doubles, both with separate bath: £95. 2 singles, both with separate shower room: £55.
Meals	Dinner, 3 courses, £30. Pub 5 miles.
Closed	Rarely.

Tel	+44 (0)1229 716295
Email	dilewthwaite@bghouse.co.uk
Web	www.broadgate-house.co.uk

Diana Lewthwaite
Broadgate,
Millom, Broughton-in-Furness, LA18 5JZ

The Malabar

Surrounded by stone walls, sheep and Howgill Fells... in the glorious Yorkshire Dales National Park. Well-travelled Fiona and Graham have restored the barn next to their farmhouse into deeply comfortable, smart spaces. Graham was born in India and tea plays a big part here! Arrive to a mound of scones, meringues, triple choc brownies. Sitting and dining rooms are upstairs: high rafters, Indian art, colourful elephant side tables. Tuck into breakfast: wild boar bacon, venison sausages, veggy choices, homemade bread; lively dinners too. Sedburgh is a hop; return to a sunny terrace, toasty wood-burners, a wonderfully luxurious bed.

Rooms	3 doubles: £140-£190. 3 suites for 2: £190-£240. Singles from £120.
Meals	Afternoon tea included. Soup & charcuterie supper, £17.50 (Mon-Thurs). Friday feast, 3 courses, £30. Last Thursday of month Indian supper, £30. Pubs/restaurants 2 miles.
Closed	Mon-Wed in Jan & Feb.

Fiona Lappin
The Malabar,
Garths, Marthwaite, Sedbergh, LA10 5ED

Tel	+44 (0)1539 620200
Mobile	+44 (0)7594 550046
Email	info@themalabar.co.uk
Web	www.themalabar.co.uk

Summerhow House

In four acres of fine landscaping and fun topiary is a large and inviting home of flamboyant wallpapers and shades of aqua, lemon and rose. Stylish but laid-back, grand but unintimidating, both house and hosts are a treat. Bedrooms have gilt frames and marble fireplaces, Molton Brown goodies and garden views, there are two sitting rooms to retreat to and breakfasts to delight you – fruits from the orchard, eggs from Sizergh Castle (John's family home). Two miles from Kendal: hop on the train to the Lakes. Walkers, sailors, water-skiers, food-lovers, dog-lovers will be charmed... aspiring actors too (talk to Janey!).

Rooms	1 double, 1 twin: £80-£120.
	Singles £50-£69.
Meals	Pub/restaurant 1.5 miles.
Closed	Occasionally.

Tel	+44 (0)1539 720763
Mobile	+44 (0)7976 345558
Email	janeyfothergill@googlemail.com
Web	www.summerhowbedandbreakfast.co.uk

Janey & John Hornyold-Strickland
Summerhow House,
Shap Road, Kendal, LA9 6NY

Gilpin Mill

Come to be seriously spoiled. Down leafy lanes is a pretty white house by a mill pond, framed by pastures and trees. Steve took a year off to build new Gilpin Mill, and Jo looks after their labs and guests – beautifully. In the country farmhouse sitting room oak beams span the ceiling and a slate lintel sits above the log fire. Bedrooms are equally inviting: beds are topped with duck down, luscious bathrooms are warm underfoot. Alongside is a lovely old barn where timber was made into bobbins; in the mill pond is a salmon and trout ladder and a dam, soon to provide power for the grid. And just six cars pass a day! *Children over 10 welcome.*

Rooms	3 twin/doubles: £95-£115.
	Singles £95-£115.
Meals	Pub 2.5 miles.
Closed	Christmas.

Jo & Steve Ainsworth
Gilpin Mill,
Crook, Windermere, LA8 8LN

Tel	+44 (0)1539 568405
Email	info@gilpinmill.co.uk
Web	www.gilpinmill.co.uk

Fellside Studios

Off the beaten tourist track, a piece of paradise in the Troutbeck valley: seclusion, stylishness and breathtaking views. Prepare your own candlelit dinners, rise when the mood takes you, come and go as you please. The flower beds spill with heathers, hens cluck, and there's a decked terrace for continental breakfast in the sun – freshly prepared by your gently hospitable hosts who live in the attached house. In your studio apartment you get oak floors, slate shower rooms, immaculate kitchenettes with designer touches, DVD players, comfy chairs, luxurious towels. Wonderful.
Minimum stay: 2 nights.

Rooms	1 double, 1 twin/double, both with kitchenette: £80-£100. Singles £50-£60.
Meals	Continental breakfast. Pub/restaurant 0.5 miles.
Closed	Rarely.

Tel	+44 (0)1539 434000
Email	brian@fellsidestudios.co.uk
Web	www.fellsidestudios.co.uk

Monica & Brian Liddell
Fellside Studios,
Troutbeck, Windermere, LA23 1NN

Brownber Hall

Peter and Amanda, London escapees keen on cycling and walking, have stylishly restored this big old house, adding contemporary touches and all the comforts. The atmosphere is relaxed and sociable, there's an honesty bar with local craft beers and excellent wines, plenty of space to chill, and heaps of bedrooms with deeply comfortable beds to choose from. The rooms at the front have the views. Breakfast tables have white cloths and wild flower posies; wake to homemade granola, sausages, bacon, sourdough toast and great coffee. Join the Coast to Coast path by foot or bike, hop on the wonderfully scenic Settle to Carlisle railway. *Dog-friendly rooms available.*

Rooms	4 doubles, 2 twin/doubles: £100-£200. 1 suite for 2: £180-£220. 1 single: £70-£80. Dogs £5. Cot available, £10. Extra bed £15 per night inc. breakfast.
Meals	Dinner for walkers available by arrangement. Pub/restaurants 5 miles.
Closed	Christmas.

Peter & Amanda
Brownber Hall,
Newbiggin-on-Lune,
Kirkby Stephen, CA17 4NX

Tel +44 (0)1539 623208
Mobile +44 (0)7412 504765
Email peter@brownberhall.co.uk
Web www.brownberhall.co.uk

Wood House

Wood House sits quietly in a sea of green... Reached over stunning mountain passes where sheep cling to the roadsides, it's surrounded by trees – with Crummock Water at the end of the valley. Tony is affable and gives you an elegant drawing room with open fire, art, piano, antiques; a dining room with polished oak floor and china-laden table; comfortably furnished bedrooms with wonderful lake views. Breakfast is a Cumbrian spread with famous sausages, granola, homemade bread; there's dinner too if you want. Wordsworth House nearby, a private woodland path to the lake and Tony can sort canoeing, guided walks, mountain biking and more.

Rooms	1 double, 2 twins: £130. Singles £90.
Meals	Dinner £28.50.
	Pubs/restaurants 15-minute walk.
Closed	Rarely.

Tel	+44 (0)1768 770208
Email	wood.house@icloud.com
Web	www.woodhousebuttermere.uk

Tony McKenzie
Wood House,
Buttermere, Cockermouth, CA13 9XA

Greenah

Tucked into the hillside off a narrow lane, this 1750s smallholding is surrounded by fells, so is perfect for walkers. Absolute privacy for friends or family with your own entrance to a beamed, stone-flagged sitting room with a wood-burning stove, and cheery floral curtains. Warm bedrooms have original paintings, good beds, hot water bottles, bathrobes and a sparkling bathroom with a loo with a remarkable view. Malcolm and Marjorie are totally committed to organic food – you get a welcoming pot of tea and cake on arrival and a fabulous breakfast. They'll give you good advice about the local area too. Fell walking is not compulsory! *Children over 8 welcome.*

Rooms	1 double, 1 twin, sharing shower, let to same party only: £96-£100. Singles £60-£65.
Meals	Pubs/restaurants 3 miles.
Closed	30 November to 28 February.

Marjorie & Malcolm Emery
Greenah,
Matterdale, Penrith, CA11 0SA

Tel	+44 (0)1768 483387
Mobile	+44 (0)7767 213667
Email	info@greenah.co.uk
Web	www.greenah.co.uk

Lowthwaite

Leave your worries behind as you head up the lanes to the farmhouse tucked into the fell. Jim, ex-hiking guide, and Danish Tine are charming, helpful and well-travelled. Their barn is dotted with Tanzanian furniture and your peaceful bedrooms are in the view-filled wing. Beds are made of recycled dhow wood, sparkling bathrooms sport organic soaps; the garden room has its own patio. Breakfasts with homemade granola, bread and muffins are delicious – perhaps halloumi with mushrooms, tomatoes and egg or smoked salmon with creamed spinach. Birds galore in the garden, a trickling stream... endless fells to explore too – advice is happily given.

Rooms	2 twin/doubles: £95-£100.
	2 family rooms for 4: £100-£130.
	Singles £65-£73.
Meals	Pubs 2.5 miles. Packed lunch £4.50-£8.
Closed	Christmas.

Tel	+44 (0)1768 482343
Email	info@lowthwaiteullswater.com
Web	www.lowthwaiteullswater.com

Tine & Jim Boving Foster
Lowthwaite,
Matterdale, Penrith, CA11 0LE

Robyns Barn

Wow, fabulous views – fells and mountains in every direction including Blencathra, the most climbed fell in the Lakes. Robyns Barn is attached to the main house, and it's all yours. Step into a large, welcoming open-plan space: limewashed walls, big oak table, beams, antique pine, toasty wood-burner and plenty of DVDs, books and games. Inviting bedrooms, upstairs, have sheepskins on wooden floors. Wake when you want – Kathryn leaves a continental breakfast with local bread, muesli, fruit, yogurts; there's a farm shop close by serving excellent cooked breakfasts too. The garden has a picnic area, barbecue – and those views! *Minimum stay: 2 nights. Children over 8 welcome.*

Rooms	1 double, 1 twin, let to same party only: £90-£120.
Meals	Continental breakfast. Pubs/restaurants 1 mile.
Closed	Rarely.

Adrian & Kathryn Vaughan
Robyns Barn,
Lane Head Farm, Troutbeck,
Keswick, Penrith, CA11 0SY

Tel	+44 (0)1768 779841
Email	robynsbarn@hotmail.co.uk
Web	www.robynsbarn.co.uk

Johnby Hall

You are ensconced in the quieter part of the Lakes and have independence in this Elizabethan manor. Once a fortified Pele tower, it's a fascinating historic house yet very much a lived-in family home with a wonderful atmosphere. The airy bedrooms have a sitting room each with books, children's videos and squashy sofas. Beds have patchwork quilts, windows have stone mullions and all is peaceful. Henry gives you sturdy breakfasts by the fire in the great hall: sausages and bacon from the free-range pigs, eggs from the hens and jams from the orchard. Children will have fun – animals to feed, garden toys galore and woods to roam – and dogs are very welcome too.

Rooms	1 twin/double, with sitting room: £130. 1 family room for 4 with sitting room: £130. Singles £90. Extra bed/sofabed £20 per person per night. Extra child £15. Under-5s stay free.
Meals	Cold platters £15. Supper, 2 courses, £22.50. Pub 1 mile.
Closed	Rarely.

Tel	+44 (0)1768 483257
Email	bookings@johnbyhall.com
Web	www.johnbyhall.co.uk

Henry & Anna Howard
Johnby Hall,
Johnby, Penrith, CA11 0UU

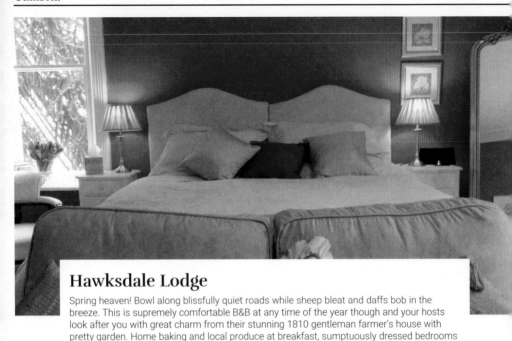

Hawksdale Lodge

Spring heaven! Bowl along blissfully quiet roads while sheep bleat and daffs bob in the breeze. This is supremely comfortable B&B at any time of the year though and your hosts look after you with great charm from their stunning 1810 gentleman farmer's house with pretty garden. Home baking and local produce at breakfast, sumptuously dressed bedrooms with plenty of space and seating, warm and inviting bathrooms with proper windows. The National Park is only six miles away for strenuous walking and cycling, the northern Lakes and fells beckon, Hadrian's wall is near. Return to something homemade and delicious. Lovely. *Minimum stay: 2 nights at Easter & New Year.*

Rooms	1 double; 1 double with separate bath: £125-£150. Singles £95-£130.
Meals	Packed lunch on request, from £6. Pubs/restaurants less than 1 mile.
Closed	Rarely.

Lorraine Russell
Hawksdale Lodge,
Dalston, Carlisle, CA5 7BX

Mobile	+44 (0)7810 641892
Email	enquiries@hawksdalelodge.co.uk
Web	www.hawksdalelodge.co.uk

Hopton House, page 327

Yorkshire

Ponden Hall, page 359

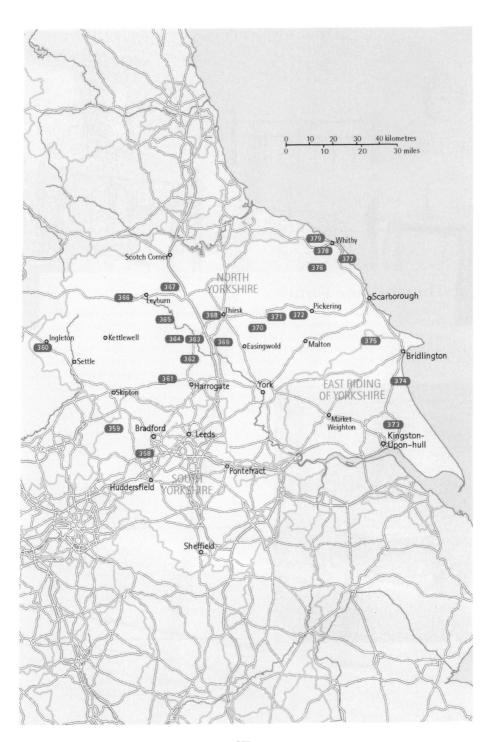

0   10   20   30   40 kilometres
0   10   20   30 miles

Scotch Corner

NORTH YORKSHIRE

379 Whitby
378
377
376

367
366 Leyburn
365
368 Thirsk
371 372 Pickering
Scarborough
370
360 Ingleton
364 363
369 Easingwold
Malton
375
Kettlewell
Settle
362
Bridlington
361
EAST RIDING OF YORKSHIRE
374
Skipton
Harrogate
York
359 Bradford Leeds
Market Weighton
373
358
Kingston-Upon-hull
Pontefract
Huddersfield
SOUTH YORKSHIRE

Sheffield

Thurst House Farm

This solid Pennine farmhouse, its stone mullion windows denoting 17th-century origins, is English to the core. Your warm, gracious hosts give guests a cosy and carpeted sitting room with an open fire in winter and shelves of books to browse; bedrooms are equally generous, with inviting, very comfortable brass beds, lovely antique linen and fresh flowers. The garden has masses of roses, sunny places to sit, a hammock to snooze in and beautiful views. Tuck into homemade bread, marmalade and jams at breakfast, and good traditional English dinners, too – just the thing for walkers who've trekked the Calderdale or the Pennine Way.

Rooms	1 double: £80.
	1 family room for 4: £80-£160.
	Singles by arrangement.
	No charge for children under 4.
Meals	Dinner, 4 courses, £25. BYO. Packed
	lunch £5. Restaurants within 0.5 miles.
Closed	Christmas.

David & Judith Marriott
Thurst House Farm,
Soyland, Ripponden,
Sowerby Bridge, HX6 4NN

Tel	+44 (0)1422 822820
Mobile	+44 (0)7759 619043
Email	judith@thursthousefarm.co.uk
Web	www.thursthousefarm.co.uk

Ponden Hall

A house brimming with atmosphere and said to be the inspiration for *Wuthering Heights*. Julie's knowledge of the history is impressive and she offers tours of her fascinating home. Arrive for tea and home-baked cake and soak up the mullion windows, huge flagstones, period pieces and original paintings. Bedrooms have just the right balance of luxury and individuality: an amazing box bed, rocking horse, raftered ceilings – and log stoves in two. A full Yorkshire breakfast is served in the magnificent main hall. Walk the Pennine Way, hop on a steam train at Keighley; Haworth is close too – for all things Brontë and independent shops.

Rooms	2 doubles: £95-£180.
	1 family room for 4: £160.
Meals	Pubs/restaurants 10-minute walk.
Closed	24-30 December.

Tel	+44 (0)1535 648608	**Julie Akhurst**
Email	stay@ponden.force9.co.uk	Ponden Hall,
Web	www.ponden-hall.co.uk	Ponden Lane, Stanbury,
		Haworth, Keighley, BD22 0HR

Lane House

Pam and art restorer Richard are chatty and friendly – they love having guests, and are happy to advise on trips. Their converted barn has an artistic vibe throughout. The big, attractive open-plan living space has a galleried landing above; airy bedrooms have soaring beams, striking light fittings, colourful throws; bathrooms are smart. Pam likes to cook so you're in for a treat: tuck in to local produce, eggs from the hens, homemade granola, breads and jams; delicious, perhaps Lebanese or Moroccan, dishes for dinner too. The 50 acres are yours to wander: farmland, woods, a beck – and there's a four-mile Heritage Trail to Bentham. *Pets by arrangement.*

Rooms	2 doubles: £89-£110. Singles £70. Extra bed/sofabed £30 per person per night.
Meals	Dinner £15. BYO. Pubs/restaurants 0.5 miles.
Closed	Christmas.

Pam Zahler
Lane House,
Fowgill, High Bentham,
Lancaster, LA2 7AH

Tel	+44 (0)15242 61998
Email	pamzahler@hotmail.com
Web	www.lanehouseandcottage.co.uk

Cold Cotes

Sue and Mark give you relaxation and a dollop of contemporary chic in their 1890s farmhouse on the edge of the Yorkshire Dales. Smart bedrooms have sitting areas with garden views; those in the barn are just as swish and comfortable. Wake for a delicious breakfast served at separate tables: porridge, local bacon and sausages and homemade jams. There's a sitting room to settle in too with stacks of books and squashy sofas. Outside you'll find a beautiful woodland walk, impressive sweeping borders and a cobblestone walk along a stream. A little lawned area surrounded by cherry trees has a perfect seating spot. *Minimum stay: 2 nights.*

Rooms	2 twin/doubles: £89.
	6 suites for 2 : £99-£109.
Meals	Cold platters & snacks available.
	Pub/restaurant 2 miles.
Closed	Mid-December to mid-February.

Tel	+44 (0)1423 770937
Mobile	+44 (0)7970 713334
Email	info@coldcotes.com
Web	www.coldcotes.com

Sue Bailey & Mark Dyson
Cold Cotes,
Felliscliffe, Harrogate, HG3 2LW

The Old Vicarage

South Stainley is a small village, with pub, church and this fine vicarage, six miles from Ripon, ten from Harrogate. Come for the races, the Dales... Sleep peacefully in a charming room up under the eaves. Julia has decorated her guest room unfussily, tucked in a sofa and added an antique wardrobe and blanket chest. The bathroom's really smart and big, with separate shower and bath. Linger over your Aga breakfast – full English, scrambled eggs, smoked salmon – in the lofty new garden room with leafy views, pastel colours, original art. You're welcome to use the swimming pool and tennis court, and you can walk to the pub for dinner. *Minimum stay: 2 nights in high season.*

Rooms	1 double: £90–£120.
Meals	Pubs/restaurants 5-minute walk.
Closed	Rarely.

Julia Roe
The Old Vicarage,
South Stainley, Harrogate, HG3 3NE

Tel	+44 (0)1423 770216
Mobile	+44 (0)7956 154786
Email	info@oldvicarageharrogate.co.uk
Web	www.oldvicarageharrogate.co.uk

Mallard Grange

Perfect farmhouse B&B. Hens, cats, sheepdogs wander the garden, an ancient apple tree leans against the wall, guests unwind and feel part of the family. Enter the rambling, deep-shuttered 16th-century farmhouse, cosy with well-loved family pieces, and feel at peace with the world. Breakfast is generous – homemade muffins, poached pears with cinnamon, a sizzling full Monty. A winding steep stair leads to big, friendly bedrooms, two cheerful others await in the converted 18th-century smithy, and Maggie's enthusiasm for this glorious area is as genuine as her love of doing B&B. It's a gem!
Over 12s welcome.

Rooms	4 twin/doubles: £85-£125.
	Singles £85-£110.
Meals	Pubs/restaurants 10-minute drive.
Closed	Christmas & New Year.

Tel	+44 (0)1765 620242
Mobile	+44 (0)7720 295918
Email	maggie@mallardgrange.co.uk
Web	www.mallardgrange.co.uk

Maggie Johnson
Mallard Grange,
Aldfield, Ripon, HG4 3BE

Laverton Hall

The hall is a beauty, even on a dull day, and the village is a dream. Half an hour from Harrogate find space, beauty, history (it's 400 years old), three walled gardens and comfort in great measure: beloved antiques, a rocking horse in the hall, feather pillows, thick white towels. Sumptuous breakfasts include seasonal fruit salad, croissants, cereals and a full English spread. The sunny guest sitting room is elegant and charming, the cream and white twin and the snug little single have long views to the river. The area is rich with abbeys and great houses, and then there are the glorious Dales to be explored.

Rooms	1 twin/double: £100.
	1 single: £70.
Meals	Pubs/restaurants 2 miles.
Closed	Christmas.

Rachel Wilson
Laverton Hall,
Laverton, Ripon, HG4 3SX

Tel	+44 (0)1765 650274
Mobile	+44 (0)7711 086385
Email	rachel.k.wilson@hotmail.co.uk
Web	www.lavertonhall.co.uk

Firs Farm

The landscape is rural and rolling, the lanes are quiet, and Healey is pretty-as-a-picture. Richard and Sarah, relaxed and genial, offer homemade cakes and coffee and the cosy feel of their home will put you instantly at ease. Sit by the fire, sleep well in comfortable bedrooms, admire the vases of flowers in every corner. Sarah uses local ingredients for breakfast: dry cure bacon, award-winning black pudding, Wensleydale butter, home-laid eggs, kippers, or a continental with croissants and jams.

Set off afterwards for long walks in the beautiful Dales. Admire the views from the walled garden, spot all the different birds; there are lively market towns, castles and stately homes nearby. Further afield, Harrogate is 45 minutes – for the famous Betty's, Turkish Baths and great shops. *Children over 10 welcome.*

Rooms	2 doubles; 1 twin/double with separate bath/shower: £90-£115. Singles £65-£75. Extra bed/sofabed £40 per person per night.
Meals	Packed lunch £7. Pubs/restaurants 1 mile.
Closed	Christmas & New Year.

Tel	+44 (0)1765 688910
Email	sarah@firsfarmbandb.co.uk
Web	www.firsfarmbandb.co.uk

Richard & Sarah Townsend
Firs Farm,
Healey, Ripon, HG4 4LH

Stow House

Past ancient stone walls and fields of lambs you reach sleepy Aysgarth and this dignified rectory. Step inside to find – Shoreditch pizzazz! Sarah and Phil have swapped the world of London advertising for a dream house in the Dales; she does cocktails, he does breakfasts and their take on Victoriana is inspiring. Floors, banisters and sash windows have been restored, stairs carpeted in plush red, sofas covered in zinging velvet. Bathrooms are wow, bedrooms are soothing and the papier-mâché hare's head above the bar says it all. A stroll down the hill are the Aysgarth Falls, beloved of Ruskin, Wordsworth and Turner. *Minimum stay: 2 nights at weekends.*

Rooms	6 doubles: £110-£175. 1 family room for 3: £175. Extra bed/sofabed £10-£20 per person per night.
Meals	Pubs/restaurants 5-minute walk.
Closed	Rarely.

Sarah & Phil Bucknall
Stow House,
Aysgarth, Leyburn, DL8 3SR

Tel	+44 (0)1969 663635
Email	info@stowhouse.co.uk
Web	www.stowhouse.co.uk

The Garden Suite

Step from the terrace into a house full of creativity and colour. You stay in the old converted grain store, which has its own entrance and is all on one floor; find cosy places to sit and relax in your deeply comfortable suite. Colin and Wendy (both keen gardeners) are warm souls. They are keen for you to feel at home and their breakfasts include home-grown produce (strawberries, figs, raspberries, veg...), granola, yogurt and a delicious full English. Outside is a stunning creation of perfect potagers, pathways and pots of lavender, wildflower meadows, secret areas and wisteria-clad walls; there's a summer house to sit in too, while Indian Runner ducks, chickens, the friendly spaniel and eccentric pigs, Esmerelda and Finlay, add to the relaxed vibe. *Over 12s welcome.*

Rooms	1 suite for 2: £110. Extra bed/sofabed £25-£40 per person per night.
Meals	Pubs/restaurants 20-minute walk.
Closed	Christmas.

Tel	+44 (0)1748 832586
Mobile	+44 (0)7596 409632
Email	craggslane@msn.com
Web	www.craggslane.com

Colin & Wendy Gerrard
The Garden Suite,
Craggs Lane Farm, Tunstall,
Richmond, DL10 7RB

Carlton House

Quietly tucked into a corner of the sedate green, a short stride from the pub, lies a stylishly renovated 18th-century farmhouse. The old wash house, tractor shed and stable have become airy, chic, characterful rooms with beams and fabulous bathrooms. In summer, pull up a chair in a pretty yard with hanging baskets or find a tranquil spot in the charmingly secret garden. The dining room with open fire is a delight, so linger over a breakfast of delicious local produce, then set off for market towns, dales and moors. There's a big-hearted family feel here – Denise's oat and raisin crunchies and soda bread are to die for! Lovely.

Rooms	2 doubles, 1 twin/double: £75-£85. Singles £55-£65. Extra bed/sofabed £20-£30 per person per night.
Meals	Pub/restaurant 2-minute walk.
Closed	Rarely.

Denise & David Mason
Carlton House,
Sandhutton, Thirsk, YO7 4RW

Tel	+44 (0)1845 587381
Email	info@carltonbarns.co.uk
Web	www.carltonbarns.co.uk

Cundall Lodge Farm

Ancient chestnuts, crunchy drive, sheep grazing, hens free-ranging. This four-square Georgian farmhouse could be straight out of Central Casting. Smart, traditional rooms have damask sofas, comfy armchairs, bright wallpapers and views to Sutton Bank's White Horse or the river Swale – and tea and oven-fresh cakes welcome you. Spotless bedrooms are inviting: pretty fabrics, antiques, flowers, Roberts radios. This is a working farm and the breakfast table groans with eggs from the hens, homemade jams and local bacon. The garden and river walks guarantee peace, and David and Caroline are generous and delightful. *Over 14s welcome.*

Rooms	1 double, 2 twin/doubles: £90-£110.
Meals	Packed lunch £7.
	Pubs/restaurants 2 miles.
Closed	Christmas, New Year.

Tel	+44 (0)1423 360203
Mobile	+44 (0)7773 494260
Email	enquiries@cundall-lodgefarm.co.uk
Web	www.cundall-lodgefarm.co.uk

Caroline Barker
Cundall Lodge Farm,
Cundall, York, YO61 2RN

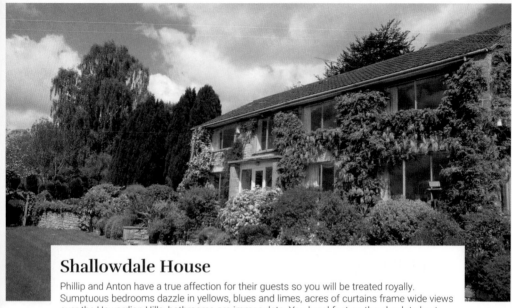

Shallowdale House

Phillip and Anton have a true affection for their guests so you will be treated royally. Sumptuous bedrooms dazzle in yellows, blues and limes, acres of curtains frame wide views over the Howardian Hills, bathrooms are immaculate. You breakfast on the absolute best: fresh fruit compotes, dry-cured bacon or Whitby kippers, homemade rolls and marmalade. Admire the amazing garden, then walk off in any direction straight from the house. Return to a cosily elegant drawing room with a fire in winter, and an enticing library. Dinner is a real treat – coffee and chocolates before you crawl up to bed? Bliss. *Over 12s welcome.*

Rooms	2 twin/doubles; 1 double with separate bath/shower: £130-£165. Singles £100-£125.
Meals	Dinner, 4 courses, £45. Pub 0.5 miles.
Closed	Christmas & New Year.

Anton van der Horst & Phillip Gill
Shallowdale House,
West End, Ampleforth, YO62 4DY

Tel	+44 (0)1439 788325
Email	stay@shallowdalehouse.co.uk
Web	www.shallowdalehouse.co.uk

Croft House

A welcoming house in the picturesque village of Harome between the North York Moors and the Howardian Hills. Find inviting bedrooms with pampering extras: bath robes, fluffy towels, spa treats and flowers. Come down to a scrumptious breakfast of local farm shop sausages, bacon and black pudding, eggs from the hens and freshly baked bread. For a lighter start, choose croissants or the breakfast booster – a refreshing mix of fruit, toasted jumbo oats and honey-soaked nuts. Frances loves to bake, so look forward to homemade cake each afternoon of your stay. There's a snug sitting room with books and magazines to delve into; decamp to the summerhouse in the garden on warm days. Dinner is a stroll away – try the acclaimed Star Inn, pretty and thatched with seasonal menus and leafy garden.

Rooms	2 doubles: £120-£130.
Meals	Pub 5-minute walk.
Closed	Christmas & New Year.

Tel	+44 (0)1439 772320
Mobile	+44 (0)7722 912864
Email	crofthouseharome@gmail.com
Web	www.crofthouseharome.co.uk

Frances Outram
Croft House,
High Street, Harome, YO62 5JE

The Stable Annex

You have independence from the main house, and you can come and go from this snug self-contained space that's been created out of an old stable. Choose a picnic spot in the garden or orchard, arrange to barbecue your supper, head off on walks down the footpath from the end of the garden. It's a household of foodies and breakfast, delivered on a tray, includes fresh orange juice and local sausage and bacon sandwiches, or pastries, Bircher muesli and berries from the garden. On Fridays and Saturdays in the winter you can join Tom and Sara for dinner – or have it in your room; in summer it's often served outside. French doors open to a patio with outdoor seating and pretty views over flowers and veg patch. Wander out to sit by the warming firepit and gaze up at the stars before tucking in for the night.

Rooms	1 double: £90-£115. Extra bed/sofabed £15 per person per night.
Meals	Dinner, 3 courses, £40; Friday & Saturday only, on request. Pubs/restaurants 15-minute drive.
Closed	Christmas, New Year & occasionally.

Sara Hall
The Stable Annex,
Orchard House, Marton,
Sinnington, YO62 6RD

Tel	+44 (0)1751 430616
Email	sarahallyork@gmail.com

Dowthorpe Hall

Caroline is lovely, cooking is her passion and she trawls the county for the best; fish and seafood from Hornsea, Dexter beef, game from the local shoot; her fruits and veg are home-grown. All is served in a sumptuous Georgian dining room by flickering candlelight, after which you retire to a comfortable drawing room; this is a marvellously elegant, and happy, house. Sleep peacefully on a luxurious mattress, wake to the aroma of bacon, sausages, eggs and home-baked bread. There are acres of gorgeous garden to roam – orchards, pathways, potager and pond – and a trio of historic houses to visit.

Rooms	1 twin/double; 1 double with separate bathroom: £100-£110. Singles £70.
Meals	Dinner £25. Pubs 0.25-5 miles.
Closed	Rarely.

Tel	+44 (0)1964 562235
Email	john.holtby@farming.co.uk
Web	www.dowthorpehall.com

John & Caroline Holtby
Dowthorpe Hall,
Skirlaugh, Hull, HU11 5AE

Village Farm

Tucked behind houses and shops, this was once the village farm with land stretching to the coast. Now the one-storey buildings overlooking a courtyard are large bedrooms in gorgeous colours with luxurious touches. Chrysta, who moved from London, is living her dream and looks after you well: baths are deep, beds crisply comfortable, heating is underfoot. Delicious breakfasts are served at wooden tables in a cheerful light room and if you don't want to venture out you can have supper on a tray – homemade bread, cheese and fruit. Stride the cliffs, watch birds at Flamborough Head or make for Spurn Point – remote and lovely. *Pets by arrangement.*

Rooms	1 double, 1 twin/double: £85.
	1 family room for 4: £100. Singles £65.
Meals	Supper £8.50.
	Pubs/restaurants 3 miles.
Closed	Rarely.

Chrysta Newman
Village Farm,
Back Street, Skipsea,
Driffield, YO25 8SW

Tel	+44 (0)1262 468479
Email	info@villagefarmskipsea.co.uk
Web	www.villagefarmskipsea.co.uk

The Wold Cottage

Drive through mature trees, and a proper entrance with signs, to a listed Georgian manor house in 300 glorious acres; tea awaits in the guest sitting room. The graceful dining room has heartlifting views across the landscaped gardens, and there are many original features: fan-lights, high ceilings, broad staircases. Bedrooms are sumptuous, traditional, with lots of thoughtful extras: chocolates, biscuits, monogrammed waffle robes. You are warmed by straw bale heating, and the food is local and delicious. An award-winning breakfast sets you up for a day of discovery: visit RSPB Bempton Cliffs, and the Wolds that have inspired David Hockney. *Minimum stay: 2 nights at weekends.*

Rooms	3 doubles, 2 twins: £100-£130. 1 family room for 4: £100-£165. Singles £60-£75.
Meals	Supper £28. Wine from £15.
Closed	Rarely.

Tel	+44 (0)1262 470696
Mobile	+44 (0)7811 203336
Email	katrina@woldcottage.com
Web	www.woldcottage.com

Derek & Katrina Gray
The Wold Cottage,
Wold Newton, Driffield, YO25 3HL

The Farmhouse

Chris and Clare own and run a Swiss ski chalet and their traditional farmhouse has the same vibe: friendly, communal, open-house. It's set in two acres of gardens at the centre of a 100-acre estate enclosed by ancient oak woodland. Foodies will thrive: tea and cake in the garden or next to the log fire when you arrive; packed lunches for day trips; lavish picnics. Weekend dinners include local game, fish from Whitby, cider from the monks at Ampleforth. Sleep well

in stylish rooms: the airy Garden Room, the Pigeon Loft with its double-ended bath, the sleekly simple Potting Shed that's tucked in the garden and has its own kitchen. You're in the heart of the North York Moors with hikes and bike trails galore; the nearest pub is a ten-minute walk, Whitby and the coast are close. Take the steam train from the village to Whitby or Pickering, explore the spectacular coastline. You can pre-book a star gazing session with an expert astronomer. *Minimum stay: 2 nights; 3 nights in the annexe. Over 16s welcome.*

Rooms	2 doubles: £125. 1 suite for 2: £140. 1 annexe for 2 with kitchen: £165. Singles £90-£125.
Meals	Dinner £45, Fridays & Saturdays; rest of week by arrangement. Pubs/restaurants 10-minute walk.
Closed	January – March.

Chris & Clare Carr
The Farmhouse,
Orchard Farm, Orchard Lane,
Goathland, Whitby, YO22 5JX

Tel +44 (0)1947 896391
Email enquiries@thefarmhouseyorkshire.co.uk
Web www.thefarmhouseyorkshire.co.uk

Thorpe Hall

Arrive and listen: nothing, bar the wind in the trees and the odd seagull. The eye gathers glimmering sea and mighty headland, the final edge of the moors... are there still smugglers? This old listed house smells of polish and flowers, the drawing room breathes history. Angelique is a delight and has furnished it all, including TV-free bedrooms (one downstairs), with an eclectic mix of old and new; wonky walls and creaky floors add to the atmospheric feel. She's hung contemporary art on ancient walls and made a veg patch with daughter Phoebe. David helps out with simple breakfast when he's not globetrotting. The very opposite of stuffy. *Minimum stay: 2 nights. Pets by arrangement.*

Rooms	3 doubles, 1 twin; 3 doubles, sharing separate bath & shower rooms: £75-£90. Singles £70-£80. Extra bed/sofabed £15 per person per night.
Meals	Pubs 1 mile.
Closed	Usually Christmas & January.

Tel	+44 (0)1947 880667
Email	thorpehall@gmail.com
Web	www.thorpe-hall.co.uk

Angelique Russell
Thorpe Hall,
Middlewood Lane, Fylingthorpe,
Whitby, YO22 4TT

Union Place

A listed Adam Georgian townhouse – elegance epitomised. Lofty well-proportioned rooms with polished floors and cornices and fireplaces intact are delightfully dotted with sophisticated, quirky *objets*: bead-and-embroidery lampshades and chandeliers, bone china, a small mirrored Indian ceramic child's dress – and your urbane host Richard's accomplished paintings. Bedrooms, one painted duck egg blue, one green with floral wallpaper, are beautiful, with lots of lace and fine linen; the claw-foot roll top in the shared bathroom cuts a dash. Breakfast is unbeatable... then it's off to explore the North Yorkshire Moors. Superb. *Pets by arrangement.*

Rooms	2 doubles sharing bath, extra wc available: £80.
Meals	Pubs/restaurants within walking distance.
Closed	Christmas.

Richard & Jane Pottas	**Tel** +44 (0)1947 605501
Union Place,	**Email** pottas1@btinternet.com
9 Upgang Lane, Whitby, YO21 3DT	**Web** www.unionplacewhitby.co.uk

Nineteen

You'll be fascinated ambling round Whitby with its cobbled streets, independent shops and deliciously dark literary links – there's a great beach and Rick Stein recommended fish and chips too. Return to the prettiest terrace in town where the first floor is yours, the beds are for conking out in extreme comfort and light streams in through sash windows with shutters intact. Peter and Lucy have good taste, original art and exquisite antiques so everywhere you look there's something beautiful. Breakfast is hidden in your own mini fridge: bread from Bothams, jams, yogurts and proper ground coffee. Walkers can tramp straight onto the moors. *Minimum stay: 2 nights.*

Rooms	2 doubles both with separate bathroom: £75-£95.
Meals	Pubs/restaurants 3-minute walk.
Closed	24-26 December.

Tel	+44 (0)1947 606385
Email	info@19sthildas.uk
Web	www.19sthildas.uk

Lucy Weller & Peter Trickett
Nineteen,
19 St Hilda's Terrace, Whitby, YO21 3AE

North East

Swinburne Castle, page 385

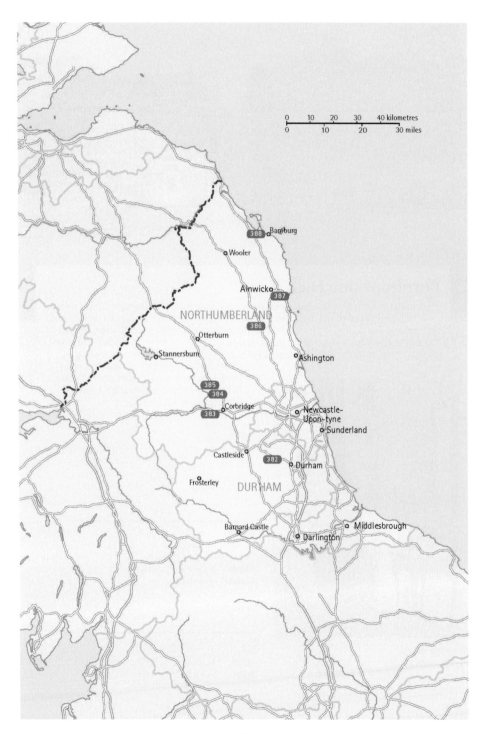

Burnhopeside Hall

It's peaceful, traditional, pristine, and nothing is too much trouble for Christine. Welcome to a listed Georgian house on a 475-acre estate near Durham, its elegant sitting rooms furnished with pictures and photos, log fires and big sofas, billiards and a baby grand, and great sash windows with garden and woodland views. Resident springer spaniels Max and Barney love all dogs, so bring yours; stroll the magnificent lawns, cycle alongside the river. Breakfast? Eggs from the hens, bacon from the pigs, honey and fruits from the walled garden: a perfect start to the day. Enormous beds, luxurious linen and fresh flowers await your return.

Rooms	6 doubles: £100-£120.
	1 apartment for 6: £100-£150.
	Singles £70-£85.
Meals	Pubs/restaurants 4 miles.
Closed	Rarely.

Christine Hewitt
Burnhopeside Hall,
Durham Road, Lanchester, DH7 0TL

Tel	+44 (0)1207 520222
Email	harmerchristine@hotmail.com
Web	www.burnhopeside-hall.co.uk

3 Ada Crescent

Rosemary, warm and cultured, and Garlic the terrier, greet you with homemade cake and encourage you to feel at home. Her bright home and its bookshelves reflect her interests in art and history. She'll happily arrange collection from the railway station or bus stop; a packed lunch for a day out – perhaps to Hadrian's Wall, or the races – will be no problem either. Breakfasts in the kitchen/dining room can be as leisurely as you like, with homemade jams and muesli and traditionally cured bacon.

And you're welcome to take your coffee and a newspaper and relax in the little courtyard or sitting room before strolling across the park to the Abbey, museum or market. Join one of several heritage walks around the town or hike through the wonderful National Park which incorporates the International Dark Skies Park. Return for a hot bath, much warmth and comfort and a short stroll into town for supper. *Children over 10 welcome.*

Rooms	1 twin/double with separate bathroom: £90–£100. Singles £60. Extra room available.
Meals	Pubs/restaurants 10-minute walk.
Closed	Rarely.

Tel	+44 (0)1434 694242
Mobile	+44 (0)7850 375535
Email	rosemary.stobart@btinternet.com

Rosemary Stobart
3 Ada Crescent,
Hexham, NE46 3DR

Errington House

Carolyn is a superb cook; breakfast on homemade bread, jams and marmalade, eggs from their hens, local sausages and bacon. You eat around the big dining table with other guests. The Dowies' handsome farmhouse and gardens are deeply peaceful and you can make yourself completely at home. Watch birds from a comfortable chair outside, sit and read in your airy bedroom or take a cup of tea to the guest sitting room and throw another log on the fire. You can walk from the house (or drive ten minutes) to Hadrian's Wall. Corbridge and Hexham have plenty of interest for an afternoon out and hum with shops, cafés and restaurants. Bring a group of friends for a walking holiday if you stay between June and October – Lex is hugely knowledgeable about the county. *Minimum stay: 2 nights at weekends.*

Rooms	3 twin/double; 1 twin/double with separate bathroom: £75-£100. Singles £85-£95.
Meals	Pubs/restaurants 5 miles.
Closed	Christmas & New Year.

Carolyn Dowie
Errington House,
Humshaugh, HexhamNE46 4HP

Tel	+44 (0)1434 672389
Email	carolyn@erringtonwalks.co.uk
Web	www.erringtonwalks.co.uk

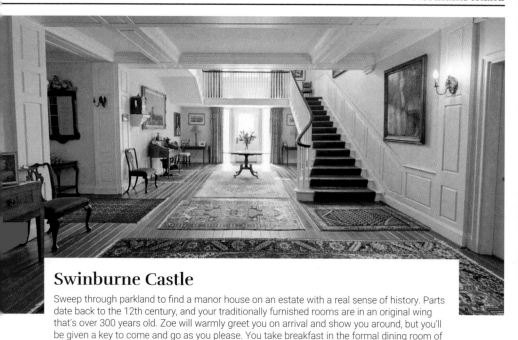

Swinburne Castle

Sweep through parkland to find a manor house on an estate with a real sense of history. Parts date back to the 12th century, and your traditionally furnished rooms are in an original wing that's over 300 years old. Zoe will warmly greet you on arrival and show you around, but you'll be given a key to come and go as you please. You take breakfast in the formal dining room of the main house – local produce and home-laid eggs – and you're welcome to make use of the garden and tennis court. Walking routes pass by the house and the area is great for cycling. Good pubs and restaurants nearby include the Barrasford Arms, a half hour walk away. It's an easy drive to Hadrian's Wall, as well as the Northumberland National Park, Kielder Water and Forest Park.

Rooms	1 double, 1 twin sharing bathroom, let to same party only: £85.
Meals	Pubs/restaurants 3 miles.
Closed	Christmas & New Year.

Mobile	+44 (0)7786 610542
Email	ztrg24@yahoo.co.uk

Zoe Murphy
Swinburne Castle,
Swinburne, Hexham, NE48 4DQ

Thistleyhaugh

Enid is one of those very special people who lifts your heart with her generosity of spirit, warmth and humour. Her passions are pictures, cooking and people, and you will be fed exceptionally well too – breakfasts are delicious and include local farm eggs. Choose any of the four large, lovely bedrooms and stay the week; they are awash with old paintings, silk fabrics and crisp linen. Wake refreshed and nip downstairs, past the log fire, to a laden and sociable table, head off afterwards to find 720 acres of organic farmland and a few million more of the Cheviots beyond. Wonderful hosts, a glorious region, a happy house.

Rooms	3 doubles, 1 twin: £100. Singles £90. Extra bed/sofabed £15 per person per night.
Meals	Light supper available. Pub/restaurant 2 miles.
Closed	Christmas, New Year & January.

Henry & Enid Nelless
Thistleyhaugh,
Longhorsley, Morpeth, NE65 8RG

Tel	+44 (0)1665 570098
Email	thistleyhaugh@hotmail.com
Web	www.thistleyhaugh.co.uk

Bilton Barns

A solidly good farmhouse B&B whose lifeblood is still farming. The Jacksons know every inch of the surrounding countryside and coast; it's a pretty spot. They farm the 400 acres of mixed arable land that sweeps down to the sea yet always have time for guests. Dorothy creates an easy and sociable atmosphere with welcoming pots of tea and convivial breakfasts – all delicious and locally sourced. Comfortable, smartly done bedrooms have a traditional feel, bathrooms have underfloor heating, the huge conservatory is filled with sofas and chairs and there's an elegant guest sitting room with an open fire and views to the sea.

Rooms	1 double, 1 twin, 1 four-poster: £84-£95. Singles £47.50-£75.
Meals	Packed lunch £4-£6. Pub/restaurant 2 miles.
Closed	Christmas.

Tel	+44 (0)1665 830427
Mobile	+44 (0)7939 262028
Email	dorothy@biltonbarns.com
Web	www.biltonbarns.com

Brian & Dorothy Jackson
Bilton Barns,
Alnmouth, Alnwick, NE66 2TB

Post Office House

Claire and ex-chef Simon have converted the old Belford post office with flair. The red pillar box is still in use, jaunty stamp fabrics and post box blinds give you colourful reminders, and the wood-burning stove in the dining room keeps it all cosy. Bedrooms have robes, comfy chairs, brimming trays and espresso machines; morning sun in one, evening rays in the other. Breakfast at one convivial table is a local and home-baked spread: Bamburgh bacon and sausages, Craster kippers, homemade baked beans and marmalade. Pretty garden and heaps to do nearby: unspoilt Northumbrian beaches, Farne Islands, castles, brilliant walks. *Minimum stay: 2 nights in high season. Over 15s welcome.*

Rooms	2 doubles, 1 twin: £89-£105. Singles £79-£95.
Meals	Pub within 5-minute walk & pubs/restaurants 5 miles.
Closed	Rarely.

Claire Jarmain
Post Office House,
2 Church Street, Belford, NE70 7LS

Tel	+44 (0)1668 219622
Email	enquiries@postofficehouse.com
Web	www.postofficehouse.com

Long Acre Farm, page 174

Wales

Pengwern Country House, page 406

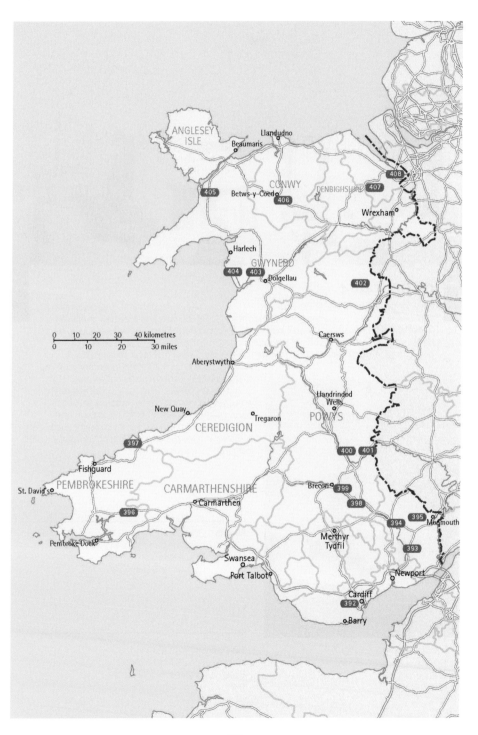

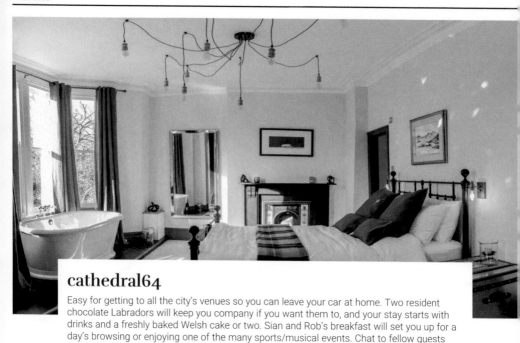

cathedral64

Easy for getting to all the city's venues so you can leave your car at home. Two resident chocolate Labradors will keep you company if you want them to, and your stay starts with drinks and a freshly baked Welsh cake or two. Sian and Rob's breakfast will set you up for a day's browsing or enjoying one of the many sports/musical events. Chat to fellow guests over compote, yogurt and granola followed by a cooked spread of local sausage, black pudding, duck eggs, tomatoes, mushrooms, baked beans... or pastries from an award-winning Scandinavian bakery. Find a piano that you're welcome to play and comfy seats for settling down with the papers. There's a good pub next door, a popular Italian restaurant down the road and plenty more places for eating out in nearby leafy Pontcanna village.

Rooms	2 doubles: £99-£140. 1 suite for 2 with separate bathroom: £120-£150.
Meals	Pubs/restaurants 1-minute walk.
Closed	Christmas & New Year.

Rob & Sian Doyle
cathedral64,
64 Cathedral Road,
Cardiff, CF11 9LL

Tel	+44 (0)2920 191138
Mobile	+44 (0)7435 611880
Email	info@cathedral64.com
Web	www.cathedral64.com

Allt-y-bela

It's a rare treat to come here. This beautiful medieval farmhouse sits in its own secret valley and is reached down a narrow lane. Built between 1420 and 1599, Allt-y-bela is now perfectly presented for the 21st century. You'll find conviviality and warmth, soaring beams, period furniture and an enormous log fire. Bedrooms soothe with limewashed walls, fabulous beds, stunning art. Wander through the magical garden created by the owner, Chelsea Gold Medal winner Arne Maynard. Find formal topiary, dramatic earth sculpture and gentle native planting which allows the garden to melt into the landscape with no boundaries at all. In the spring there are massed snowdrops and wild narcissus which give way to carpets of primroses and bluebells. Blossom abounds in pleached fruit trees and all through the hedgerows, perfect vegetables are freshly picked for the table. Summer brings wild orchids to the fields around the house and innumerable other rare and beautiful wildflowers. Visitors can relax here all day or walk and explore the valley with its streams, coppiced woods, pastures and drove-ways.

Rooms	2 doubles: £200. Stays of 2 nights or more: 1st night £200, subsequent nights £150.
Meals	Farmhouse supper £30. Pubs/restaurants 3 miles.
Closed	Rarely.

Mobile	+44 (0)7892 403103
Email	alltybela@icloud.com
Web	www.alltybela.co.uk

William Collinson & Arne Maynard
Allt-y-bela,
Llangwm Ucha, Usk, NP15 1EZ

Penpergwm Lodge

A rambling Edwardian house... Margot and Maud, resident pug and terrier, make a characterful welcoming party and you step into a warmly painted hall with old rugs on wooden boards. Simon and Catriona give you tea and biscuits in a sunny, lived-in sitting room: heaps of books, family bits and pieces, squashy sofa by the fire. Breakfast is served here, or round the long table in the dining room. Bedrooms are time-worn trad with embroidered covers and chintz; bathrooms are a skip across the landing. Enjoy the beautiful garden with parterre, potager, orchard and brick follies, bring a jumper in winter and don't mind the worn corners... a charming home.

Rooms	2 twins both with separate bath: £85. Singles £55.
Meals	Pub 2 miles.
Closed	Rarely.

Catriona Boyle
Penpergwm Lodge,
Penpergwm, Abergavenny, NP7 9AS

Tel	+44 (0)1873 840208
Email	boyle@penpergwm.co.uk
Web	www.penplants.com

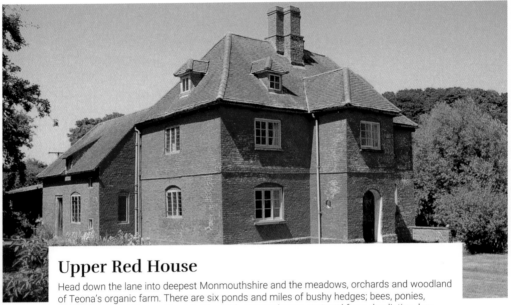

Upper Red House

Head down the lane into deepest Monmouthshire and the meadows, orchards and woodland of Teona's organic farm. There are six ponds and miles of bushy hedges; bees, ponies, peafowl and wild flowers flourish. The 17th-century house, restored from dereliction, has lovely views, flagstones and oak, limewashed walls and a magical feel. Up steep stairs are rustic bedrooms with beams, lots of books, no TV; the attic rooms get the best views of all. Bathrooms are simple, one has a huge old roll top tub. After a good vegetarian breakfast at the long kitchen table take a farm tour, explore Offa's Dyke or the Wye Valley – and enjoy the silence.

Rooms	1 double; 1 double sharing bath with 2 singles, let to same party only: £80-£95. 2 singles sharing bath with double, let to same party only: £35-£45.
Meals	Vegetarian packed lunch £8. Pubs/restaurants 3.5 miles.
Closed	Rarely.

Tel	+44 (0)1600 780501
Email	upperredhouse@mac.com
Web	www.upperredhouse.co.uk

Teona Dorrien-Smith
Upper Red House,
Llanfihangel-Ystern-Llewern,
Monmouth, NP25 5HL

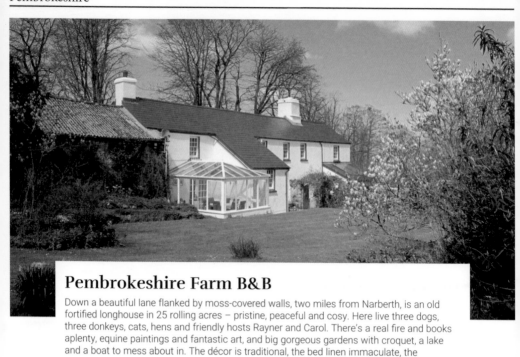

Pembrokeshire Farm B&B

Down a beautiful lane flanked by moss-covered walls, two miles from Narberth, is an old fortified longhouse in 25 rolling acres – pristine, peaceful and cosy. Here live three dogs, three donkeys, cats, hens and friendly hosts Rayner and Carol. There's a real fire and books aplenty, equine paintings and fantastic art, and big gorgeous gardens with croquet, a lake and a boat to mess about in. The décor is traditional, the bed linen immaculate, the bathrooms are spanking new and the views to the Preseli Hills gorgeous. Narbeth's restaurants are good but Carol's cooking is fabulous. *Over 14s welcome.*

Rooms	1 double; 1 double with separate bathroom: £100-£110.
Meals	Dinner, 3 courses, from £35. Pubs/restaurants 2 miles.
Closed	Rarely.

Rayner & Carol Peett
Pembrokeshire Farm B&B,
Caermaenau Fawr,
Clynderwen, SA66 7HB

Tel	+44 (0)1834 860338
Mobile	+44 (0)7796 615332
Email	info@pembrokeshirefarmbandb.co.uk
Web	www.pembrokeshirefarmbandb.co.uk

The Old Vicarage Moylegrove

A breath of fresh air close to the beautiful Pembrokeshire Coastal Path. Energetic young owners have completely redecorated their new home and it feels bright, uncluttered, easy-going. Welsh blankets, Edwardian tiling, glass and fireplaces blend their charm with stripped boards, simple blinds, painted and bistro-style furniture. Chalkboards tell you what's for breakfast, and supper – Meg's a good cook and sources as locally as possible. Beds are wide and deep, views are peacefully green. Walk to Newport or St Dogmaels, catch the Poppit Rocket back and watch the sun set over the distant sea. The old vicar would surely approve! *Minimum stay: 2 nights at weekends.*

Rooms	4 doubles: £100. Singles £85-£90. Extra bed/sofabed £25 per person per night.
Meals	Dinner £10-£20. Pubs/restaurants 3.5 miles.
Closed	Rarely.

Tel	+44 (0)1239 881711
Email	stay@theoldvicbedandbreakfast.co.uk
Web	www.oldvicaragemoylegrove.co.uk

Megan van Soest
The Old Vicarage Moylegrove,
Moylegrove, Cardigan, SA43 3BN

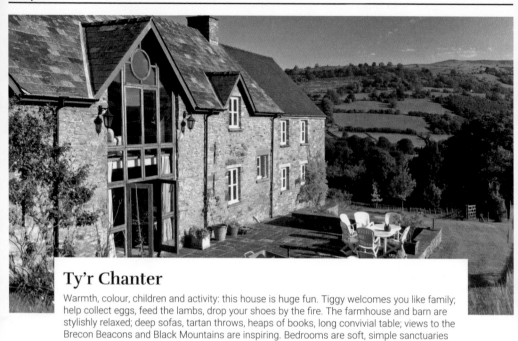

Ty'r Chanter

Warmth, colour, children and activity: this house is huge fun. Tiggy welcomes you like family; help collect eggs, feed the lambs, drop your shoes by the fire. The farmhouse and barn are stylishly relaxed; deep sofas, tartan throws, heaps of books, long convivial table; views to the Brecon Beacons and Black Mountains are inspiring. Bedrooms are soft, simple sanctuaries with Jo Malone bathroom treats. The children's room zings with murals; toys, kids' sitting room, sandpit – it's child heaven. Walk, fish, canoe, book-browse in Hay or stroll the estate. Homemade cakes and whisky to help yourself to: fine hospitality and Tiggy is wonderful.

Rooms	3 doubles: £100. 1 children's twin room with separate bath/shower: £20 per child. Singles £55.
Meals	Packed lunch £8. Pub 1 mile.
Closed	Rarely.

Tiggy Pettifer
Ty'r Chanter,
Gliffaes, Crickhowell, NP8 1RL

Tel	+44 (0)1874 731144
Mobile	+44 (0)7802 387004
Email	tiggy@tyrchanter.com
Web	www.tyrchanter.com

The Old Store House

If a spick and span house gives you pleasure, read no further. Peter has filled his home mostly with books, but chickens and swans might wander in too. Things are moved out of the way rather than put away, there are no hard and fast breakfast times and guests are welcome to use the kitchen. Bedrooms are large, light and comfy with sofas and armchairs; two have wood fires and the room at the top has exterior stone steps and a door that stays open all summer – fledgling swallows might sit on the beam between flying practices. The sitting room is cosy with a big fire, the lived-in conservatory looks across the valley... come and go as you please.

Rooms	3 doubles, 1 twin: £90. Singles £45.
Meals	Packed lunch £4.
	Pub/restaurant 0.75 miles.
Closed	Rarely.

Tel	+44 (0)1874 665499
Email	oldstorehouse@btconnect.com
Web	www.theoldstorehouse.co.uk

Peter Evans
The Old Store House,
Llanfrynach, Brecon, LD3 7LJ

Hafod Y Garreg

A unique opportunity to stay in the oldest house in Wales – a fascinating, 1402 cruck-framed hall house, built for Henry IV as a hunting lodge. Informal Annie and John have filled it with a charming mix of Venetian mirrors, Indian rugs, pewter plates, rich fabrics and oak pieces. Dine by candlelight in the romantic dining room – all sorts of delicious dishes; tuck into a big breakfast in the sweet conservatory. Bedrooms are luxuriously comfortable with embroidered linen, quirky lamps, nifty bathrooms. Reach this relaxed retreat by a bumpy track up across gated fields crowded with chickens, cats... a peaceful, special place.

Rooms	2 doubles: £98. Singles £93.
Meals	Dinner, 3 courses, £28. BYO.
	Pubs/restaurants 2.5 miles.
Closed	Christmas.

Annie & John McKay
Hafod Y Garreg,
Erwood, Builth Wells, LD2 3TQ

Tel	+44 (0)1982 560400
Email	johnanniehafod@gmail.com
Web	www.hafodygarreg.co.uk

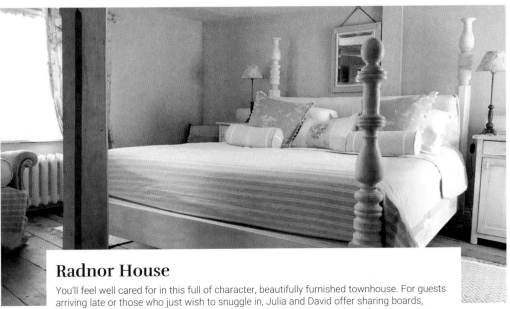

Radnor House

You'll feel well cared for in this full of character, beautifully furnished townhouse. For guests arriving late or those who just wish to snuggle in, Julia and David offer sharing boards, homemade soup, salads and local cheeses – served downstairs or brought to your room. Wake to a breakfast table laden with fresh fruit and juices, homemade granola and cake, as well as a generous full English and seasonally changing menu. You can walk to everything. Explore the castle, walk along the river to the Warren (great for picnics, wild swimming, kayaking), browse galleries, studios and of course the famous bookshops. Foodies have much choice in the popular cafés, restaurants and bars – from tapas, veggie and vegan to traditional pub food. Order a picnic hamper and head off for the top of Hay Bluff – views from the top soar all the way to the Welsh Marches. Join Offa's Dyke from here and you can walk all day. Return to the cosy sitting room with a wood-burner, board games and well-stocked bar. *Minimum stay: 2 nights at weekends. Over 16s welcome.*

Rooms	3 doubles, 1 twin/double: £90-£135. Singles £75-£115. Extra bed/sofabed £20 per person per night. Gift cards available.
Meals	Pubs/restaurants within walking distance.
Closed	Rarely.

Tel	+44 (0)1497 821180
Mobile	+44 (0)7507 615733
Email	enquiries@radnorhousehay.co.uk
Web	www.radnorhousehay.co.uk

David Bartlett & Julia Joplin
Radnor House,
Church Street, Hay-on-Wye, HR3 5DQ

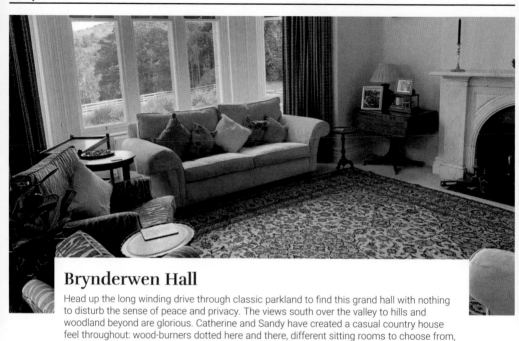

Brynderwen Hall

Head up the long winding drive through classic parkland to find this grand hall with nothing to disturb the sense of peace and privacy. The views south over the valley to hills and woodland beyond are glorious. Catherine and Sandy have created a casual country house feel throughout: wood-burners dotted here and there, different sitting rooms to choose from, ballroom, big bedrooms (three en suite, one with a separate bathroom, and a double and twin sharing a Jack and Jill bathroom) with garden or valley views, a utility room/kitchen for wine storage and wet boots and dogs and a loft space with enormous TV and WiFi for teenagers. Sit on the terrace for tea or a sundowner or two, wake in the morning for cereals, croissants and breads followed by a full cooked breakfast with produce from nearby. The only sounds you'll hear are birdsong, lambs in the fields and the wind in the pines. *Minimum stay: 2 nights. Pets by arrangement.*

Rooms	3 doubles; 1 double with separate bathroom; 1 double, 1 twin sharing bathroom: £90-£120.
Meals	Pubs/restaurants 2 miles.
Closed	Christmas & occasionally.

Catherine Chapple Gill
Brynderwen Hall,
Llanfyllin, SY22 5LH

Tel +44 (0)1691 648266
Email cchapple_gill@yahoo.co.uk

The Slate Shed at Graig Wen

Sarah and conservationist John spent months travelling in a camper looking for their own special place and found this lovely old Welsh slate cutting mill... captivated by acres of wild woods and stunning views. You'll feel at ease as soon as you step into their eclectic modern home with its reclaimed slate and wood, cosy wood-burners, books, games, snug bedrooms (one downstairs) and superb bathrooms. Breakfast communally on local eggs and sausages, honey from the mountainside, homemade bread and granola. Hike or bike the Mawddach Trail, climb Cadair Idris, wonder at the views... and John's chocolate brownies. *Minimum stay: 2 nights at weekends & in high season. Children over 10 welcome.*

Rooms	4 doubles, 1 twin/double: £80-£130. Singles £65.
Meals	Packed lunch £7.50. Pub 5 miles.
Closed	5 November – 14 February.

Tel	+44 (0)1341 250482	**Sarah Heyworth**
Email	hello@graigwen.co.uk	The Slate Shed at Graig Wen,
Web	www.slateshed.co.uk	Arthog, LL39 1YP

Coes Faen Lodge

Effortless simplicity is the key to this new spa B&B. A glass and rock entrance, a hallway suffused with light: this Victorian lodge on the edge of Mawddach Estuary has been stunningly, meticulously revived. Bedrooms are cocoons of sleek opulence, bathrooms are rich in slate and stone, and detailing is sublime: mood lighting, hands-free technology, pearlescent tiles that reflect the light. Choose a sauna smelling of cedar or a rooftop hot tub and terrace... Richard and Sara have Welsh roots and love both place and landscape. Acres of woodland garden await behind; breakfasts and dinners are original and exquisite.

Rooms	6 doubles: £165-£275.
Meals	Dinner from £35.
	Pubs/restaurants 0.5 miles.
Closed	Rarely.

Richard & Sara Parry-Jones
Coes Faen Lodge,
Coes Faen, Abermaw, LL42 1TE

Tel	+44 (0)1341 281632
Email	richard@coesfaen.com
Web	www.coesfaen.co.uk

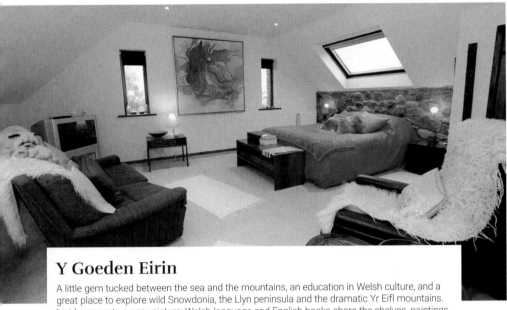

Y Goeden Eirin

A little gem tucked between the sea and the mountains, an education in Welsh culture, and a great place to explore wild Snowdonia, the Llyn peninsula and the dramatic Yr Eifl mountains. Inside presents a cosy picture: Welsh-language and English books share the shelves, paintings by contemporary Welsh artists enliven the walls, an arty 70s décor mingles with sturdy Welsh oak in the bedrooms – the one in the house the best – and all bathrooms are super. Wonderful food is served alongside the Bechstein in the beamed dining room – the welcoming, thoughtful Eluned has created an unusually delightful space.

Rooms	2 doubles, 1 twin: £65-£100. Singles £65-£70.
Meals	Packed lunch available. Pub/restaurant 3 miles.
Closed	Christmas, New Year & occasionally.

Tel	+44 (0)1286 830942
Email	eluned.rowlands@tiscali.co.uk
Web	www.ygoedeneirin.co.uk

Eluned Rowlands
Y Goeden Eirin,
Dolydd, Caernarfon, LL54 7EF

Pengwern Country House

The steeply wooded Conwy valley snakes down to this stone and slate property set back from the road in Snowdonia National Park, and the walks are wonderful. Inside has an upbeat traditional feel: a large sitting room with tall bay windows and pictures by the Betws-y-Coed artists who once lived here. Settle with a book by the wood-burner; Gwawr and Ian are naturally friendly and treat guests as friends. Bedrooms have rough plastered walls, colourful fabrics and super bathrooms; one comes with a double-ended roll top tub and views of Lledr Valley. Breakfast on fruits, herb rösti, soda bread – superb. *Minimum stay: 2 nights.*

Rooms	1 double, 1 twin/double, 1 four-poster: £75-£95.
Meals	Packed lunch £5.50. Pubs/restaurants within 1.5 miles.
Closed	Christmas & New Year.

Gwawr & Ian Mowatt
Pengwern Country House,
Allt Dinas, Betws-y-Coed, LL24 0HF

Tel   +44 (0)1690 710480
Email gwawr.pengwern@btopenworld.com
Web   www.snowdoniaaccommodation.co.uk

Tower

A grand yet wonderfully relaxed and friendly country house on the Welsh borders. Overlooking a lake and first mentioned in 1465, Tower has been in John's family for hundreds of years, and he is more than happy to share his knowledge on its extensive, fascinating history. Breakfast is served at one long polished table in the impressive dining room, bedrooms are elegant with high ceilings, antiques, portraits and masses of space; the garden is perfect for a stroll. Head out to historic Chester, climb Snowdon or explore lively Mold with its umpteen places to eat. Return to relax by the fire in the drawing room.

Rooms	2 doubles, 1 twin; 1 double with separate bathroom: £90-£125. Singles £75. Extra beds available.
Meals	Restaurants 0.5 miles.
Closed	Rarely.

Mobile	+44 (0)7964 008772
Email	info@tower.wales
Web	www.tower.wales

John Wynne-Eyton
Tower,
Nercwys Road, Mold, CH7 4EW

Gladstone's Library

If this glorious, unusual, historic and stunning place fails you as a retreat, then look deep within yourself. You have 150,000 books, silence, space, convivial company if you need it, Theatre Clwyd and Chester but 15 minutes away. Eucharist is held every weekday, delicious local food is there for you in the bistro, an open fire and sofas in the Gladstone room. The staff are lovely, the mood sheer old-fashioned decency. It is a Roberts radio,

rather than TV, place. Bedrooms are warm, simple and unpretentious. Come for as long as you need to recover from this mad world. It will, for all adults, feel like a privilege. *Reception 8.30-5pm. Check in from 2pm, check out 10am; you are welcome to use the facilities and library once you have checked out. If arriving after 5pm please do let us know in advance. Hairdryers, Roberts Radio and WiFi in all rooms.*

Rooms	14 doubles, 3 twins: £90-£100. 7 singles: £66-£77.
Meals	Restaurant on site. Breakfast 8-9am; 8.30-9.30am, Sat & Sun. Lunch 12-2pm. Dinner 6.45-7.15pm.
Closed	Christmas & New Year.

Gladstone's Library
Gladstone's Library,
Church Lane, Hawarden,
Deeside, CH5 3DF

Tel	+44 (0)1244 532350
Email	enquiries@gladlib.org
Web	www.gladstoneslibrary.org/ accommodation/sleeping-with-books

The Slate Shed at Graig Wen, page 403

Scotland

Singdean, page 415

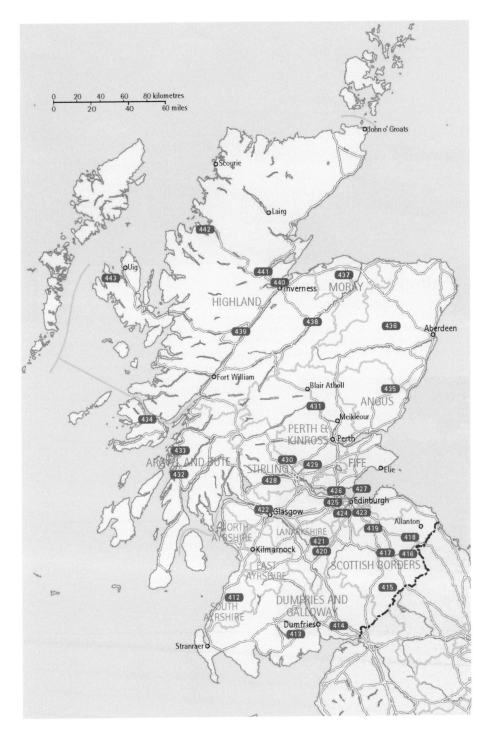

0 20 40 60 80 kilometres
0 20 40 60 miles

○ John o' Groats

○ Scourie

○ Lairg

442

443 ○ Uig

441
440 ○ Inverness 437 MORAY
HIGHLAND 438 436 Aberdeen ○

439 ○ Fort William

○ Blair Atholl 435
431 ANGUS
○ Meikleour
434 PERTH &
KINROSS ○ Perth
433
432 ARGYLL AND BUTE
STIRLING 430 429 FIFE ○ Elie
428
426 427
422 ○ Glasgow 425 ○ Edinburgh
424 423
NORTH 419 Allanton ○
AYRSHIRE LANARKSHIRE 421 418
○ Kilmarnock 420
EAST 417 416
AYRSHIRE SCOTTISH BORDERS
412 415
SOUTH DUMFRIES AND
AYRSHIRE GALLOWAY
○ Dumfries 414
413
○ Stranraer 413

Alton Albany Farm

Discover Ayrshire... pine forests, hills and wild beauty. Alasdair and Andrea (sculptor/garden photographer) are generous hosts who love having you to stay – your visit starts with tea, coffee and cake. There's an arty vibe with their work on display; the dining room brims with garden books and games; large bedrooms have cosy lamps and more books. Big breakfasts by a log fire are a treat, perhaps with haggis, garden fruit, homemade bread; hearty dinners too. Rich in wildlife and orchids the garden has a rambling charm, the salmon-filled river Stinchar runs past and dogs are welcome – resident Daisy, Clover and Tansy are friendly.
Minimum stay: 2 nights.

Rooms	1 double; 1 double, 1 twin, sharing bath, let to same party only: £115. Singles £75.
Meals	Dinner £17.95. Pubs/restaurants 10 miles.
Closed	Rarely.

Andrea & Alasdair Currie
Alton Albany Farm,
Barr, Girvan, KA26 0TL

Tel	+44 (0)1465 861148
Mobile	+44 (0)7881 908764
Email	alasdair@gardenexposures.co.uk
Web	www.altonalbanyfarm.com

Chipperkyle

This beautiful Scottish-Georgian family home has not a hint of formality, and sociable Willie puts you at your ease. Your sitting and dining rooms connect through a large arch; find gloriously comfy sofas, family pictures, rugs on wooden floors, masses of books and a constant log fire. Upstairs: good linen, striped walls, armchairs and windows with views – this wonderful house just gets better and better. There are 200 acres, dogs, cats, donkeys and hens – children can collect the eggs and go on tractor rides. The countryside is magnificent, beaches fabulous and this is a classified dark sky area. A house full of flowers and warmth.

Rooms	2 doubles; 1 double with separate bathroom; 1 twin with separate bath/shower: £115. 10% off for 3 nights or more. Discounts for children. Singles £75.
Meals	Supper, 4 courses, £25. Pub 3 miles.
Closed	Rarely.

Tel	+44 (0)1556 650223
Mobile	+44 (0)7917 610008
Email	willie@chipperkyle.co.uk
Web	www.chipperkyle.co.uk

Willie Dickson
Chipperkyle,
Kirkpatrick Durham,
Castle Douglas, DG7 3EY

Knockhill House

This comfortable self-contained flat has books for rainy days and detailed local info for explorers. Good walking routes can be joined on foot from the door and there are local gin and whisky distilleries to visit. Lucinda likes to cook. Breakfast is brought to your living room: a full English of local produce with eggs from the garden hens – she'll cook dinner too if you ask, or you can opt to fend for yourself in the neat kitchen. Many guests break their journey north here, but if you're staying longer it's all about enjoying the great outdoors – and you can organise fishing on the river.

Rooms	1 twin: £90.
Meals	Dinner with wine, £20.
	Pubs/restaurants 5 miles.
Closed	Rarely.

Lucinda Morgan
Knockhill House,
Hoddom, Lockerbie, DG11 1AW

Tel	+44 (0)1576 300477
Mobile	+44 (0)7790 619307
Email	loobystucley@hotmail.com

Singdean

Twist through woodlands to this remote retreat high in the hills away from the hustle and bustle. Your cosy Alpine-style suite has its own entrance in a glorious off-grid cottage with solar panels and its own fresh spring water.Take a deep breath out, light the candles, laze in the hot tub and look up at the stars... romantics will be happy and a mountain feast of a breakfast is delivered through a secret door each morning. Head out into glorious countryside with a picnic or hop in the car to find good places to eat within 20-minutes. Browse Christa and Del's Alpine lifestyle shop, or venture down to Hawick (15 miles) for cashmere – though awe-inspiring walks and wildlife are on your doorstep, and Kielder Water and Forest Park, with its astronomical observatory, is less than ten miles away.

Rooms	1 suite for 2: £185.
Meals	Packed lunch included by prior arrangement; voluntary contribution to the Landscaping fund. Pub 6 miles.
Closed	Rarely.

Tel	+44 (0)1450 860622
Email	hello@singdean.co.uk
Web	www.singdean.co.uk

Christa & Del Dobson
Singdean,
Newcastleton, TD9 0SP

Parkside

Take tea out into Edythe's burgeoning garden; the stone wall surrounding the property makes it hard to believe the town centre's so close – no need to take a car for dinner in town or a day at the Races. There's a cosy, open-fired guest sitting room and smart, peaceful, high-ceilinged bedrooms – two with garden views – and space to sit and ponder the day's fishing on the Tweed, or what to choose for breakfast: anything from kippers to continental, as locally sourced as possible. And, with notice, Edythe will gladly help if she can with any special requests. Two friendly dogs live here, and yours will be made very welcome with good advice on best local walks; you could take in sections of the Pennine Way or the Cheviot Hills; pick-up St Cuthbert's Way from nearby Melrose and visit the monastic ruins. Edinburgh's just over an hour's drive. *Minimum stay: 2 nights at weekends. Children over 10 welcome.*

Rooms	2 doubles, 1 twin/double: £80-£120.
Meals	Pubs/restaurants 5-minute walk.
Closed	Christmas & New Year.

Edythe Hogg
Parkside,
Edenside Road, Kelso

Tel	+44 (0)1573 229624
Email	hoggedythe@gmail.com
Web	www.parksidehousekelso.co.uk

Fauhope House

Near to Melrose Abbey and the glorious St Cuthbert's Walk, this solid 1890s house is immersed in bucolic bliss. Views soar to the Eildon Hills through wide windows with squashy seats; all is luxurious, elegant, fire-lit and serene with an eclectic mix of art. Bedrooms are warm with deeply coloured walls, pale tartan blankets and soft velvet and linen; bathrooms are modern and pristine. Breakfast is served with smiles at a flower-laden table and overlooking those purple hills. A short walk through the blooming garden and over a footbridge takes you to the interesting town of Melrose, with shops, restaurants and its own theatre.

Rooms	3 twin/doubles: £140-£160. Singles £98.
Meals	Pub/restaurant 0.5 miles.
Closed	Rarely.

Tel	+44 (0)1896 823184
Mobile	+44 (0)7816 346768
Email	info@fauhopehouse.com
Web	www.fauhopehouse.com

Ian & Sheila Robson
Fauhope House,
Gattonside, Melrose, TD6 9LU

Eastfield House

Throw back the duvet and revel in the view from your room across the fields to the Cheviot Hills. Full breakfasts are served at the mahogany dining table. Bilingual French-Belgian Francis loves to cook and also produces sumptuous dinners, while florist Camilla fills the house with fragrant displays. Walk, cycle, fish (local guest permits available), discover castles, abbeys and glorious beaches less than an hour away. Slump in front of the fire, read a book in the conservatory, then retire to elegant rooms with comfy beds, chequered headboards and pretty fabrics. Bathrooms are sparkling, fresh and hung with eye-catching pictures. *Well behaved children & pets welcome.*

Rooms	1 double; 1 double with separate bathroom: £100-£125.
Meals	Dinner £10-£50. Pubs/restaurants 5-minute drive.
Closed	Rarely.

Francis & Camilla Raeymaekers
Eastfield House,
Greenlaw, TD10 6YJ

Tel +44 (0)1361 810750
Mobile +44 (0)7788 560326
Email raeymaekers@aol.com

Crookston House

Scots Baronial grandeur complete with turrets, balustrades, ancestral portraits and impressive entrance... yet a family home with life and warmth. Engaging hosts welcome you with tea and a homemade something. A splendid staircase leads to huge traditional bedrooms with antiques, art and cosy gowns. Watch the wild birds tucking in as you breakfast too, on home-laid eggs and local treats. The 47 acres have swathes of snowdrops in spring and colour all year. Georgina and Malcolm know the area well; heaps to do: river Tweed fishing, walks, mountain bike trails. Return to a toasty, red sitting room with comfy sofas, log fire and lots of interesting books. *Over 12s welcome.*

Rooms	1 double, 1 twin; 1 double with separate shower room): £100-£140.
Meals	Pubs/restaurants 11 miles.
Closed	Christmas, New Year.

Tel	+44 (0)1875 835661
Email	georgina@crookstonhouse.com
Web	www.crookstonhouse.com

Georgina Leslie
Crookston House,
Heriot, EH38 5YS

Cormiston Farm

Richard and Kate make you feel like you're staying with friends in the country for the weekend – they're relaxed and entertaining. Breakfasts are moreish – eggs from the quails and fresh things from the mature walled garden; and you can book supper too. The Georgian farmhouse is tucked into the soft hills of the Clyde Valley; there are 26 acres of farmland to soak up with Hebridean sheep, horses, kune-kune pigs and friendly alpacas children love to pet. You're only two miles from the market town of Biggar, you can walk there along the old Glasgow to Peebles road, now only a faint track. It's pleasant to retire to quiet, spacious rooms with bucolic views after a day marauding around this untamed landscape – there's a walk through fields to the Clyde river for trout fishing and a ten-minute drive takes you to the base of Tinto Hill, a steep scramble rewards you with views to the Trossachs (on a clear day). Later, tuck nippers up in bunks and slip back for a snifter in front of the log fire in the sitting room.

Rooms	2 doubles, both with separate bath: £96. 1 bunk room for 2 children (2-15 years old): £15.
Meals	Dinner, 4 courses, £25-£30. Supper, 2 courses, £20. Pub 2 miles.
Closed	Rarely.

Richard Philipps
Cormiston Farm,
Cormiston Road, Biggar, ML12 6NS

Tel   +44 (0)1899 221507
Email   info@cormistonfarm.com
Web   www.cormistonfarm.com

The Lint Mill

Fields of sheep and a rushing river surround this peaceful converted mill. You have your own wing with sitting room, separate entrance and garden so you'll feel nicely private. Your hosts' passion for living off the land is inspiring – meet their rare breeds of sheep, pigs and hens whose meat and eggs will end up on your plate, along with fruit and veg from the kitchen garden. Peacocks wander and the dogs, Golden Guernsey goats and geese are all part of life on this working smallholding – and you can sign up for craft and farm courses or a rejuvenating 'solo retreat'. You're very well looked after: tea and cake in the conservatory, tasty breakfasts, a lunch platter if you don't want to go out, or a packed lunch for day trips, and seasonal dinner with a bit of notice. It's a two-mile wander to the pub. *Please see owners' website for availability.*

Rooms	1 double with sitting room & conservatory: £90-£135. Singles £60. Extra bed £45 per person per night.
Meals	Dinner, 3 courses, £25. Supper, 2 courses, £20. Platter for 2 £18. Packed lunch £6. Restaurants 9 miles.
Closed	Rarely.

Tel	+44 (0)1555 840042
Mobile	+44 (0)7966 164742
Email	info@thelintmill.co.uk
Web	www.thelintmill.co.uk

Colin & Deborah Richardson-Webb
The Lint Mill,
Carnwath, Biggar, ML11 8LY

64 Partickhill Road

Be greeted by three free-range hens and Gertie the terrier on arrival at this relaxed family home. It's the bustling West End but the road is peaceful and there's a lovely big garden. Caroline and Hugh are lovers of the arts: the house is full of pictures, vintage finds and books. There are wood floors, rugs, a fire in the comfy sitting room and your bedroom is bright and spacious. Tuck into a delicious breakfast, in the conservatory, of good croissants, organic bacon and sausages, homemade bread and jams. Easy for the underground, trendy cafés and delis, museums, theatres and the university. A city treat.

Rooms	1 double: £85–£95. Extra twin available
Meals	Packed lunch available.
	Pubs/restaurant 0.25 miles.
Closed	Occasionally.

Caroline Anderson
64 Partickhill Road,
Glasgow, G11 5NB

Tel   +44 (0)141 339 1946
Mobile +44 (0)7962 144509
Email carolineanderson64@gmail.com

Claremont House

This handsome Victorian mansion stands in the widest residential street in Edinburgh, a 20-minute walk from Holyrood Park and a quick bus ride into the centre. Two streets away is the lively Old Bell, serving real ale and Scottish fare... but for peacefulness and views you could not be better placed. Start the day with breakfast in the morning room: cooked or continental, it's one of the best. End the day with a stroll in the garden. Here, everything is a treat, from the log fires lit at the first chill to the decanters of whisky replenished every day. All thanks to your hostess, warm-hearted, generous Gill. Catch the bus from the end of the road into the centre for booming cannons, the castle with its Crown Jewels, the medieval Old Town, Botanic Gardens and a myriad of restaurants. Return to delicious chocolates in your large, luxurious room. *Minimum stay: 2 nights.*

Rooms	1 double, 1 twin/double: £120-£180.
Meals	Pubs/restaurants 5-minute walk.
Closed	November – January.

Mobile	+44 (0)7885 411209
Email	claremonthouse3@gmail.com

Gillian Hunter
Claremont House,
Edinburgh, EH9 2LL

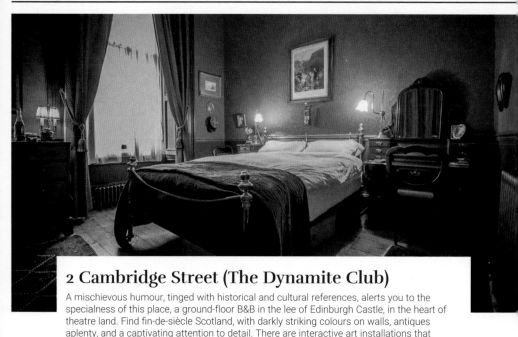

2 Cambridge Street (The Dynamite Club)

A mischievous humour, tinged with historical and cultural references, alerts you to the specialness of this place, a ground-floor B&B in the lee of Edinburgh Castle, in the heart of theatre land. Find fin-de-siècle Scotland, with darkly striking colours on walls, antiques aplenty, and a captivating attention to detail. There are interactive art installations that sing and play, a line of old theatre seats up on the wall, photos and 'objets' serving startling and original purposes. Erlend and Hélène are delightful and free-spirited; Erlend, a quietly spoken (but don't be fooled) Shetlander, serves a breakfast to remember.

Rooms	2 doubles: £100-£160. Singles £90-£110.
Meals	Pubs/restaurants 1-minute walk.
Closed	Christmas.

Erlend & Hélène Clouston
2 Cambridge Street (The Dynamite Club),
Edinburgh, EH1 2DY

Tel	+44 (0)131 478 0005
Email	erlendclouston@gmail.com
Web	www.wwwonderful.net

7 Gloucester Place

It's restful here. Those who want to explore Edinburgh's treasures are close to the Royal Mile, Botanical Gardens, museums, galleries and theatres, traditional and innovative restaurants and live music from the concert halls and pubs. Memorably good breakfasts (often accompanied by classical music or jazz) at the convivial dining table include freshly-squeezed orange juice, homemade jams and full Scottish if you like. Naomi is relaxed and happy to chat to you about the local music and art scene, or to leave you in peace. Up the cantilevered staircase in walnut and mahogany, below a hand-painted cupola find restful bedrooms full of finds from travels to far-flung places. One faces the street but they are both quiet at night. *Italian & French spoken*

Rooms	1 double; 1 double with separate bath: £110-£140. Singles £90-£115.
Meals	Pubs/restaurants 5-minute walk.
Closed	Christmas, New Year & occasionally.

Mobile	+44 (0)7803 168106
Email	naomijennings@hotmail.com
Web	www.stayinginscotland.com

Naomi Jennings
7 Gloucester Place,
Edinburgh, EH3 6EE

14 Hart Street

The brightly lit Georgian house has a smart front of polished brass and glossy paint. The warm raspberry hall is lined with art, and the graceful dining room is just as inviting: decanters on the sideboard, period furniture, glowing lamps, and a welcoming home-baked something. Fresh bright bedrooms are elegant and comfortable with whisky and wine on a tray and smart, sparkling bathrooms. Wake for breakfast at a beautifully polished table, with plenty of coffee, newspapers and chat; Angela is easy to talk to and loves having guests to stay. Perfect for a peaceful city break, and Princes Street is a five-minute walk. *Minimum stay: 2 nights. Over 12s welcome.*

Rooms	2 doubles, 1 twin: £110-£170.
Meals	Restaurants 2-minute walk.
Closed	Rarely.

Angela Wilson
14 Hart Street,
Edinburgh, EH1 3RN

Tel	+44 (0)131 557 6826
Mobile	+44 (0)7795 203414
Email	hartst.edin@gmail.com
Web	www.14hartstreet.co.uk

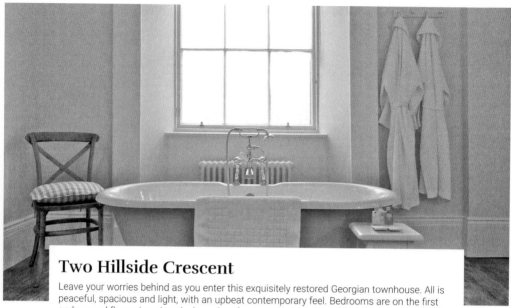

Two Hillside Crescent

Leave your worries behind as you enter this exquisitely restored Georgian townhouse. All is peaceful, spacious and light, with an upbeat contemporary feel. Bedrooms are on the first and second floors: imagine sleek modern furniture, big beds, superb mattresses, clouds of goose down, crisp linen, and immaculate bathrooms with organic toiletries and lashings of hot water. Over a superb breakfast your charming hosts will help you get the most out of your stay. Calton Hill is across the road for the best views of the city, and you're a stroll from the start of the Royal Mile. Wonderful.

Rooms	5 twin/doubles: £125-£165. Singles from £95.
Meals	Pubs/restaurants across the road.
Closed	Rarely.

Tel	+44 (0)131 556 4871
Email	info@twohillsidecrescent.com
Web	www.twohillsidecrescent.com

Elaine Adams
Two Hillside Crescent,
Edinburgh, EH7 5DY

Cardross

Dodge the lazy sheep on the long drive to arrive (eventually!) at a sweep of gravel and lovely old Cardross in a gorgeous setting. Bang on the enormous ancient door and either Archie or Nicola (plus labradors and lively Jack Russells) will usher you in. And what a delight it is; come here for a blast of Scottish history! Traditional big bedrooms have airiness, long views, antiques, wooden shutters, towelling robes and good linen; one bathroom has a cast-iron period bath. The drawing room is vast, the house is filled with warm character, the Orr Ewings can tell you all the history. *Over 14s welcome.*

Rooms	1 twin; 1 twin with separate bath: £110-£120. Singles £70-£75.
Meals	Occasional dinner £35. Pubs/restaurants 3-6 miles.
Closed	Christmas & New Year.

Sir Archie & Lady Orr Ewing
Cardross,
Port of Menteith, Kippen, FK8 3JY

Tel	+44 (0)1877 385223
Email	enquiries@cardrossestate.com
Web	www.cardrossestate.com

Powis House

A sprawling 18th-century mansion with the volcanic Ochil Hills as a stunning backdrop and a colourful entrance hall of antlers and stuffed animals. Country style bedrooms invite with polished old floors, tartan throws, garden views and original bathrooms. You have a huge dining room with warming wood-burner, a guest lounge on the first floor, a sunny stone-flagged patio with places to sit and acres of estate with a woodland walk to explore. Colin and Jane are caring and interesting; Colin is a keen cook and has ghost stories galore to share. Historical Stirling is close: castle, university, festival and more.

Rooms	2 doubles, 1 twin: £110. Singles £75.
Meals	Pub/restaurant 3 miles.
Closed	1 November – 1 April.

Tel	+44 (0)1786 460231
Email	colinkilgour1@gmail.com
Web	www.powishouse.co.uk

Jane & Colin Kilgour
Powis House,
Stirling, FK9 5PS

Old Kippenross

What a setting! Old Kippenross rests in 150 peaceful acres of gorgeous park and woodland overlooking the river Allan – spot red squirrels and deer, herons, dippers and otters. The 15th-century house has a Georgian addition and an air of elegance and great courtesy, with its rustic white-vaulted basement, and dining and sitting rooms strewn with soft sofas and Persian rugs. Sash-windowed bedrooms are deeply comfortable, warm bathrooms are stuffed with towels. Susan and Patrick (an expert on birds of prey) are welcoming, the food is good and there's a croquet lawn in the walled garden. *Children over 10 welcome. Dogs by arrangement only.*

Rooms	1 double; 1 twin/double with adjoining single room, let to same party only: £108-£112. Singles £69-£71.
Meals	Dinner £30. BYO. Pub 1.5 miles.
Closed	Rarely.

Susan & Patrick Stirling-Aird
Old Kippenross,
Kippenross, Dunblane, FK15 0LQ

Tel	+44 (0)1786 824048
Email	kippenross@hotmail.com

Cuil an Duin

Rhododendrons form a brilliant guard of honour to escort you to the front door, and you arrive to tea and scones in the drawing room. Admire mountain views, head off into woodland, roam the gardens – the 20 acres are stunning. Inside is just as good: elegant rooms, Persian rugs, modern art, flowers, a gleaming grand piano; sunny bedrooms are luxuriously comforting. Happy hens foraging in the fields lay your breakfast eggs, artisan shops provide the trimmings. Sally and David are charming, Flora the Labrador and Chloe the cat stay behind the kitchen door until given the all clear, and there are outdoor pursuits galore. *Minimum stay: 2 nights. Over 12s welcome.*

Rooms	1 double, 1 twin/double; 1 double with separate bath: £130–£160. Singles £115–£145.
Meals	Pubs/restaurant 1.5 miles.
Closed	Rarely.

Tel	+44 (0)1796 482807
Email	enquiries@cuil-an-duin.com
Web	www.cuil-an-duin.com

Sally Keay & David Royce
Cuil an Duin,
Ballinluig, Pitlochry, PH9 0NN

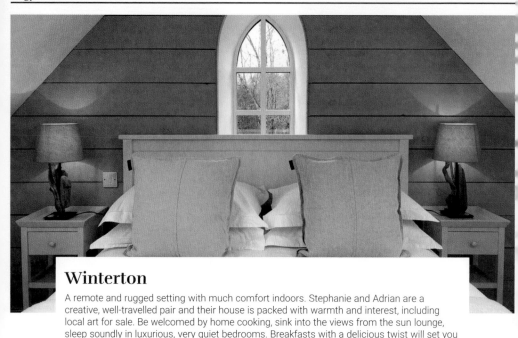

Winterton

A remote and rugged setting with much comfort indoors. Stephanie and Adrian are a creative, well-travelled pair and their house is packed with warmth and interest, including local art for sale. Be welcomed by home cooking, sink into the views from the sun lounge, sleep soundly in luxurious, very quiet bedrooms. Breakfasts with a delicious twist will set you up for a wonderful day walking in the footsteps of the first Scots through this fascinating history-steeped landscape. Explore the beach, sea loch and woods, discover 'Britain's most beautiful short cut by sea' and from there sail to the Corryvreckan. You won't have to go out again in the evening, as the house is licensed and Stephanie and Adrian's dinners are well worth arranging too. *Minimum stay: 2 nights.*

Rooms	2 doubles: £110-£125.
Meals	Dinner, 3 courses, from £32.
	Pubs/restaurants 5 miles.
Closed	Christmas & New Year.

Stephanie Schwind-Parsons
Winterton,
Crinan Ferry, Lochgilphead, PA31 8QH

Tel	+44 (0)1546 510567
Email	stephanie@crinanferry.co.uk
Web	www.crinanferry.co.uk

Melfort House

A truly seductive combination of a wild landscape of ancient woods and hidden glens with rivers that tumble to a blue sea and a big, beautiful house with views straight down the loch. The whole place glows with polished antiques, oak floors, exquisite fabrics, prints and paintings. And Yvonne and Matthew are brilliant at looking after you – whether you're super-active, or not – their fabulous Scottish food's a treat. Bedrooms have soft plaids, superb views and handmade chocolates; bathrooms have huge towels and locally made soaps. Sally forth with boots or bikes, return to a dram by the log fire. Don't book too short a stay!

Rooms	2 twin/doubles: £120-£130. 1 suite for 2: £140. Singles £80. Extra bed/sofabed £20 per person per night.
Meals	Dinner, 4 courses, from £37. Packed lunch £10. Pub/restaurant 400 yds.
Closed	Rarely.

Tel	+44 (0)1852 200326
Mobile	+44 (0)7795 438106
Email	relax@melforthouse.co.uk
Web	www.melforthouse.co.uk

Yvonne & Matthew Anderson
Melfort House,
Kilmelford, Oban, PA34 4XD

Callachally House

By the small fishing river at the mouth of the Glen, settled into its own wooded grounds, is a big Scottish farmhouse (once a drovers' inn) where on a still summer night you can hear the lapping of the sea. A fine, traditional, cultured place, it's been in Ian's family since time began and overflows with colour and character. Bedrooms share bathrooms and each is a gem: old polished floors topped with bright rugs, chalky blue walls hung with paintings; you might hear sheepdogs barking at night. Wake to a fine breakfast (Ian loves to cook), head off down winding roads with views of islands and mountains, return to sprawling armchairs by the log fire.

Rooms	3 doubles sharing 2 bathrooms; adjoining twin available: £90. Singles £75.
Meals	Restaurants 2 miles away.
Closed	December – March.

Ian Mazur
Callachally House,
Glenforsa, Aros, Isle of Mull, PA72 6JN

Mobile	+44 (0)7887 950126
Email	ianmazur@icloud.com
Web	www.largeholidayhousemull.co.uk

Newtonmill House

The house and grounds are in perfect order; the owners are warm, charming and discreet. This is a little-known part of Scotland, with glens and gardens to discover; fishing villages, golf courses and deserted beaches, too. Return to a cup of tea in the sitting room or summerhouse, a wander in the lovely walled garden, and a marvellous supper of local produce; Rose grows interesting varieties of potato and her hens' eggs make a great hollandaise! Upstairs are crisp sheets, soft blankets, feather pillows, flowers, homemade fruit cake and warm sparkling bathrooms with thick towels. Let this home envelop you in its warm embrace. *Dogs by arrangement.*

Rooms	1 twin; 1 double with separate bath: £75-£130. Singles £70-£80.
Meals	Dinner, £30-£36. BYO. Packed lunch £10. Pub 3 miles.
Closed	Rarely.

Tel	+44 (0)1356 622533
Mobile	+44 (0)7793 169482
Email	rrickman@srickman.co.uk
Web	www.newtonmillhouse.co.uk

Rose & Stephen Rickman
Newtonmill House,
Brechin, DD9 7PZ

Lynturk Home Farm

The stunning drawing room, with pier-glass mirror, baby grand and enveloping sofas, is reason enough to come; the food, served in a candlelit deep-sage dining room, is delicious too, with produce from the farm. A home full of life where you're treated as friends – your hosts are delightful, helped along by a very personable Jack Russell. It's peaceful, too, on the Aberdeenshire Castle Trail. The handsome farmhouse has been in the family since 1762 and you can roam the rolling 300 acres. Inside: flowers, polished furniture, Persian rugs, family portraits and supremely comfortable bedrooms with fine linen. "A blissful haven," says a guest. *Pets by arrangement.*

Rooms	1 double, 2 twin/doubles: £100. Singles £60.
Meals	Dinner, 4 courses, £30. Pub 1 mile.
Closed	Rarely.

John & Veronica Evans-Freke
Lynturk Home Farm,
Alford, AB33 8HU

Tel	+44 (0)1975 562504
Mobile	+44 (0)7773 389793
Email	lynturk@hotmail.com

Westfield House

Sweep up the drive to the grand home of an illustrious family: Macleans have lived here since 1862, and there are 500 peaceful acres of farmland. Veronica cooks sublimely; a proper Scottish breakfast and dinner served at a long candle-lit table, with vegetables from the garden. A winter fire crackles in the guest sitting room, old-fashioned bedrooms are inviting (biscuits, books, lovely views), the peace is deep. The coast is close and the walking is splendid. Stride out on walks straight from the doorstep, the Moray Firth, with Spey Bay's pod of dolphins, is less than 30 minutes away, or head to Elgin (ten minutes) for a whisky trail around the local distilleries and cathedral ruins. You can borrow bikes here and explore the quiet coastal roads.

Rooms	1 twin; 1 twin with separate bath & shower: £100. 1 single with separate bath: £55. Extra bed/sofabed £20 per person per night.
Meals	Supper, 2 courses, £20. Pub 3 miles.
Closed	Rarely.

Tel	+44 (0)1343 547308
Email	veronica.maclean@yahoo.co.uk
Web	www.westfieldhouseelgin.co.uk

Veronica Maclean
Westfield House,
Elgin, IV30 8XL

The Old Ferryman's House

This 200-year-old former ferryman's house is small, homely and well lived-in. Mountain views, the river Spey close by and a garden with a tray of tea and homemade treats... Plants tumble from whisky barrels and pots and there are woodpeckers and otters to spy. The sitting room is cosy with the wood-burner and brimming with books. Elizabeth, a keen traveller who has lived in the Sudan, cooks delicious breakfasts: eggs from her hens, homemade bread and preserves, heather honey and sometimes herbs and veg from the garden. There's no TV – no need here: it's an unmatched spot for explorers and nature lovers. Good value too.

Rooms	1 twin/double, 1 double: £85. 1 single: £43. All rooms share 1 bath and 2 wcs.
Meals	Hotel/bistro within 10-15 minute walk.
Closed	Occasionally in winter.

Elizabeth Matthews
The Old Ferryman's House,
Boat of Garten, PH24 3BY

Tel	+44 (0)1479 831370
Email	tofhbbnw@gmail.com

Lock Chambers @ The Caledonian Canal Centre

These comfortable, airy bedrooms are set above an interpretation room dedicated to the famous Scottish engineer Thomas Telford and the history of the Caledonian Canal. They're just off the main road through Fort Augustus and have views of the canal, the village and the hills beyond. Downstairs you'll find a souvenir shop, a grab and go with sandwiches and good coffee and the café. Here you can have breakfast – continental, full Scottish with haggis, vegetarian or a roll with fillings. Simple lunches including homemade Caledonian fish chowder are served until the afternoon. The Boathouse in the grounds of St Benedict's Abbey on the shores of Loch Ness, five minutes away is worth a visit and there are three pubs serving food just across the bridge too. The wonderful landscape makes the area inspiring walking and biking country – the Great Glen Way passes through the village – or you can explore the canals by canoe. Urquhart Castle on Loch Ness is half an hour away, Fort William, Ben Nevis and Inverness are an hour. *Minimum stay: 2 nights in high season.*

Rooms	3 doubles, 2 twin/doubles: £70-£105. 1 quadruple: £85-£105. 1 bunk room for 2: £70-£90. Sofa bed available.
Meals	Full Scottish breakfast & lunch, £6.95.
Closed	Never.

Tel	+44 (0)1463 725581
Email	stay@scottishcanals.co.uk
Web	www.scottishcanals.co.uk/destinations/ fort-augustus/caledonian-canal-centre/

Ben Verbeeren

Lock Chambers @ The Caledonian Canal Centre, Canalside, Fort Augustus, PH32 4BA

Craigiewood

The best of both worlds: Highland remoteness (red kites, wild goats) and Inverness just four miles away. The landscape surrounding this elegant cottage exudes a sense of ancient mystery... woodpeckers, deer, glorious roses all round. Araminta is a delightful host and her home has a lovely family feel; bedrooms are old-fashioned and cosy; the drawing room is snug with stove and books. Gavin built the house almost single-handed, planting a glorious garden here, and many throughout Scotland – his special touch remains. Meander up through rowan trees to a view point, sit and enjoy the peace. Inverewe, Attadale and Cawdor – all on the doorstep. *Minimum stay: 2 nights in high season.*

Rooms	2 twins: £96-£108. Singles £55-£70.
Meals	Pub 2 miles.
Closed	Christmas & New Year.

Araminta Dallmeyer
Craigiewood,
North Kessock, Inverness, IV1 3XG

Tel	+44 (0)1463 731628
Mobile	+44 (0)7831 733699
Email	minty@craigiewood.co.uk
Web	www.craigiewood.co.uk

Knockbain House

This is a well-loved farm, its environmental credentials supreme, and David and Denise are warm and interesting. A beautiful setting, too: landscaped gardens, a 700-acre farm (cows, lambs, barley) and rolling countryside stretching to Cromarty Firth. A grandfather clock ticks away time to relax, by floor-to-ceiling windows and a wood-burner in the antiques-filled sitting room; over a breakfast of local and home-grown produce; with a drink on the pond-side terrace; in bedrooms with fresh bathrooms and stunning views. David can advise on great walks, and has made maps of the farm's footpaths. Revel in the glorious unspoilt nature. *Babes in arms & over 10s welcome.*

Rooms	1 double, 1 twin: £75-£95.
	Singles £45-£70.
Meals	Dinner from £25.
	Pubs/restaurants 1 mile.
Closed	Christmas & New Year.

Tel	+44 (0)1349 862476
Mobile	+44 (0)7736 629838
Email	denise@knockbainhouse.co.uk
Web	www.knockbainhouse.co.uk

David & Denise Lockett
Knockbain House,
Dingwall, IV15 9TJ

The Peatcutter's Croft

Some say there's more beauty in a mile on the west coast than in the rest of the world put together – vast skies, soaring mountains, shimmering water, barely a soul in sight. Pauline and Seori left London to give their family the freedom to roam. Now they have a colourful cast of companions: sheep, hens, ducks, rabbits – all live here. In the adjoining byre: country simplicity, a Norwegian wood-burner, colour, texture and style. Sea eagles patrol the skies, porpoises bask in the loch, red deer come to eat the garden. This, coupled with Pauline's home cooking, makes it very hard to leave. Dogs and children are very welcome.

Rooms	1 apartment for 2: £80-£110. Singles £60-£80.
Meals	Dinner, 3 courses, £30. BYO. Pub/restaurant 30 miles.
Closed	Christmas.

Seori & Pauline Burnett
The Peatcutter's Croft,
Croft 12, Badrallach, Dundonnell,
Garve, Ullapool, IV23 2QP

Tel	+44 (0)1854 633797
Email	seori@yahoo.com
Web	www.peatcutterscroft.com

The Cottage Stein

John and Fiona are warm and welcoming – you'll feel at home straight away. They've renovated their 200-year-old crofter's cottage with love and contemporary style, the views from bedrooms and guest sitting room are astonishing and a short walk takes you to the edge of the loch. Wake to breakfast in the cosy dining room – continental and cooked options, including full Scottish and lighter and sweeter choices, are all served with John's delicious homemade bread. Heaps to do nearby: boat trips, art galleries, Dunvegan castle and great walks. Supper is easy: it's a stroll to Skye's oldest inn and a fabulous restaurant – both right on the water. *Minimum stay: 2 nights in high season. Over 12s welcome.*

Rooms	1 double, 1 twin/double: £125-£140. Singles £100-£115.
Meals	Pubs/restaurants 1-minute walk.
Closed	December – February.

Tel	+44 (0)1470 592734
Mobile	+44 (0)7742 193901
Email	stay@thecottagestein.co.uk
Web	www.thecottagestein.co.uk

John & Fiona Middleton
The Cottage Stein,
Stein, Waternish, IV55 8GA

Index by town

Index by town

Index by town

Who are we?

Alastair Sawday began publishing books quite by chance – which explains a lot. Twenty-five years ago he was a tour guide in France, exploring the country and getting to know its secrets and its characters. Eventually he turned his scruffy, wine-stained notes into a book about unusual places to stay, so that other travellers could engage with authentic owners and guests in interesting and soul-filled places.

We're now over sixty people working from an office overlooking the eclectic Bristol harbourside, but we're still committed to reflecting our values in our culture. We will continue to rail against the iniquities of bland corporate travel by seeking out special places, visiting them personally, writing about them honestly and making no apology for our choices. We celebrate quirkiness, generosity of spirit and all the good, nurturing things that encourage small, local businesses to flourish.

In 2018 we entered into a unique version of Employee Ownership, in which the company was divided between the employees (52%), a Charitable Trust (24%) and the Sawday family (24%). Over the next few years, the Charitable Trust will grow with the company, developing into a real force for good and suppporting causes we all decide on and believe in.

Read more at www.sawdays.co.uk/about